化学工业出版社“十四五”普通高等教育规划教材

食品专业英语

吴澎 徐康 刘玉茜 主编

化学工业出版社

·北京·

内 容 简 介

《食品专业英语》全书共 5 章，主要内容包括食品营养与健康、食品化学、食品技术、食品安全和管理以及写作。全书以中英文对照的形式编排，有助于学生对照学习参考。以独具特色的记忆窍门教学生学习专业词汇分析，课文配以翻译，难句分析，并穿插课后作业、阅读文选和科技论文写作常用句型总结。

本书可作为食品科学与工程、食品质量与安全、食品营养与健康等相关专业的本科生、研究生专业英语教材，也可作为相关领域的科研人员、生产单位从业人员的参考书。

图书在版编目（CIP）数据

食品专业英语 / 吴澎，徐康，刘玉茜主编. -- 北京 : 化学工业出版社，2025. 8. --（化学工业出版社“十四五”普通高等教育规划教材）. -- ISBN 978-7-122-48191-7

Ⅰ. TS2

中国国家版本馆 CIP 数据核字第 20257QC198 号

责任编辑：尤彩霞　　文字编辑：朱雪蕊
责任校对：李雨函　　装帧设计：韩　飞

出版发行：化学工业出版社
（北京市东城区青年湖南街 13 号　邮政编码 100011）
印　　装：三河市双峰印刷装订有限公司
787mm×1092mm　1/16　印张 $12^{1}/_{4}$　字数 314 千字
2025 年 9 月北京第 1 版第 1 次印刷

购书咨询：010-64518888　　售后服务：010-64518899
网　　址：http://www.cip.com.cn
凡购买本书，如有缺损质量问题，本社销售中心负责调换。

定　　价：45.00 元

【形态特征】

甘薯根分为须根、柴根和块根。须根呈纤维状，有根毛，根系向纵深伸展，一般分布在30厘米土层内，深可超过100厘米，具有吸收水分和养分的功能。柴根粗1厘米左右，长可达30～50厘米，是须根在生长过程中遇到土壤干旱、高温、通气不良等原因，以致发育不完全而形成的畸形肉质根，没有利用价值。块根是贮藏养分的器官，也是供食用的部分，分布在5～25厘米土层中，其形状分为纺锤形、圆筒形、球形和块形等；皮色有白、黄、红、淡红、紫红等；肉色分为白、黄、淡黄、橘红、紫等；具有根出芽特性，是育苗繁殖的重要器官。

【分布习性】

世界甘薯主要产区分布在北纬40°以南，据联合国粮食及农业组织（FAO）统计，世界上共有50多个国家栽培甘薯，主要分布在亚洲、非洲的发展中国家，其次为拉丁美洲，欧洲分布面积极少。

我国近年甘薯种植面积为560万公顷左右，占世界甘薯种植面积的70%～75%。我国单产水平现为19吨/公顷，相当于世界平均水平的130%。

甘薯在我国分为5个薯区：北方春薯区，包括辽宁、吉林、河北、陕西北部等地；黄淮流域春夏薯区，种植面积约占全国甘薯总面积的40%；长江流域夏薯区——除青海和川西北高原以外的整个长江流域；南方夏秋薯区——北回归线以北的长江流域以南地区；南方秋冬薯区——北回归线以南的沿海陆地和台湾等岛屿。

【化学成分】

甘薯淀粉含量高，一般块根中淀粉含量占鲜重的15%～26%，高的可达30%；可溶性糖类占3%左右。每100克鲜薯中含糖类29克、蛋白质2.3克、脂肪0.2克、粗纤维0.5克、无机盐0.9克（其中钙18毫克、磷20毫克、铁0.4毫克）。此外，甘薯的维生素含量丰富，每千克鲜薯含维生素C 300毫克、维生素B_1 0.4毫克、烟酸5毫克。维生素B_1和维生素B_2含量为面粉的2倍，维生素E含量为小麦的9.5倍，纤维素为面粉的10倍，维生素A和维生素C的含量较高。

【综合利用】

甘薯最大的特点是它独有的脱氢表雄甾酮（DHEA），这种物质具有防癌潜力，是一种与哺乳动物体内肾上腺所分泌激素相类似的类固醇，国外学者称其为“冒牌荷尔蒙”。大量试验证实，它可能抑制乳腺癌和结肠癌的发生与发展。

甘薯另一个特点是可供给人体大量胶体和黏液多糖类物质，此为一种多糖和蛋白质的混合物。它对人体的消化系统、呼吸系统和泌尿系统各器官组织的黏膜具有特殊保护作用。

甘薯还有一个特点是富含胡萝卜素（1.31毫克每100克）、维生素C（30毫克每100克）、赖氨酸（26毫克每100克）等。

甘薯的食用方法很多，按其形式来分，可分为主食、副食两种类型。甘薯作为主同时还含有黄酮类化合物等活性成分。葛的根、茎、叶所含化学成分有很大差异，且不同品种和不同地区生长的葛成分含量也有很大差异。此外，葛中还含钙、磷、铁、锌、铜等多种矿物质及皂角苷、三萜类化合物、生物碱、维生素和多种氨基酸。葛根含有人体必需氨基酸含量（以100克干物质计）为：赖氨酸＞7.54毫克、苯丙氨酸＞9.65毫克、苏氨酸＞9.63毫克、异亮氨酸＞7.45毫克、亮氨酸＞11.54毫克。

【综合利用】

医药开发与利用，主要是从葛中提取黄酮类生物活性成分，将其制成药物，即将葛根黄酮浸膏经干燥、造粒后制成中成药浸膏或将浸膏进行纯化，制成粉型等不同剂型药品。目前国内已开发生产多种葛根药品，主要有以下几种：① 葛根素（注射剂），用于预防心肌梗死、冠心病、心绞痛、突发性耳聋等，是近年新开发的一种较高端产品，效果好，应用面广；② 葛根素浸膏粉；③ 愈风宁心片；④ 心血宁片；⑤ 葛根芩连片；⑥ 其他含葛根成分中成药。

食品方面利用，主要是从葛根中提取淀粉，作为食品原料或加工成各类食品。葛粉具有清香可口，洁白细腻，淀粉糊透明度高、黏度稳定性强等良好加工性能，适于食品加工。这类食品主要可分为两类：一类是从葛根提取淀粉加工成普通食品（黄酮类物质很少或几乎没有）；另一类是从葛根提取淀粉时采用物理化学方法，使葛中黄酮类活性物质尽可能多保留在淀粉中（或在加工食品时将葛中提取黄酮类物质添加到食品中），然后加工成功能性食品。现已开发的葛食品有普通葛淀粉（生葛淀粉）、速溶葛根淀粉、葛粉果冻、葛粉食糖、葛根汁饮料、葛根黄酮酒、速溶葛奶粉、葛根挂面、葛根粉丝、葛根冰淇淋、葛根红肠、葛根罐头、葛根饼干等系列产品。

工业、农业方面利用主要有以下几种。

① 造纸及填充物：根提取淀粉后，其渣纤维可作填充物及造纸原料，加入油漆又可作修理船板的填充物等。

② 纺织物：藤茎皮可剥皮纤维，打绳，编织麻袋；与亚麻混纺织成麻布；还可作人造棉的原料。

③ 润滑油：种子含油15%，可榨油，供作机器的润滑油。

④ 饲料：嫩茎叶及加工淀粉后剩的渣滓，是良好的家畜饲料。

⑤ 生物农药：葛具有良好的杀虫效能。其藤及根有胃毒和触杀作用，并兼有一定的乳化效能，因此，葛是一种大有开发前景的生物农药资源。

5.5.6 甘薯

【植物名】

甘薯（*Dioscorea esculenta*）又名甜薯，为薯蓣科薯蓣属缠绕草质藤本。

本书编者名单

主　编：吴　澎　徐　康　刘玉茜

副主编：李　锋　路　飞　庞　杰　杨凌宸

其他参加编写人员（按姓氏拼音排序）：

毕艳红

Carol Yongmei Zhang（英）

崔婷婷

董鹏程

蓝蔚青

李苏红

刘　锦

刘亚平

彭　强

单长松

唐文婷

王文亮

许方舟

薛友林

张　晨

张　慧

周　涛

前　言

随着科技的进步和全球贸易的发展，英语的重要性日渐突出，目前全国各高校专业均开设了专业英语课程。本书由编者结合多年的食品专业英语教学经验和知识积累编写而成，主要突出以下三个特点：

（1）立足中国共产党的二十大报告中“树立大食物观”“构建多元化食物供给体系”的要求，对全篇的内容、词句表述、格式做了修整，使逻辑更加分明，内容更有条理。

（2）根据授课经验，将中文翻译课文分段置于英文原课文下方，有助于读者加深理解。

（3）配套有相应的多媒体资源，通过登录化工教育网（www.cipedu.com.cn）可以方便获取相关课件、视频等丰富的资源，学生可以结合教材在课下利用网站资源进行自学、预习与复习。

本着由浅入深、循序渐进的原则，本书以专业的基本词汇、短小精悍的论文，提高学生的阅读兴趣；中文翻译侧重于授之以渔，讲技巧，配有课后作业；写作方面强调熟练掌握科技论文题目、摘要的英语写作，以备毕业论文的写作需要，为研究生阶段的科技论文写作打下基础。

本书分 5 个章节：营养与健康、食品化学、食品技术、食品安全和管理与写作。以独具特色的记忆窍门教学生学习专业词汇分析，课文配以翻译、阅读链接、难句分析，并穿插作业、阅读文选。本书可作为食品科学与工程、食品质量与安全、食品营养与健康等相关专业本科生、研究生专业英语教材和相关科研人员的参考书。

本书由山东农业大学（吴澎、周涛、李锋、张慧、董鹏程、张晨、刘玉茜、徐康、许方舟）联合沈阳师范大学（路飞）、福建农林大学（庞杰）、辽宁大学（薛友林）、苏州大学（刘锦）、上海海洋大学（蓝蔚青）、西北农林科技大学（彭强）、沈阳农业大学（李苏红）、山西农业大学（山西省农业科学院）（刘亚平）、南京农业大学（单长松）、湖南农业大学（杨凌宸）、青岛农业大学（唐文婷）、齐鲁工业大学（山东省科学院）（崔婷婷）、淮阴工学院（毕艳红）、山东省农业科学院农产品研究所（王文亮）及英国皇家农业大学（Carol Yongmei Zhang）16 所高等院校及科研单位联合编写，编者均为从事相关课程教学与研究的在职人员。

在本书编书过程中，尽管各位编者同心协力，但由于内容庞杂，编者水平有限，书中难免存在不足或问题，敬请读者批评指正，以便进一步修改、补充和完善。

编　者

2024 年 10 月

目 录

Chapter 1 Nutrition and Health
第1章 营养与健康

1.1 Carbohydrate
1.1 碳水化合物

1.1.1 Glossary
专业词汇分析

① carbohydrate *n.* 碳水化合物

[记忆窍门] 将该词分解成 "carbo" 和 "hydrate" 两个字母组合，"carbo"形似 "carbon"，词义为"碳"，"hydrate"词义为"水合物"，合起来就是碳水化合物。

② metabolism *n.* 新陈代谢

[记忆窍门] meta 超过，改变 + bolism 代谢，合起来就是新陈代谢。

③ biosynthesis *n.* 生物合成

[记忆窍门] 该词可以分解为 "bio" 和 "synthesis"，分别为"生物"和"合成"的意思，加起来就是生物合成。

④ photosynthesis *n.* 光合作用

[记忆窍门] 该词可以分解为 "photo" 和 "synthesis"，其中 "photo-" 是光、照相术；"synthesis"是合成的意思。综合起来即为光合作用。

⑤ organism *n.* 有机体；生物体；微生物

[记忆窍门] organ 为"组织、器官"之意，-ism 表状态或行为，合在一起即为有机体。

⑥ nutrient *n.* 营养物

[记忆窍门] nutri 滋养，赡养 + …ent 名词词缀 → 营养品

⑦ nondigestible *adj.* 不易消化的

[记忆窍门] 该词可以被分解为 “non” 和 “digestible”, 分别为“非, 不”和“可消化的”意思，加起来就是不易消化的。

⑧ glucose *n.* 葡萄糖

[记忆窍门] 通常用该词的首字母大写 “G” 来表示葡萄糖。词中 “ose” 是糖的后缀。

⑨ deoxysugar *n.* 脱氧糖

[记忆窍门] 该词由 “deoxy” 和 “sugar”组成，分别为“脱氧的”和“糖”意思，加起来就是脱氧糖。

⑩ carboxylic *adj.* 羧基的

⑪ monosaccharide *n.* 单糖

[记忆窍门] 该词可以被分解为 “mono” 和 “saccharide”, 分别为“单的”和“糖”的意思，加起来就是单糖。

⑫ oligosaccharide *n.* 寡糖

[记忆窍门] 该词可以被分解为 “oligo” 和 “saccharide”, 分别为“寡”和“糖”的意思，加起来就是单糖。

⑬ polysaccharide *n.* 多糖

[记忆窍门] 该词可以分解为 “poly” 和 “saccharide”, 分别为“多, 复”和“糖”的意思，加起来就是多糖。

⑭ polyhydroxy *adj.* 多羟基的

[记忆窍门] 该词可以分解为 “poly” 和 “hydroxy”, 分别为“多”和“羟基”的意思，加起来就是多羟基的。

⑮ fructose *n.* 果糖

[记忆窍门] 通常用该词的首字母大写 “F” 来表示果糖，而 “ose” 是单糖的后缀。

⑯ galactose *n.* 半乳糖

[记忆窍门] 该词可以分为 “ga” 和 “lactose” 两部分。“lactose” 是乳糖的意思，乳糖是由葡萄糖和半乳糖构成的双糖，所以一个乳糖分子去掉一个葡萄糖 “G”，就剩下就是一个半乳糖了。

⑰ disaccharide *n.* 双糖

[记忆窍门] 该词可以被分解为 “di-” 和 “saccharide”, 分别为“二”和“糖类, 糖化物”的意思，加起来就是双糖。

⑱ sucrose *n.* [有机化学][食品] 蔗糖

[记忆窍门] 其中 “ose”为糖的后缀。

⑲ saccharose *n.* [食品] 蔗糖

[记忆窍门] 其中 “ose” 为糖的后缀。

⑳ lactose *n.* 乳糖

[记忆窍门] 其中 “ose” 为糖的后缀，可与 galactose（半乳糖）对比记忆。

㉑ maltose *n.* 麦芽糖；饴糖

[记忆窍门] 该词可以分解为“malt”和“ose”,“malt”意为“麦芽”;“ose”为糖的后缀;加起来就是麦芽糖。

㉒ trisaccharide *n.* 三糖

[记忆窍门] 该词可以分解为“tri-”和“saccharide”,“tri”意为“三”;“saccharide”为糖类;加起来就是三糖。

㉓ raffinose *n.* 棉子糖;蜜三糖

[记忆窍门] 其中“ose”为糖的后缀。

㉔ tetrasaccharide *n.* 四糖

[记忆窍门] 该词可以分解为“tetra-”和“saccharide”,“tetra-”意为“四”;“saccharide”为糖的意思;加起来就是四糖。

㉕ stachyose *n.* 水苏糖;水苏四糖

[记忆窍门] 该词可以分解为“stachy”和“ose”,“stachy”形似“starch”,“starch”为淀粉、含淀粉的食物;“ose”为糖的后缀;合在一起意为水苏糖。

㉖ starch *n.* 淀粉,浆粉

[记忆窍门] 由 starch 发音可尝试联想到 start(开始),ch 音似吃,合起来就是“开始吃”,吃什么呢?很多人是吃米饭或馒头,而米饭或馒头里不是有很多淀粉吗?

㉗ cellulose *n.* 纤维素

[记忆窍门] 其中“cell”意为细胞,纤维素是来源于植物细胞的细胞壁,本质上属于多糖(“ose”)。

㉘ pectin *n.* 果胶

㉙ hygroscopicity *n.* 吸湿性;吸水性

㉚ chloroform *n.* 氯仿;三氯甲烷

[记忆窍门] 该词可以分解为“chloro”和“form”,“chloro”意为“氯代”;“form”可谐音为“仿”;合在一起可记为氯仿。

㉛ benzene *n.* 苯

[记忆窍门] 可谐音记忆。

㉜ mannose *n.* 甘露糖;甘糖醇

[记忆窍门] 其中“ose”为糖的后缀。

㉝ gentiobiose *n.* 龙胆二糖

[记忆窍门] 其中“ose”为糖的后缀。

㉞ sorbitol *n.* 山梨醇;山梨糖醇

[记忆窍门] “sorbit”形似“sorbate(山梨酸盐)”,“ol”通常为醇的后缀,因此合起来就是“山梨醇”。

㉟ mannitol *n.* 甘露醇;甘露糖醇

[记忆窍门] “ol”通常为醇的后缀,可结合 mannose 进行对比记忆。

㊱ xylitol *n.* 木糖醇

[记忆窍门] “xylose”意为木糖,“ol”通常为醇的后缀,结合转化为木糖醇。

㊲ hydrogenation　*n.* 氢化作用

[记忆窍门] "hydro-" 一般是指与氢有关，"genation" 是动词 "generate"（产生，生成）的变异，合在一起意为氢化作用。

㊳ ketose　*n.* 酮糖

[记忆窍门] 其中 "keto" 为酮类的意思。

㊴ pentitol　*n.* 戊糖醇；戊五醇

[记忆窍门] 其中 "pent" 形似"pentene"为戊稀的意思，"ol" 通常为醇的后缀，合在一起意为戊糖醇。

㊵ glucitol　*n.* 山梨（糖）醇；葡萄糖醇

[记忆窍门] 与 sorbitol[山梨（糖）醇]对比记忆。

㊶ dicarboxylic　*adj.* 二（双）羧酸的；二羧基的

[记忆窍门] "di-" 为前缀多为"二，双"的意思，与 "carboxylic，羧酸，(含）羧基的" 合在一起意为二羧酸的。

㊷ pyranose　*n.* 吡喃糖

[记忆窍门] "pyran" 意为吡喃，"ose" 通常为糖的后缀，合在一起即为吡喃糖。

㊸ dilactone　*n.* 双内酯

[记忆窍门] "di-" 为前缀多为"二，双"的意思，与 "lactone"（内酯）合在一起意为双内酯。

㊹ mannuronic acid　甘露糖醛酸

[记忆窍门] 该词可拆解为"mann"（"mannose" 甘露糖）+ uronic（糖醛酸）　acid（酸）

㊺ guluronic acid　古罗糖醛酸

[记忆窍门] 该词可拆解为"gul"（"gulose"古洛糖）+uronic（糖醛酸）　acid（酸）

㊻ caramelization　*n.* 焦糖化反应

[记忆窍门] "caramel"（焦糖）→ "caramelize"（使变成焦糖）→ "caramelization"（焦糖化反应）

㊼ glycoside　*n.* 糖苷

[记忆窍门] 该词中 "glycol"联想到 glucose（葡萄糖）,"side"为一侧、旁边，由此联想到糖作为一部分出现就是糖苷。

㊽ nonenzymatic　*adj.* 非酶的

[记忆窍门] 该词中 "non-" 为"非，不"，"enzymatic" 为"酶的"，合在一起意为非酶的。

㊾ peptide　*n.* 肽

㊿ melanoidin　*n.* 类黑素

[记忆窍门] 可与 "melanin"（黑色素）对比记忆。

(51) pasteurization　*n.* 巴氏杀菌

[记忆窍门] "Pasteur" 为法国化学以及生物学家，其发明了"巴氏杀菌法"。

1.1.2 Texts and Translations

课文及翻译

Carbohydrate 碳水化合物

Carbohydrates are the most widely distributed and abundant organic compounds on earth. They have a central role in the metabolism of animals and plants. Carbohydrate biosynthesis in plants starting from carbon dioxide and water with the help of light energy, i.e., photosynthesis, is the basis for the existence of all other organisms which depend on the intake of organic substances with food.

碳水化合物是地球上分布最广泛、含量最丰富的有机化合物。它们在动植物的新陈代谢中起着核心作用。植物在光能作用下，利用二氧化碳和水进行碳水化合物的生物合成，即光合作用，这是所有其他依赖于食物摄入有机物质的生物体的生存基础。

Carbohydrates represent one of the basic nutrients and are quantitatively the most important source of energy. Their nutritional energy value amounts to 17 kJ/g or 4 kcal/g. Even nondigestible carbohydrates, acting as bulk material, are of importance in a balanced daily nutrition. Other important functions in food are fulfilled by carbohydrates. They act, for instance as sweetening, gel or paste-forming and thickening agents, stabilizers and are also precursors for aroma and coloring substances, especially in thermal processing.

碳水化合物是基础营养素之一，在数量上是最重要的能量来源。其营养能量值为17 kJ/g (4 kcal/g)。即使是不消化的碳水化合物，也起到填充作用，对于日常营养平衡也很重要。碳水化合物在食物中还发挥着其他重要作用，例如，可以作为甜味剂、凝胶或合剂、增稠剂、稳定剂等，特别是在食品热加工过程中，还是产生香气和色泽的前体物质。

The term carbohydrate goes back to times when it was thought that all compounds of this class were hydrates of carbon, on the basis of their empirical formula, e.g. glucose, $C_6H_{12}O_6$ ($6C+6H_2O$). Later, many compounds were identified which deviated from this general formula, but retained common reactions and, hence, were also classed as carbohydrates. Carbohydrates are commonly divided into monosaccharides, oligosaccharides and polysaccharides. Monosaccharides are polyhydroxy-aldehydes or -ketones, generally with an unbranched C-chain. Well known representatives are glucose, fructose and galactose. Oligosaccharides are carbohydrates which are obtained from <10 carbohydrate units, which formally polymerize from monosaccharides with the elimination of water to give full acetals. Well known representatives are the disaccharides saccharose (sucrose), maltose and lactose, and the trisaccharide raffinose, and the tetrasaccharide stachyose.

碳水化合物一词可追溯到人们根据它的经验公式认为所有这类化合物都是碳的水合物的时代，例如葡萄糖，其分子组成为 $C_6H_{12}O_6$，即 $6C+6H_2O$。后来，随着更多的化合物被鉴定出，其分子组成并不符合这一通用的分子式，但却呈现碳水化合物的常见反应，因此也被归类为碳水化合物。一般将碳水化合物分为单糖、寡糖和多糖。单糖是多羟基醛或多羟基酮，通常带有不分支的碳链。其代表性糖如葡萄糖、果糖和半乳糖。寡糖是由小于

10 个单糖单位通过单糖分子间脱水聚合成的完整缩醛结构。代表性的糖有二糖（蔗糖、麦芽糖和乳糖），三糖（棉子糖）以及四糖（水苏糖）等。

In polysaccharides, consisting of *n* monosaccharides, the number *n* is, as a rule, >10. Hence, the properties of these high molecular weight polymers differ greatly from other carbohydrates. Thus, polysaccharides are often considerably less soluble in water than mono- and oligosaccharides. They do not have a sweet taste and are essentially inert. Well known representatives are starch, cellulose and pectin.

多糖是由 *n* 个单糖组成的聚合物，*n* 的数目通常大于 10。这些高分子量聚合物的性质与其他碳水化合物差异较大。因此，多糖通常比单糖和寡糖在水中的溶解度要小得多，且无甜味，呈惰性。最具代表性的有淀粉、纤维素和果胶。

1.1.2.1 Physical Properties 物理性质

(1) Hygroscopicity and Solubility

吸湿性和溶解性

The moisture uptake of sugars in crystallized form is variable and depends, for example, on the sugar structure, isomers present and sugar purity. Solubility decreases as the sugars cake together, as often happens in sugar powders or granulates. On the other hand, the retention of food moisture by concentrated sugar solutions, e.g., glucose syrup, is utilized in the baking industry.

结晶糖的吸湿性是可变的，这与糖的结构、同分异构体以及糖的纯度有关。当糖结块时，其溶解度会下降，这在糖粉或糖粒中经常发生。另外，在焙烤工业中，常用浓缩糖溶液，如葡萄糖糖浆，来保持食品中的水分。

The solubility of mono-and oligosaccharides in water is good. However, anomers may differ substantially in their solubility, as exemplified by α- and β- lactose. Monosaccharides are soluble to a small extent in ethanol and are insoluble in organic solvents such as ether, chloroform or benzene.

单糖和寡糖在水中的溶解性良好。然而异构件在溶解性上会有所差异，如 α-乳糖和 β-乳糖。单糖微溶于乙醇，不溶于乙醚、氯仿、苯等有机溶剂。

(2) Sensory Properties

感官性质

Mono-and oligosaccharides and their corresponding sugar alcohols, with a few exceptions, are sweet. β-D-Mannose has a sweet-bitter taste, and some oligosaccharides are bitter, e.g. gentiobiose. The most important sweeteners are saccharose (sucrose), starch syrup (a mixture of glucose, maltose and malto-oligosaccharides) and glucose. Invert sugar, fructose-containing glucose syrups (high fructose corn syrup), fructose, lactose and sugar alcohols, such as sorbitol, mannitol and xylitol, are also of importance. The sugars differ in quality of sweetness and taste intensity. Saccharose is distinguished from other sugars by its pleasant taste even at high concentrations. The taste intensity of oligosaccharides drops regularly as the chain length increases.

单糖和寡糖及其对应的糖醇，除了个别外，都具有甜味。β-D-甘露糖有甜苦味。一些寡糖是苦的，如龙胆二糖。最重要的甜味剂是甘蔗糖（蔗糖）、淀粉糖浆（葡萄糖、麦芽糖和低聚麦芽糖的混合物）以及葡萄糖。转化糖、含果糖的葡萄糖浆（高果糖玉米糖浆）、果糖、乳糖和糖醇如山梨糖醇、甘露醇和木糖醇，也是非常重要的甜味剂。这些糖在甜度和口感强度上有所差异。蔗糖与其他糖的区别在于即使在高浓度下仍具有令人愉悦的味道。寡糖的甜味强度会随着链长的增加有规律地下降。

1.1.2.2 Chemical Reactions and Derivatives 化学反应及衍生物

(1) Reduction to Sugar Alcohols

还原为糖醇

Monosaccharides can be reduced to the corresponding alcohols by $NaBH_4$, electrolytically or via catalytic hydrogenation. Two new alcohols are obtained from ketoses, e.g., fructose, since a new chiral center is formed.

单糖以电解或催化加氢的方式被 $NaBH_4$ 还原为相应的糖醇。由于形成了一个新的手性中心，因此可以从果糖等酮糖中获得两种新的糖醇。

The alcohol name is derived from the sugar name in each case by replacing the suffix -ose or -ulose with the suffix-itol. The sugar alcohols of importance in food processing are xylitol, the only one of the four pentitols used, and only D-glucitol (sorbitol) and D-mannitol of the ten stereo isomeric forms of hexitols. They are used as sugar substitutes in dietetic food formulations to decrease water activity in "intermediate moisture foods", as softeners, as crystallization inhibitors and for improving the rehydration characteristics of dehydrated food. Sorbitol is found in nature in many fruits, e.g., pears, apples and plums. Maltitol, the reduction product of the disaccharide maltose, is being considered for wider use in food formulations.

糖醇的命名衍生于相应的糖，用后缀-itol 替换后缀-ose 或-ulose。在食品加工中，比较重要的糖醇有木糖醇，它是四种戊糖醇中唯一应用的一种，以及己糖醇十种立体异构体形式中唯一的 D-葡萄糖醇（山梨醇）和 D-甘露糖醇。这些糖醇常被用作减肥食品配方中糖的替代品以降低“中等水分食品”中的水活度，或作为软化剂，或作为结晶抑制剂，或者用于改善脱水食品的复水特性。山梨糖醇存在于自然界的许多水果中，如梨、苹果和李子。麦芽糖醇，麦芽糖二糖的还原产物，正被考虑更广泛地应用于食品配方中。

(2) Oxidation to Aldonic, Dicarboxylic and Uronic Acids

氧化生成醛糖酸、二羧酸和糖醛酸

Under mild conditions, e.g., with bromine water in buffered neutral or alkaline media, aldoses are oxidized to aldonic acids. Oxidation involves the lactol group exclusively. β-Pyranose is oxidized more rapidly than the α-form. Since the β-form is more acidic, it can be considered that the pyranose anion is the reactive form. The oxidation product is the δ-lactone which is in equilibrium with the γ-lactone and the free form of aldonic acid. The latter form prevails at pH > 3.

在温和条件下，例如，在中性或碱性缓冲介质中加入溴水，醛糖被氧化为醛糖酸。而氧化反应仅涉及内半缩醛基团。β-吡喃糖比 α-吡喃糖被氧化的速度更快。由于 β-吡喃糖酸性更强，因此可以认为吡喃糖阴离子是反应形式。氧化产物为 δ-内酯，与 γ-内酯和游离醛糖酸处于平衡状态。当 pH 为> 3 时，产物以后者为主。

Glucono-δ-lactone is utilized in food when as low acid release is required, as in baking powders, raw fermented sausages or dairy products.

葡萄糖酸-δ-内酯可用于需要释放低酸的食品中，如发酵粉、生发酵香肠或乳制品中。

Treatment of aldose with more vigorous oxidizing agents, such as nitric acid, brings about oxidation of the C-1 aldehyde group and the CH_2OH-group, resulting in formation of a dicarboxylic acid. Thus, galactaric acid (common or trivial name: mucic acid) is obtained from galactose. The dicarboxylic acid can, depending on its configuration, form mono-or dilactones. Oxidation of the CH_2OH-group by retaining the carbonyl function at C-1, with the aim of obtaining uronic acids (aldehydocarboxylic acids), is possible only by protecting the carbonyl group during oxidation. A suitable way is to temporarily block the vicinal HO-groups by ketal formation which, after the oxidation at C-6 is completed, are deblocked under mild acidic conditions.

用较强的氧化剂如硝酸处理醛糖时，C-1 醛基和—CH_2OH 基团同时发生氧化反应得到二羧酸。因此，半乳糖二酸（俗名或惯用名：黏液酸）是从半乳糖获得的。二羧酸根据其构型可以形成单内酯或双内酯。在氧化过程中，通过保护羰基，也就是保留 C-1 的羰基功能，仅使—CH_2OH 基团氧化以获得糖醛酸（醛羧酸）是可能的。一种适宜的方法是通过生成酮缩醛暂时保护邻位羟基，当 C-6 位羟基氧化完全后，可在弱酸性条件下将邻位羟基释放出来。

A number of uronic acids occur fairly abundantly in nature. Some are constituents of polysaccharides of importance in food processing, such as gel-forming and thickening agents, e.g. pectin (D-galacturonic acid) and sea weed-derived alginic acid (D-mannuronic acid, L-guluronic acid).

自然界中存在着大量的糖醛酸。有些多糖组分在食品加工中具有重要作用，例如凝胶形成剂和增稠剂，果胶（D-半乳糖醛酸）以及海藻衍生的海藻酸（D-甘露糖醛酸、L-古洛糖醛酸）。

(3) Caramelization

焦糖化反应

Brown-colored products with a typical caramel aroma are obtained by melting sugar or by heating sugar syrup in the presence of acidic and/or alkaline catalysts. The process can be directed more towards aroma formation or more towards brown pigment accumulation. Heating of saccharose syrup in a buffered solution enhances molecular fragmentation and, thereby, formation of aroma substances. On the other hand, heating glucose syrup with sulfuric acid in the presence of ammonia provides intensively colored polymers. The stability and solubility of these polymers are enhanced by bisulfite anion addition to double bonds.

在酸性和/或碱性催化剂存在下，通过熔化糖或加热糖浆可以得到具有典型焦糖香气的棕色产品。该过程可以导致更多的香气生成或更多褐色色素的累积。在缓冲溶液中加热蔗糖糖浆会增强分子的碎裂，从而生成芳香物质。另一方面，在氨的存在下，用硫酸加热葡萄糖糖浆会产生色泽浓重的聚合物。亚硫酸氢盐阴离子加成到双键上，可提高这些聚合物的稳定性和溶解度。

(4) Reactions with Amino Compounds (Maillard Reaction)

与氨基化合物的反应（美拉德反应）

N-glycosides are widely distributed in nature (nucleic acids, NAD, coenzyme A). They are formed in food whenever reducing sugars occur together with proteins, peptides, amino acids or amines. They are obtained more readily at a higher temperature, low water activity and on longer storage.

N-糖苷广泛分布于自然界[核酸、烟酰胺腺嘌呤二核苷酸（NAD）、辅酶 A]中。当还原糖与蛋白质、多肽、氨基酸或胺同时存在时，食物中就会形成 *N*-糖苷。在较高的温度、低水活度和较长的储存时间下，*N*-糖苷更容易生成。

On the sugar side, the reactants are mainly glucose, fructose, maltose, lactose and, to a smaller extent, reducing pentoses, e.g., ribose. On the side of the amino component, amino acids with a primary amino group are more important than those with a secondary because their concentration in foods is usually higher. Exceptions are, e.g., malt and corn products which have a high proline content. In the case of proteins, the ε-amino groups of lysine react predominantly. However, secondary products from reactions with the guanidino group of arginine are also known. In fact, imidazolin-ones and pyrimidines, which are formed from arginine and reactive α- and β-dicarbonyl compounds obtained from sugar degradation, have been detected.

从糖的角度而言，反应物主要是葡萄糖、果糖、麦芽糖、乳糖，还有少量的还原性戊糖，如核糖。从氨组分而言，含伯氨的氨基酸比含仲氨的氨基酸更加重要，因为它们在食物中的浓度通常更高。但也有例外，如脯氨酸含量较高的麦芽和玉米产品。在蛋白质中，主要是赖氨酸的 ε-氨基发生反应。此外，还发现了与精氨酸的胍基反应生成的次级产物。事实上，已检测到由精氨酸和糖降解得到的活性 α-和 β-二羰基化合物形成的咪唑啉酮类和嘧啶类物质。

These reactions result in:

这些反应形成了：

• Brown pigments, known as melanoidins, which contain variable amounts of nitrogen and have varying molecular weights and solubilities in water. Little is known about the structure of these compounds. Studies have been conducted on fragments obtained after Curie point pyrolysis or after oxidation with ozone or sodium periodate. Browning is desired in baking and roasting, but not in foods which have a typical weak or other color of their own (condensed milk, white dried soups, tomato soup).

棕色色素，称为类黑素，含氮量不同，其分子量不同，在水中的溶解度也不同。然而，人们对这些化合物的结构知之甚少。人们已对居里点热解或臭氧氧化或高碘酸钠氧化后得到的碎片进行了研究。烘焙和烤制时需要产生褐变，但本身具有典型浅色或其他颜色的食品（炼乳、白汤粉、番茄汤汁）例外。

• Volatile compounds which are often potent aroma substances. The Maillard reaction is important for the desired aroma formation accompanying cooking, baking, roasting or frying. It is equally significant for the generation of off-flavors in food during storage, especially in the dehydrated state, or on heat treatment for the purpose of pasteurization, sterilization and roasting.

• 挥发性化合物，通常是强效的芳香物质。美拉德反应对烹饪、烘焙、烘烤或油炸时生成理想香气非常重要。对在食品贮存过程中，特别是在脱水状态下，或在巴氏杀菌、灭菌和烘烤的热处理过程中产生的异味也同样重要。

• Flavoring matter, especially bitter substances, which are partially desired (coffee) but can also cause an off-taste, e.g., in grilled meat or fish (roasting bitter substances).

风味物质，特别是一些苦味成分，部分食品是需要的（如咖啡），但也会产生异味，如烤肉或鱼（烧烤的苦味物质）。

• Compounds with highly reductive properties (reductones) which can contribute to the stabilization of food against oxidative deterioration.

具有高还原性的化合物（还原酮类），有助于食品的稳定，防止氧化变质。

• Losses of essential amino acids (lysine, arginine, cysteine, methionine).

必需氨基酸（赖氨酸、精氨酸、半胱氨酸、蛋氨酸）的损失。

• Compounds with potential mutagenic properties.

具有潜在致突变性的化合物。

• Compounds that can cause cross-linkage of proteins.

能引起蛋白质交联的化合物。

• Reactions of this type apparently also play a role *in vivo* (diabetes).

这类反应显然在体内（糖尿病患者）也起到一定作用。

1.1.3 Homework

课后作业

1.1.3.1 Sentence Translation

句子翻译

(1) Original Sentences

原句

① Current dietary guidelines recommend that the fat intake in Western countries should be decreased from around 40% at present to not more than 30% of the energy intake.

② In recent years, however, the specific nutritional importance of the carbohydrates as such has been more and more emphasized, and new classification of the different food carbohydrates as a basis for more specific recommendations.

③ Simple sugars, or food products containing large amounts of simple sugars, have often been referred to as “bad”carbohydrates, mostly as a method of describing the fact that they contain little additional nutritional value other than the provision of calories.

④ Continuing this process of size reduction, mechanical action of the stomach increases both the rate of gastric emptying of food from the stomach into the small intestine and the surface area of the food particles made accessible to intestinal enzymes.

(2) Translations

翻译

① 在西方国家，目前的膳食指南推荐的脂肪摄入量占能量摄入的比例应从现在 40% 左右减少到不足 30%。

② 然而，近年来，碳水化合物本身的特殊重要性越来越受到重视，不同的食物碳水化后物被重新分类，作为更具体建议的基础。

③ 简单的糖，或含有大量的单糖的食物，常常被称为“坏”的碳水化合物，事实上，和其他供给热量的物质相比，它们很少有额外的营养价值。

④ 胃的机械作用，会继续减小食物颗粒大小，并提高食物从胃进入小肠的排空速度，并使食物颗粒和肠酶充分接触。

(3) 翻译文中划线句子

1.1.3.2 Common Sentence Patterns of Scientific Papers 科技论文常见句型

(1) 摘要

This paper derives the…

This paper puts forward a new method to …

(2) 引文

① 研究目的（purpose of the study）

This problem concerned (deals, bears) (briefly, meanly, largely) with …

This is a problem relating to …

Our work is devoted to…

The primary goal of the present research is...

The work presented in this paper focuses on…

The work presented in this paper focuses on several aspects of …

The chief aim of study is …

The laboratory study demonstrates (suggests, indicates, reveals, establishes) …

Doing this work, we intend (hope, expect, attempt) to…

Carrying out (undertaking, performing, initiating) this study, we hope to …

The principal purpose (objective, task) of the present (preliminary, further) work is to investigate the features of (mechanisms involved in, effects produced by) …

② 背景和历史（background and history）

This problem was (first) advanced by …

The problem under discussion was formulated (raised, posed, brought up, put forward) by …

Since then the problem has attracted (fascinated) many scientists (workers in this field) ...

This problem has been clarified (dated, solved) …

The problem, as can be seen (is to know) is (still) poorly (inadequately) understood.

Compared with the current research, the previous work was in connection with …

The work we are doing is closely related to the deliberations described in …

The new findings from the experiment agree well with the results obtained in …

Several (numerous, many, few) studies are made (carried out, performed) to elucidate the nature (understand the behavior, reveal the cause) of …

A study of this kind has (never) been made (until now, until a few years ago)

③ 问题的难易程度（difficulty of the problem）

It seems (exceedingly, enormously) difficult to obtain knowledge of the problem …

It proves (totally, quite) impossible (unrealistic) to try …

It is rather difficult to solve the problem …

The problem is rather involved …

The problem involves (certain, tremendous) difficulties.

It is easy to present (reveal, analyze, discuss) the problem in all its complexity (in every detail).

It is no easy task to gain an insight into the intricate detail of …

④ 问题的范围（scope of the problem）

The main aspect (core, essence) of the problem is …

Studies of these effects cover various aspects of …

Our studies with this technique are confined to …

The problem is within the scope of …

Our problem lies beyond the range of …

(3) 正文

① 理论说明（theoretical explanations）

Our theory is based on the assumption that …

This theory proceeds from the idea (principle) of …

The underlying concept of the theory is as follows.

There is a similar (alternative, tentative) theory that …

The basic (essential, fundamental) feature of this theory is …

The object of this theory is to …

The newly advanced theory has some advantages (assets, strong points, positive features, deficiencies, drawbacks, inadequacies, flaws, shortcomings).

The validity of the theory has become obvious in the light of recent findings.

This newly-developed theory finds experimental support...

The theory received universal recognition (general acceptance).

② 公式推导（formulas derivation）…

…is given by:

… as follows:

… as in the following:

… the following equation is obtained.

… this becomes

therefore, we have

… can be expressed as

… can be derived:

… can be written:

… can be described by …

… can be represented as

③ 方法介绍（method introduction）

The method of … was first developed by …

The method of …came into use as long ago as …

The original proposal of this method was first published in …

The method we used differs from the conventional one.

The newly-elaborated technique is different from the one previously used.

The method is now greatly improved …

The procedure we followed has certain advantages over the existing method.

One of the assets of the technique is its simplicity (reliability, sensitivity).

Another good feature of this method is …

This method allows us to demonstrate …

The above procedure makes it possible to evaluate …

This method is capable of providing …

④ 实验描述（experiment description）

We made (carried out, performed, initiated) this experiment to show (demonstrate, elucidate, evaluate) a correlation between (certain phenomena, the mechanism of, the hypothesis of, some features of) …

Experiments on … are made (underway) to …

Earlier (previous) experiments with this technique were intended (designed, designated) to …

The experiments reported here demonstrate a variety of changes in (a correlation between, a resistance to) …

Our experiment supports our assumption (hypothesis, evidence) that …

Recent experiments with … furnish some new information (for the data, new evidence) about the mechanism (the influence) of …

Further experiments in this area lead us to conclude (believe, suggest) that …

From these experiments we can conclude that …

(4) 结论

① 结果的意义（meaning of the results）

The results presented in this paper are (seem) …

The findings reported here are (quite) striking (remarkable, fascinating).

These preliminary findings are very reliable (encouraging, promising, convincing, ambiguous)

The results reported here prove (confirm, support, bear out) the hypothesis (assumption, observation) that …

The above findings can be viewed (approached) as follows (in terms of ... from other standpoints).

We can consider (interpret, look at) these results as fully reliable (consistent with) …

This fruitful work gives explanation to …

② 导致结论（conclusion deduced）

Our findings suggest that …

These findings lead the other to a conclusion that …

Our data leave an open the question of whether …

In the future, we will extend the present studies to …

Our work has contributed to the understanding of …

The research work has brought about a discovery of …

Further progress can be provided by this experiment

1.2 Lipids

1.2 脂类

1.2.1 Glossary

专业词汇分析

① palatability *n.* 嗜食性，适口性，风味

[记忆窍门] 该词可以分成“pala”、“tab”、“ility”三部分，“pala”和宫殿“palace”拼写形似；“tab”和餐桌“table”拼写相似，这两部分合起来就是宫殿里的餐桌，想象为宫殿里的桌子上一定有很多美味的食物；“ility”是名词的后缀，因此为“适口性”。

② triacylglycerol *n.* [医]三酰基甘油；甘油三酯

[记忆窍门] 该词中“tri-”为“三”；“acyl”为“酰基”；“glycerol”为“甘油”；合起来就是三酰基甘油，即甘油三酯。

③ sterols *n.* 甾醇类；固醇类

[记忆窍门] 单词中“erols”是酯的后缀，再加上“s”为固体的第一个字母，进而联想到为固醇类。

④ bile *n.* 胆汁

[记忆窍门] 胆汁（bile）为胆囊（bile cyst）中的液体。

⑤ diacylglycerol *n.* 二酰基甘油；甘油二酯

[记忆窍门] 该词中“di-”为“二”；“acyl”为“酰基”；“glycerol”为“甘油”，合起来就是甘油二酯。

⑥ cholesterol *n.* 胆固醇

[记忆窍门] 该词中“chole”为胆汁；“sterol”为固醇类，合起来就是胆汁中固醇类，即胆固醇。

⑦ sitosterol *n.* 谷甾醇

[记忆窍门] 该词中“sito”为食物，而中国人以谷物为主；“sterol”为甾醇类，合起来就是谷甾醇。

⑧ acylglycerol *n.* 酰基甘油，甘油酯

[记忆窍门] 该词中“acyl”为酰基；“glycerol”为甘油，合起来就是“酰基甘油”。

⑨ phospholipid *n.* [医]磷脂（类）

[记忆窍门] 该词中“phosph”和磷酸盐“phosphate”拼写很相似；第二部分“lipid”为脂类，将二者合起来就是磷脂。

⑩ glycolipid *n.*[医]糖脂（类），配糖脂

[记忆窍门] 该词中“glyco”为糖词根；“lipid”为脂类；将二者合起来就是糖脂。

⑪ sphingolipid *n.*（神经）鞘脂类

[记忆窍门] 该词的第一部分“sphingo”和（神经）鞘氨（基）脂“sphingoin”形似；“lipid”为脂类；将二者合起来就是（神经）鞘脂类

⑫ ruminant *n.* 反刍动物

[记忆窍门] 单词可以分解为“rumin”和“ant”，第一部分和瘤胃（rumen）相似。而只有反刍动物有瘤胃，进而联想到反刍动物。

⑬ hibernate *vi.*（某些动物）冬眠，蛰伏

[记忆窍门] 该词中“hibe”和隐藏“hide”拼写很相似；联想到动物在冬天藏起来，往往是“冬眠”。

⑭ linolenic acid 亚麻酸

[记忆窍门] 该词中“linolenic”为“亚麻酸的”；“acid”是“酸”；合起来就是亚麻酸。

⑮ adipocyte *n.* 脂肪细胞

[记忆窍门] 该词中“adipo”的含义为脂肪；“cyte”为细胞；合起来就是脂肪细胞。

⑯ adipose *adj.* 含动物脂肪的；动物脂肪（似）的；脂肪质的；脂肪多的；*n.*（储于脂肪组织中的）动物脂肪；肥胖

[记忆窍门] 该词为脂肪“adipo”的派生词。

⑰ carotenoid *n.* 类胡萝卜素

[记忆窍门] 该词中“carot”是胡萝卜，联想到胡萝卜含有类胡萝卜素。

⑱ leptin *n.* 瘦蛋白

[记忆窍门] 由单词中“ptin”联想到蛋白质 protein，说明是蛋白质的一种。

⑲ homeostasis *n.* 动态静止；动态平衡

[记忆窍门] 该词中“homeo”为（拉丁语）相同或类似；而“stasis”和静止“static”拼写很相似；合起来就是动态静止。

1.2.2 Texts and Translations

课文及翻译

Lipids 脂类

Lipids form a group of compounds, the chemical nature of which is extremely varied. They have physical, chemical, and physiological properties that make them important both in nutrition and in food technology. Lipids make an important contribution to food characteristics, such as texture and palatability. In addition to fats ingested as food, there are specific lipids synthesized by the human body that are essential to life.

脂类构成了一大类化合物，其化学性质差别很大。它们具有物理、化学和生理特性，使得在营养和食品加工中显得十分重要。脂类对于食品的质地和口感等特性具有重要贡献。除了作为食物摄入的脂肪外，人体还合成了对生命至关重要的特定脂质。

Lipids are insoluble in water and this profoundly affects the particular phenomena associated with their digestion, absorption, transport in the blood, and metabolism at the cellular level. Fat is easily recognized when it accumulates within the body, but the chemical and technical definition of fats and lipids are more difficult. Of nutritional interest are triacylglycerols (TAG), phospholipids (PL), sterols, and some derived lipids — results of the hydrolysis or enzymatic breakdown of simple and compound lipids.

脂质不溶于水，这严重影响了与它们的消化、吸收、在血液中的运输和细胞水平的代谢相关的特殊现象。当脂肪在体内累积时很容易被识别，但是脂肪和脂质从化学和技术的角度来定义和区别就比较难。最有营养价值的是三酰甘油（TAG）、磷脂（PL）、甾醇和一些衍生脂质——简单和复合脂质水解或酶解的结果。

TAG represents the bulk of ingested lipids. The second major group of lipids contained in a normal diet, the PL, contributes only an estimated 2% to the total fat intake, but an additional 12 g PL is secreted in the bile every 24 hours. Other lipids are either present in such minute quantities that they do not play a role in digestion and absorption, or they are poorly absorbed (e.g., wax and wax-like compounds).

甘油三酯代表摄入的脂质总量。正常的饮食中包含的第二大脂类，磷脂（PL），约占总脂肪摄入量的 2%，但每 24 小时胆汁中会额外分泌 12g 的 PL。其他脂类物质要么是量很小，在消化和吸收中不起作用，要么是吸收不好（如蜡和蜡样化合物）。

Fatty acids (FA) are the main constituents of food fats and oils as well as of depot fats in man and animals. Dietary fats contain practically no free FA; instead, these are present in the form of TAG.

故脂肪酸（FA）是食物脂肪和油以及人类和动物体内储存脂肪的主要成分。膳食脂肪几乎不含有自由 FA，而是以三酰甘油的形式存在。

Diacylglycerols (DAG) are found naturally as minor components in various dietary lipids. Although human adults ingest 1 g to 5 g of DAG every day, little attention has been paid to its nutritional characteristics because DAG has been recognized only as intermediates in the process of TAG digestion and absorption.

二酰甘油（DAG）是天然存在于各种膳食脂肪中的次要成分。虽然成人每天摄入 1 ~ 5g 的 DAG，但由于 DAG 在 TAG 的消化吸收过程中仅被认为是中间体，因此对其营养特性的关注很少。

Food lipids usually contain small amounts of other fat-soluble substances, including flavor components and some vitamins. Animal fats may contain vitamins A and D, and varying amounts of cholesterol, while vegetable fats may contain carotenes, vitamin E, and sitosterol, but not cholesterol.

食品脂质通常含有少量其他脂溶性物质，包括风味成分和一些维生素。动物脂肪可能含有维生素 A 和维生素 D 以及不同量的胆固醇，而植物脂可能含有胡萝卜素、维生素 E 和谷甾醇，但不含胆固醇。

1.2.2.1 Lipid Classifications
脂的分类

Classification of lipid structures is possible based on physical properties at room temperature (oils are liquid and fats are solid), their polarity (polar and neutral lipids), their essentiality for humans (essential and nonessential fatty acids), or their structure (simple or complex). Neutral lipids include fatty acids, alcohols, glycerides, and sterols, while polar lipids include glycerophospholipids and glyceroglycolipids. The separation into polarity classes is rather arbitrary, as some short chain fatty acids are very polar. A classification based on structure is, therefore, preferable. Based on structure, lipids can be classified as derived, simple, or complex. The derived lipids include fatty acids and alcohols, which are the building blocks for the simple and complex lipids. Simple lipids, composed of fatty acids and alcohol components, include acylglycerols, ether acylglycerols, sterols, and their esters and wax esters. In general terms, simple lipids can be hydrolyzed into two different components, usually alcohol and acid. Complex lipids include glycerophospholipids (phospholipids), glyceroglycolipids (glycolipids), and sphingolipids. These structures yield three or more different compounds on hydrolysis.

脂质可能是根据室温下的物理性质（油是液体，脂肪是固体）、极性（极性脂肪和中性脂肪）、对人类的重要性（必需脂肪酸和非必需脂肪酸）或结构（简单或复杂的）进行分类的。中性脂类包括脂肪酸、醇类、甘油酯和甾醇，而极性脂类包括甘油磷脂和甘油糖脂。由于一些短链脂肪酸极性很强，因此极性分类是相当随意的。所以，基于结构的分类更为可取。根据结构脂质可分为衍生脂质、简单脂质和复杂脂质。衍生脂类包括脂肪酸和醇类，它们是构成简单脂和复杂脂的组成部分。由脂肪酸和醇类组成的简单脂包括酰基甘油酯、醚酰基甘油、甾醇及其酯和蜡酯。一般来说，简单脂可以水解为两种不同组分，通常是醇和酸。复杂脂包括甘油磷脂（磷脂）、甘油糖脂（糖脂）和鞘脂。这些结构在水解时会产生三种或多种不同的化合物。

1.2.2.2 Source of Lipids in the Diet 饮食中的脂质来源

In plants, fats are formed from carbohydrates. Thus, when seeds such as sunflowers or soybeans ripen, their starch content decreases as the fat content increases. The proportion of FA in fat varies from plant to plant, and is also quite variable within a species. Fats from vegetable seeds are among the principal sources of essential FA (EFA), especially of linoleic acid (LA). Vegetable oil obtained from corn, soybean, and sunflower seeds contains less than 15% saturated FA and more than 55% polyunsaturated FA (PUFA). However, not all vegetable oils contain such large amounts of PUFA; for example, the fat contained in olive oil and coconut is less than 10% PUFA.

在植物中，脂肪是由碳水化合物转化而来的。因此，当向日葵或大豆等种子成熟时，其淀粉含量随着脂肪含量增加而下降。脂肪中脂肪酸的比例因植物而异，在同一物种内也有很大差异。源于蔬菜种子中的脂肪是必需脂肪酸（EFA）的主要来源之一，特别是亚油酸(LA)。从玉米、大豆和葵花籽中得到的植物油含有少于15%的饱和脂肪酸以及超过55%的多不饱和脂肪酸（PUFA）。然而，并不是所有的植物油中都含有如此大量的多不饱和脂肪酸；例如，橄榄油和椰子所含的脂肪含有小于10%的多不饱和脂肪酸。

Animals, including humans, store excess energy almost entirely in deposits of fat, the amount of which is very variable. As in plants, this fat can be made from carbohydrate, but the dietary carbohydrates can be starch, sugar, or cellulose (in ruminants). Animals and humans also lay down fat from their dietary fat. The FA composition in this case reflects that of the diet, except for ruminants whose digestive process normally makes the FA more saturated and/or by isomerization with a lower melting point. Animal fats have a high percentage of saturated FA with chain lengths of 14 to 18 carbon atoms. Milk fat contains about 20% 4 ~ 14 carbon FA. This short-chain FA (SCFA) and medium-chain FA (MCFA) content is specific milk fat and is partly responsible for the physical properties of butter such as melting point and for its pleasant taste. Beef and pork fats contain about 40% or more of long-chain FA (LCFA) and saturated MCFA. The PUFA content of animal fats, including fish oils, is generally between 4.0% and 30%. But, contrary to other land animals, the storage fat of hibernating animals (e.g., brown or black bear) is rich in PUFA and contains much of linolenic acid (LNA). Differences between animal and vegetable lipids in relation to composition, digestion, absorption, and in the composition and concentration of sterols incorporated in ingested fat affect the metabolism and composition of fat depots.

包括人类在内的动物几乎完全可以将多余的能量储存在脂肪沉积物中，脂肪的数量变化很大。与植物一样，这种脂肪可以由碳水化合物转化而来，而膳食碳水化合物可能是淀粉、糖或纤维素（反刍动物）。动物和人类也会从他们的膳食脂肪中储存脂肪。在这种情况下，FA 的组成反映了饮食的组成，但反刍动物的消化过程通常使脂肪酸更饱和/或通过异构化降低熔点。动物脂肪中饱和脂肪酸的比例很高，链长为 14 至 18 个碳原子。乳脂中约含有 20%的 4 ~ 14 个碳原子的脂肪酸。这种短链脂肪酸（SCFA）和中链脂肪酸（MCFA）的含量是乳脂特有的，部分程度上影响了黄油的物理性质，例如熔点以及令人愉悦的味道。牛肉和猪肉脂肪中，含有 40%甚至更多的长链脂肪酸（LCFA）。包括鱼油在内的动物脂肪的多不饱和脂肪酸含量一般在 4.0 %~30%之间。但是，和其他陆地动物相反，冬眠动物的储存脂肪（如棕熊或黑熊）富含 PUFA，并含有大量的 γ-亚麻酸（LNA）。动物脂和植物脂在组成、消化、吸收以及摄入脂肪中所含固醇的组成和浓度方面的差异，会影响储存脂肪的代谢和组成。

1.2.2.3 Lipid Functions
脂类功能

(1) Energy Reserve

能量储备

As humans grow, mature, and age, characteristic changes in body composition occur. These changes are influenced by gender, heredity, stature, and of course, food supply in relation to need. One of these changes involves the deposition of fat in adipocytes (fat cells), producing substantial deposits of body fat that can insulate against body heat loss and serve as an energy reserve. Various procedures have been used to measure the size of these adipose deposits, and about 59 million adult Americans have fat stores so large as to be classified as obese. In these individuals, intake of energy far exceeds their energy expenditure. Fat is an efficient energy storage form because every gram of fat can provide more than twice as much energy in support of body metabolism as can carbohydrate or protein. However, excess body fat is often accompanied by health problems—a serious consequence of too much food and too little exercise. Unfortunately, too little food characterizes the lives of much of the world's population, and the benefits of a substantial body fat store to buffer short periods of food scarcity are not available to them.

随着人类的生长、成熟和衰老，身体组分会发生特征性的变化。这些变化受性别、遗传、身材的影响，当然还受与需求相关的食品供应影响。其中一种变化涉及脂细胞（脂肪细胞）中的脂肪沉积，产生大量的身体脂肪沉积，可以防止身体热量损失并作为能量储备。人们使用了各种方法来测量这些脂肪沉积粒的大小。大约 59000000 名美国成年人因储存脂肪过多而被列为肥胖。在这些人身上，能量的摄入远远超过他们的能量消耗。脂肪是一种高效的能量存储形式，因为每克脂肪为支持身体代谢提供的能量是碳水化合物或者蛋白质的两倍多。然而，身体脂肪过多往往伴随着健康问题——这就是摄入食物过多和锻炼过少导致的严重后果。不幸的是，食物太少是世界上大部分人的生活特点，他们无法获得大量的体内脂肪来缓冲短时间的食物匮乏。

(2) Thermogenesis

产热

Specialized body fat deposits, with an unusually rich blood vessel supply, have been designated brown adipose tissue. They are characterized by the ability to generate heat in response to food intake or to prolonged cold exposure by a process called nonshivering thermogenesis. Although present in newborns, particularly between the shoulder blades (interscapular area) and useful in elevating body temperature after birth, brown adipose tissue appears to play little role in maintaining the body temperature of human adults.

具有异常丰富的血液供应的特殊体脂肪沉积被称为棕色脂肪组织。它们的特点是能够在摄入食物或长时间的寒冷暴露下产生热量，这一过程被称为非颤抖产热。尽管棕色脂肪组织存在于新生儿体内，特别是肩胛骨（肩胛间区域）之间，并有助于提高出生后的体温，但它在维持成人体温方面几乎没有什么作用。

(3) Cell Membrane Structure and Function

细胞膜的结构和功能

Particular fatty acids are found in phospholipids that are critical for cell membrane structure and function. They provide physical support to the membranes, serve as a source of physiologically active compounds, and modulate cross-membrane movement of metabolically active substances.

在磷脂中发现的特殊脂肪酸对细胞膜的结构和功能至关重要。它们对膜提供物理支持，作为生理活性物质的来源，并调节代谢活性物质的跨膜运动。

(4) Nutrient Transport

营养素的运输

In addition to serving as a source of essential fatty acids, lipids are involved in the transport of the lipid-soluble vitamins A, D, E, and K and provitamin A carotenoids.

除了作为一种必需脂肪酸的来源，脂质还参与了脂溶性维生素 A、维生素 D、维生素 E、维生素 K 和维生素 A 原类胡萝卜素的运输。

(5) Hormonal Activity

激素活性

Body fat is no longer considered as just a source of stored energy. In recent years, white adipose tissue has been shown to secrete over ten peptide hormones—compounds that contain two or more amino acids. By means of these hormones (such as leptin, which affects appetite and the immune system), fat serves also as an endocrine organ, sustaining energy homeostasis through regulation of glucose and lipid metabolism, modulating the immune response, and influencing reproduction.

身体脂肪不再仅仅被认为是储存能量的来源。近年来，白色脂肪组织已被证明分泌十种肽激素——含有两种或两种以上氨基酸的化合物。通过这些激素（如影响食欲和免疫系统的瘦素），脂肪还充当内分泌器官，通过调节葡萄糖和脂质代谢、调节免疫反应和影响生殖来维持能量稳态。

1.2.3 Homework

课后作业

1.2.3.1 Sentence Translation

句子翻译

(1) Original Sentences

原句

① Lipids are important energy sources and also help form cell membranes.

② Saturated fatty acids have no double bonds between carbon atoms, making them solid at room temperature.

③ Short-chain fatty acids are easily absorbed by the intestines, while long-chain fatty acids require bile salts for digestion.

④ Fat metabolism is a key pathway for energy supply, involvingfatty acid oxidation and the tricarboxylic acid (TCA) cycle.

⑤ Activating brown adipose tissue increases energy expenditure, showing potential benefits against obesity and metabolic syndrome.

⑥ Hormones influence the body's energy balance and physiological functions by regulating metabolic pathways.

(2) Translations

翻译

① 脂类是重要的能量来源，同时也参与构成细胞膜。

② 饱和脂肪酸的碳原子之间没有双键，因此它们在室温下呈固态。

③ 短链脂肪酸易被肠道吸收，而长链脂肪酸则需要胆汁盐参与消化。

④ 脂肪代谢是能量供应的关键途径，涉及脂肪酸氧化和三羧酸循环。

⑤ 激活棕色脂肪组织可增加能量消耗，对改善肥胖和代谢综合征具有潜在作用。

⑥ 激素通过调控代谢途径影响机体的能量平衡和生理功能。

(3) 翻译文中划线句子。

1.2.3.2 Common Sentence Patterns of Scientific Papers

科技论文常见句型

① The specific nutritional importance of the carbohydrates has been more and more emphasized...

② Carbohydrates can be found in ...

③ Carbohydrates can be classified according to several criteria, including those based on the structure and number of sugar molecules, as well as …

④ The fiber content of carbohydrate foods, which is largely indigestible by humans, plays an important role in …

⑤ Lipids form a group of compounds, the chemical nature of which is extremely varied.

⑥ TAG represent the bulk of ingested lipids.

⑦ Based on structure, lipids can be classified as derived, simple, or complex.

⑧ When seeds such as sunflowers or soybeans ripen, their starch content decreases as the fat content increases.

⑨ Vegetable oils obtained from corn, soybean, and sunflower seed contain less than 15% saturated FA and more than 55% polyunsaturated FA (PUFA)

⑩ As humans grow, mature, and age, characteristic changes in body composition occur.

⑪ Particular fatty acids are found in phospholipids that are critical for cell membrane structure and function.

1.3 Vitamins and Minerals

1.3 维生素和矿物质

1.3.1 Glossary

专业词汇分析

① vitamin *n.* [生化] 维生素

[记忆窍门] 维他命发音和含义都更贴切：vi（音似维）-ta（音似他）-min（音似命），维持生命的营养素就是维生素。

② mineral *n.* 矿物质

[记忆窍门] mine（矿）。

③ nerve signal 神经信号

[记忆窍门] nerve 神经；signal 信号。

④ formulate *v.* 用公式表示，明确表达

[记忆窍门] formula *n.* 公式；late（动词词缀）。

⑤ interplay *v.* 相互影响，相互作用

[记忆窍门] inter（相互的）+ play（起作用）。

⑥ micronutrient *n.* [生化] 微量营养素

[记忆窍门] micro（微小的）+ nutrient（营养）。

⑦ scurvy *n.* [内科] 坏血病

⑧ blindness *n.* 失明

[记忆窍门] blind *adj.* 失明的，盲的； -ness 名词后缀。

⑨ deficiency *n.* 缺陷，缺点

[记忆窍门] de 否定前缀，“非，不”，efficient“有效的”，cy 名词后缀，无效率也是一种缺点。

⑩ rickets *n.* [内科] 佝偻病

⑪ fortified milk *n.* 强化奶

[记忆窍门] fortify *v.* 加强，增强。

⑫ block *v.* 阻止，阻塞

[记忆窍门] b（拼音 bu，不）+lock（锁）→不锁→妨碍、阻碍。

⑬ assimilate *v.* 吸收，使同化

[记忆窍门] similar *adj.* 相似的；as similar（相似的）+ late（动词后缀）。

⑭ copper *n.* 铜

[记忆窍门] 铜的元素符号“Cu”

⑮ minor *adj.* 次要的，微量的

[记忆窍门] min 同 minimum，最小值。

⑯ overload *n.* 超载，过量

[记忆窍门] 复合词，词头 over-，“越过，在…之上”；load *v.* 负载，装载量。

⑰ manganese *n.* [化学] 锰

[记忆窍门] 化学符号 Mn。

⑱ skeletal deformities 骨头畸形

[记忆窍门] 词头 skele-形似 skeleton *n.* 骨头； -tal 是形容词词尾；deform *adj.* 畸形的。

⑲ water-soluble vitamin 水溶性维生素

⑳ be packed into 充满

㉑ bloodstream *n.* [生理] 血流，血液的流动

[记忆窍门] blood（血液）+ stream（溪流）。

㉒ digestion *n.* 消化

[记忆窍门] digest *v.* 消化；tion 是名词词尾。

㉓ urine *n.* 尿

㉔ biotin *n.* [生化] 生物素

㉕ riboflavin *n.* [生化] 核黄素

㉖ folic acid *n.* [生化] 叶酸

㉗ thiamin *n.* [生化] 硫胺

㉘ niacin *n.* [生化] 烟酸

㉙ pantothenic acid *n.* [生化] 泛酸

㉚ coenzyme *n.* [生化] 辅酶

[记忆窍门] co-（表“共同的，辅助的”一类词的词头）+ enzyme *n.* 酶。

㉛ blood vessel wall 血管壁

[记忆窍门] blood（血液）+ vessel（脉管）+ wall（墙壁，似墙之物）。

㉜ metabolise *v.* 使新陈代谢

[记忆窍门] metabo-是新陈代谢的词头+ lise 成为动词。

㉝ multiply *v.* 增殖，繁殖

[记忆窍门] 词缀 multi 表示“多”。

㉞ replenish *v.* 补充，再装满

[记忆窍门] re（“重新”词头）+ plenish *v.* 给…装备。

㉟ lymph channel 淋巴管道

[记忆窍门] lymph *n.* [解剖] 淋巴；channel *n.* 通道，管路。

㊱ intestinal *adj.* 肠的

[记忆窍门] intestine *n.* [解剖] 肠； al 形容词词缀，合起来就是肠的。

㊲ gastrointestinal *adj.* 胃肠道的

[记忆窍门] gastro- *adj.* 胃的；intestinal *n.* 肠的。

㊳ vision *n.* 视力，视野

[记忆窍门] visit *v.* “参观”的意思，这个单词前面的 vis 是表示“看”的一类词的词根，后面加上名词后缀 ion，合起来就是“视力，视野”的意思。

㊴ major mineral 常量矿物质；

㊵ minor mineral 微量矿物质

[记忆窍门] major 主要的；minor 次要的，较小的。

㊶ hamper *v.* 妨碍

㊷ excrete *v.* 排泄，分泌（从血液、组织或器官中分离废物）

[记忆窍门] ex-“外、离”的词头；crete-形似 create，创造-创造出废物-排泄。

㊸ immune response *n.* [生理] 免疫反应

[记忆窍门] 拆分+谐音联想法，immu 英语谐音“疫苗”，ne 中文谐音“能”谐音联想：疫苗能提供“免疫的”。

㊹ hemoglobin *n.* [生理] 血红蛋白

[记忆窍门] hemo（出血）+ globin（球蛋白）。

㊺ decay *v.* 腐烂 腐坏

[记忆窍门] de-（向下）+ cay（礁岩），向下掉的礁岩就是腐烂。

㊻ exacerbate *v.* 使加剧，使恶化

[记忆窍门] acerbate *v.* 使发怒，使烦恼；ex-是表示“出去，向外”一类词的词头，在 exacerbate 中，它表示一种向外的扩散或加剧的趋势+ acerbate 加剧、恶化。

㊼ thyroid *n.* 甲状腺；*adj.* 甲状腺的

㊽ hormone *n.* 激素

[记忆窍门] 谐音记忆荷尔蒙（激素）

1.3.2 Texts and Translations

课文及翻译

Vitamins and minerals 维生素与矿物质

Key Points

文章要点

① Vitamins and minerals are essential nutrients because they perform hundreds of roles in the body.

② There is a fine line between getting enough of these nutrients (which is healthy) and getting too much (which can end up harming you).

③ Eating a healthy diet remains the best way to get sufficient amounts of the vitamins and minerals you need.

① 维生素和矿物质是必不可少的营养素，因为它们在人体内起着数百种的作用。

② 在获得足够的营养物质（有益健康的）和摄入过多（最终伤害人体）之间是有细微的界限的。

③ 健康饮食仍然是获得足够的维生素和矿物质的最好方式。

1.3.2.1 Essential Nutrients for Your Body

人体必需营养素

Every day, your body produces skin, muscle, and bone. It churns out rich red blood that carries nutrients and oxygen to remote outposts, and it sends nerve signals skipping along thousands of miles of brain and body pathways. It also formulates chemical messengers that shuttle from one organ to another, issuing the instructions that help sustain your life.

每天，你的身体都在生成组成皮肤、肌肉和骨骼的细胞。它分泌出丰富的红色血液，把营养物质和氧气输送到较远的部位，并沿着数千英里❶的大脑和身体路径发送神经信号。它还形成了从一个器官穿梭到另一个器官的化学信使，发出有助于维持你生命的指令。

But to do all this, your body requires some raw materials. These include at least 30 vitamins, minerals, and dietary components that your body needs but cannot manufacture on its own in sufficient amounts.

但要做到这一切，你的身体需要一些原料。这些包括至少 30 种维生素、矿物质和膳食组分。这些成分是你的身体所需的，但自身不能合成足够的量。

Vitamins and minerals are considered essential nutrients—because acting in concert, they perform hundreds of roles in the body. They help shore up bones, heal wounds, and bolster your immune system. They also convert food into energy, and repair cellular damage.

❶ 1 英里=1609.344m。

维生素和矿物质被认为是必需的营养素。通过协调作用，它们在体内发挥着数百个重要的功能。它们帮助支撑骨骼、愈合伤口，并增强你的免疫系统。它们还将食物转化为能量，修复细胞损伤。

But trying to keep track of what all these vitamins and minerals do can be confusing. Read enough articles on the topic, and your eyes may swim with the alphabet-soup references to these nutrients, which are known mainly by their initials (such as vitamins A, B, C, D, E and K to name just a few).

但试图跟踪所有这些维生素和矿物质的作用是很复杂的事情。阅读大量有关该主题的文章时，你的眼睛可能会被这些主要以首字母缩写命名的营养素（如维生素 A、维生素 B、维生素 C、维生素 D、维生素 E 和维生素 K 等等）的字母表所淹没。

1.3.2.2 Micronutrients with a Big Role in the Body 体内具有重要作用的微量营养素

Vitamins and minerals are often called micronutrients because your body needs only tiny amounts of them. Yet failing to get even those small quantities virtually guarantees disease. Here are a few examples of diseases that can result from vitamin deficiencies:

① Scurvy: Old-time sailors learned that living for months without fresh fruits or vegetables-the main sources of vitamin C-causes bleeding gums and listlessness of scurvy.

② Blindness: In some developing countries, people still become blind from vitamin A deficiency.

③ Rickets: A deficiency in vitamin D can cause rickets, a condition marked by soft, weak bones that can lead to skeletal deformities such as bowed legs. Partly to combat rickets, the U.S. has fortified milk with vitamin D since the 1930s.

维生素和矿物质通常被称为微量营养素，因为你的身体对它们的需求量很小。但是如果未能摄取足够的这些微量的成分，也肯定会导致疾病。以下是几个维生素缺乏造成疾病的例子：

① 坏血病：古代的水手们发现在海上生活几个月，因为缺乏新鲜水果或蔬菜（维生素 C 的主要来源）而导致坏血病，出现牙龈出血和无精打采的症状。

② 失明：在一些发展中国家，仍然有人缺乏维生素 A 导致失明。

③ 佝偻病：缺乏维生素 D 会导致佝偻病，这种疾病的特征是骨头又软又脆弱，会导致骨骼发育畸形，比如出现弓形腿。在一定程度上为了防治佝偻病，美国自 20 世纪 30 年代开始在牛奶中添加维生素 D。

(1) The Difference between Vitamins and Minerals

维生素和矿物质之间的区别

Although they are all considered micronutrients, vitamins and minerals differ in basic ways. Vitamins are organic and can be broken down by heat, air, or acid. Minerals are inorganic and hold on to their chemical structure.

So why does this matter? It means the minerals in soil and water easily find their way into your body through the plants, fish, animals, and fluids you consume. But it's tougher to shuttle vitamins from food and other sources into your body because cooking, storage, and simple exposure to air can inactivate these more fragile compounds.

虽然维生素和矿物质都被当作微量营养素，但是它们的本质不同。维生素是有机的，可以被高温、空气或酸所破坏。矿物质是无机的，化学结构非常稳定。

这些有什么关系呢？这意味着土壤和水中的矿物质很容易通过你摄入的植物、鱼类、动物和液体进入到你的身体中。但很难通过食物或其他来源将维生素运送到你的身体里，因为烹饪、存储和单纯暴露在空气中就可使这些更脆弱的化合物失去活性。

(2) Interacting—In Good Ways and Bad

交互作用——好的和坏的方面

Many micronutrients interact. Vitamin D enables your body to pluck calcium from food sources passing through your digestive tract rather than harvesting it from your bones. Vitamin C helps you absorb iron.

The interplay of micronutrients isn't always cooperative, however. For example, vitamin C blocks your body's ability to assimilate the essential mineral copper. And even a minor overload of the mineral manganese can worsen iron deficiency.

许多微量营养素是相互影响的。维生素 D 能够使机体从经过消化道的食物中获取钙，而不是从骨骼中获得。维生素 C 帮助吸收铁。

然而，微量营养素之间并不总是协同作用的。例如，维生素 C 会阻碍身体吸收必需矿物质铜。矿物质锰稍有过量，就会加重铁的缺乏。

(3) A Closer Look at Water-Soluble Vitamins

近距离观察水溶性维生素

① Water-soluble vitamins are packed into the watery portions of the foods you eat. They are absorbed directly into the bloodstream as food is broken down during digestion or as a supplement dissolves. Because much of your body consists of water, many of the water-soluble vitamins circulate easily in your body. Your kidneys continuously regulate levels of water-soluble vitamins, shunting excesses out of the body in your urine. Water-soluble vitamins including B vitamins: Biotin (vitamin B_7), Riboflavin (vitamin B_2), Folic acid (folate, vitamin B_9), Thiamin (vitamin B_1), Niacin (vitamin B_3), Vitamin B_6, Pantothenic acid (vitamin B_5), Vitamin B_{12}; Vitamin C.

水溶性维生素存在于所吃食物的含水的部分。当食物在消化过程中被分解或作为一种营养补充剂溶解时，水溶性维生素被直接吸收进入血液中。因为身体的大部分是由水组成的，许多水溶性维生素很容易在体内循环。肾脏会不断调节水溶性维生素水平，将多余的部分随尿液排出体外。水溶性维生素包括 B 族维生素如生物素（维生素 B_7）、核黄素（维生素 B_2）、叶酸（维生素 B_9）、硫胺素（维生素 B_1）、烟酸（维生素 B_3）、维生素 B_6、泛酸（维生素 B_5）、维生素 B_{12}，和维生素 C。

② What They Do?

水溶性维生素的作用

Although water-soluble vitamins have many tasks in the body, one of the most important is helping to free the energy found in the food you eat. Others helps keep tissues healthy.

虽然水溶性维生素在体内有很多功能，最重要的功能之一是帮助释放你所吃食物中的能量。其他还包括帮助保持身体组织健康。

③ Words to the Wise

知识延伸

Contrary to popular belief, some water-soluble vitamins can stay in the body for long periods of time. You probably have several years' supply of vitamin B_{12} in your liver. And even folic acid and vitamin C stores can last more than a couple of days.

Generally, though, water-soluble vitamins should be replenished every few days. Just be aware that there is a small risk that consuming large amounts of some of these micronutrients through supplements may be quite harmful. For example, very high doses of B_6-many times the recommended amount of 1.3 milligrams (mg) per day for adults-can damage nerves, causing numbness and muscle weakness.

与普遍的看法相反，一些水溶性维生素在体内能停留很长一段时间。你的肝脏中可能有足够你使用几年的维生素 B_{12}。甚至是叶酸和维生素 C 的储存也可以持续超过数日。

一般来说，水溶性维生素应该每隔几天补充一下。只是要注意一个小的风险，通过食用营养品摄入大量的微量营养素可能会对人体造成危害。例如，成人每天建议维生素 B_6 的食用量为 1.3mg，如果服用非常高剂量的维生素 B_6——数倍于推荐量，会损伤神经，导致麻木和肌肉无力。

(4) A Closer Look at Fat-Soluble Vitamins

近距离观察脂溶性维生素

① Rather than slipping easily into the bloodstream like most water-soluble vitamins, fat-soluble vitamins gain entry to the blood via lymph channels in the intestinal wall. Many fat-soluble vitamins travel through the body only under escort by proteins that act as carriers. Fatty foods and oils are reservoirs for the four fat-soluble vitamins. Within your body, fat tissues and the liver act as the main holding pens for these vitamins and release them as needed.

To some extent, you can think of these vitamins as time-release micronutrients. It's possible to consume them every now and again, perhaps in doses weeks or months apart rather than daily, and still get your fill. Your body squirrels away the excess and doles it out gradually to meet your needs. Fat-soluble: Vitamin A, Vitamins D, Vitamin E, Vitamin K.

脂溶性维生素不像大多数水溶性维生素那样容易进入血液，而是通过肠壁的淋巴通道进入血液。许多脂溶性维生素只有在载体蛋白质的携带下才能进入人体。高脂食物和食用油是四种脂溶性维生素的储存库。在你的身体中，脂肪组织和肝脏是这些维生素的主要储存位置，需要时会释放出来。

在某种程度上，你可以认为这些维生素是定时释放的微量营养素。它们可以时不时地被利用，或许可以每隔几周或几个月补充而不必每天，仍然可以维持足够的水平。你的身体会存储过剩的部分然后逐渐释放来满足身体的需求。脂溶性维生素指：维生素 A、维生素 D、维生素 E 和维生素 K。

② What They Do

脂溶性维生素的作用

Together, this vitamin quartet helps keep your eyes, skin, lungs, gastrointestinal tract, and nervous system in good repair. Here are some of the other essential roles these vitamins play:

a. Build bones. Bone formation would be impossible without vitamins A, D, and K.

b. Protect vision. Vitamin A also helps keep cells healthy and protects your vision.

c. Interact favorably. Without vitamin E, your body would have difficulty absorbing and storing vitamin A.

d. Protect the body. Vitamin E also acts as an antioxidant (a compound that helps protect the body against damage from unstable molecules).

这四种维生素有助于你的眼睛、皮肤、肺、胃肠道和神经系统保持良好的状态。以下是这些维生素其他的重要作用：

构建骨骼：如果没有维生素 A、维生素 D、维生素 K，骨骼是不可能形成的。

保护视力：维生素 A 也有助于保持细胞的健康并保护你的视力。

更好的协同作用：没有维生素 E，你的身体很难吸收和储存维生素 A。

保护身体：维生素 E 也可以作为一种抗氧化剂（保护身体免受不稳定分子的损伤）。

③ Words to the Wise

知识延伸

Because fat-soluble vitamins are stored in your body for long periods, toxic levels can build up. This is most likely to happen if you take supplements. It's very rare to get too much of a vitamin just from food.

脂溶性维生素可以在你的体内长期储存，因此会产生毒性。这种情况最有可能发生在你服用补充剂之后。仅从食物中获取维生素一般不会出现过量的情况。

(5) A Closer Look at Major Minerals

近距离观察常量矿物质

① The body needs, and stores, fairly large amounts of the major minerals. These minerals are no more important to your health than the trace minerals; they're just present in your body in greater amounts. Major minerals travel through the body in various ways. Potassium, for example, is quickly absorbed into the bloodstream, where it circulates freely and is excreted by the kidneys, much like a water-soluble vitamin. Calcium is more like a fat-soluble vitamin because it requires a carrier for absorption and transport. Major minerals including phosphorus, sulfur, magnesium, sodium, potassium, chloride, calcium.

身体需要和储存了相当大量的常量矿物质。这些矿物质对你的健康并非比微量矿物质更重要，只是它们在人体内的含量更高而已。常量矿物质在体内的流动方式多种多样。例如，钾会很快被血液吸收，在血液中自由循环，然后由肾脏排出体外，这与水溶性维生素很相似。钙更像脂溶性维生素，因为它需要载体来吸收和运输。常量矿物质包括磷、硫、镁、钠、钾、氯、钙。

② What They Do

常量矿物质的作用

One of the key tasks of major minerals is to maintain the proper balance of water in the body. Sodium, chloride, and potassium take the lead in doing this. Three other major minerals—calcium, phosphorus, and magnesium—are important for healthy bones. Sulfur helps stabilize protein structures, including some of those that make up hair, skin, and nails.

常量矿物质的一个主要作用是维持体内适当的水平衡。钠、氯和钾起主要作用，其他三种常量矿物质——钙、磷、镁对骨骼的健康非常重要。硫有助于稳定蛋白质结构，包括构成头发、皮肤和指甲的一些蛋白质。

③ Words to the Wise

知识延伸

Having too much of one major mineral can result in a deficiency of another. These sorts of imbalances are usually caused by overloads from supplements, not food sources. Here are two examples:

a. Salt overload. Calcium binds with excess sodium in the body and is excreted when the body senses that sodium levels must be lowered. That means that if you ingest too much sodium through table salt or processed foods, you could end up losing needed calcium as your body rids itself of the surplus sodium.

b. Excess phosphorus. Likewise, too much phosphorus can hamper your ability to absorb magnesium.

某种常量矿物质摄入太多，会导致另一种矿物质缺乏。这类失衡通常是因为食用了过量的营养补充剂而非通过食物摄入。这里有两个例子：

盐过量：身体感觉到钠的水平需要降低的时候，钙可以和体内多余的钠结合，结合物被排出。这意味着，如果你通过食盐或加工食品摄入过多的钠，你可能会在身体排出多余的钠时失去所需的钙。

磷过量：同样，过多的磷也会阻碍人体对镁的吸收。

(6) A Closer Look at Trace Minerals

微量矿物质

① A thimble could easily contain the distillation of all the trace minerals normally found in your body. Yet their contributions are just as essential as those of major minerals such as calcium and phosphorus, which each account for more than a pound of your body weight. Trace minerals:Chromium, Manganese, Copper, Molybdenum, Fluoride, Iodine, Zinc, Selenium, Iron.

人体内所有正常存在的微量矿物质，若经提炼浓缩，一个顶针大小的容器便能轻松装下。然而这些微量矿物质的贡献与钙和磷等常量矿物质的贡献一样重要，它们各占人体质量的一磅[1]多。微量矿物质有铬、锰、铜、钼、氟、碘、锌、硒、铁。

② What They Do

微量矿物质的作用

Trace minerals carry out a diverse set of tasks. Here are a few examples:

a. Iron is best known for ferrying oxygen throughout the body.

b. Fluoride strengthens bones and wards off tooth decay.

c. Zinc helps blood clot, is essential for taste and smell, and bolsters the immune response.

d. Copper helps form several enzymes, one of which assists with iron metabolism and the creation of hemoglobin, which carries oxygen in the blood.

The other trace minerals perform equally vital jobs, such as helping to block damage to body cells and forming parts of key enzymes or enhancing their activity.

微量矿物质的作用多种多样。以下是几个例子：

a. 众所周知，铁的功能是将氧气运送到全身。

b. 氟化物可以增强骨骼，防止蛀牙。

c. 有助于凝血，对味觉和嗅觉很重要，可以增强免疫反应。

[1] 1 磅=0.45kg。

d. 铜有助于几种酶的形成，其中一种酶有助于铁的代谢和血红蛋白的生成，血红蛋白在血液中携带氧气。

其他微量矿物质执行同样重要的工作，比如有助于保护身体细胞免受破坏，形成部分关键酶或增强它们的活性。

③ Words to the Wise

知识延伸

Trace minerals interact with one another, sometimes in ways that can trigger imbalances. Too much of one can cause or contribute to a deficiency of another. Here are some examples:

a. A minor overload of manganese can exacerbate iron deficiency. Having too little can also cause problems.

b. When the body has too little iodine, thyroid hormone production slows, causing sluggishness and weight gain as well as other health concerns. The problem worsens if the body also has too little selenium.

The difference between "just enough"and "too much" of the trace minerals is often tiny. Generally, food is a safe source of trace minerals, but if you take supplements, it's important to make sure you're not exceeding safe levels.

微量矿物质之间会相互影响，有时会引发失衡。一种矿物质过多会导致或加剧另一种矿物质的缺乏。下面是一些例子：

锰轻微过量会加重缺铁，而锰太少也会导致问题。

当身体碘含量过低时，甲状腺激素的生成放缓，导致行动迟缓、体重增加以及其他健康问题。缺硒会使这种情况更加恶化。

微量矿物质的"刚刚够"和"过多"之间的区别往往很小。一般来说，食物是微量矿物质的安全来源，但如果你服用补充剂，就必须确保没有超过安全水平。

1.3.3 Homework

课后作业

1.3.3.1 Sentence Translation

句子翻译

(1) Texts

原文

① Vitamins and minerals are often called micronutrients because your body needs only tiny amounts of them. Yet failing to get even those small quantities virtually guarantees disease.

② The interplay of micronutrients isn't always cooperative, however. For example, vitamin C blocks your body's ability to assimilate the essential mineral copper.

③ Although water-soluble vitamins have many tasks in the body, one of the most important is helping to free the energy found in the food you eat. Others helps keep tissues healthy.

④ Rather than slipping easily into the bloodstream like most water-soluble vitamins, fat-soluble vitamins gain entry to the blood via lymph channels in the intestinal wall.

⑤ Calcium is more like a fat-soluble vitamin because it requires a carrier for absorption and transport.

⑥ To take targeted measures in poverty alleviation, the nutrition and health of children in poverty-stricken areas must be paid attention to, because it will not only affect the growth of children, but also affect their future education level and human capital accumulation, resulting in a further increase in the urban-rural gap in the future.

⑦ A nutritional intervention study carried out on students in poor rural areas found that the addition of micronutrients (such as multivitamins) in the lunch of primary school students can effectively reduce the anemia rate of students and significantly improve their academic performance.

(2) Translations

翻译

① 维生素和矿物质通常被称为微量营养素，因为你的身体对它们的需求量很小。但是如果未能摄取够这些微量的成分，也肯定会导致疾病。

② 然而，微量营养素之间并不总是协同作用的。例如，维生素 C 会阻碍身体吸收必需矿物质——铜。

③ 水溶性维生素在体内有很多功能，最重要的功能之一是帮助释放你所吃食物中的能量。其他功能还包括帮助保持组织健康。

④ 脂溶性维生素不像大多数水溶性维生素那样容易进入血液，而是通过肠壁的淋巴通道进入血液。

⑤ 钙更像脂溶性维生素，因为它需要载体来吸收和运输。

⑥ 精准扶贫必须关注贫困地区儿童营养健康问题，因为这不仅会影响儿童阶段的成长，还会影响其未来的教育水平和人力资本积累，造成未来城乡差距的进一步加剧。

⑦ 对贫困农村地区学生开展营养干预研究发现，在小学生午餐中额外补充微量营养素（如多种维生素），可有效降低学生贫血率，还能显著提高学生的学业表现。

(3) 翻译文中划线句子

1.3.3.2 Common Sentence Patterns of Scientific Papers 科技论文常见句型

① 研究现状

People have reported a variety of…

Nevertheless，… remains unclear.

② 研究目的

We used data from … to …

③ 定义概念

Something is defined as …

The poverty-income ratio (PIR) was defined as …

④ 实验分组

Something was categorized as follows …

Something was divided into …, as seen in the following tabulation…

⑤ 数量描述

This number is equivalent to …

⑥ 表格结果描述

Table 1 and Table 2 show （that）…

⑦ 结果描述（experiment description）

Of those taking vitamin and mineral supplements, 43% were male and 57% were female; the mean age of those taking vitamin and mineral supplements was 37 years …

From these experiments, we can conclude that …

We found that 62.1% of all folic acid users…

⑧ 结果的意义

These results suggest that…

⑨ 导致结论

Further study to … could prove valuable

Chapter 2 Food Chemistry
第 2 章 食品化学

2.1 Food Additives
2.1 食品添加剂

2.1.1 Glossary
专业词汇分析

① acidulant *n.* 酸化剂

[记忆窍门] acid，酸，酸的；lant，陈化尿液（用于清洁地板）。

② additive *n.* 添加剂

[记忆窍门] add，*v.* 添加，增加；-ive 形容词后缀。该词有形容词和名词两个词性，此处是名词。

③ anti-browning agent 抗褐变剂

[记忆窍门] anti-，是表示"反""抗"意思的词前缀；brown，褐色，变成褐色；agent，药剂。

④ antifoaming agent 消泡剂

[记忆窍门] anti-，是表示"反""抗"意思的词前缀；foam，泡沫，起泡；agent，药剂。

⑤ antimicrobial *adj.* 抗菌的；*n.* 杀菌剂

[记忆窍门] anti-，表示"对抗、防止"，而 microbiac 表示"微生物的"。因此，可以将 antimicrobial 理解为"防止微生物的"，这样有助于记忆其含义，形容词为"抗菌的，抗微生物的"，名词为"抗菌剂、杀菌剂"。

⑥ metallic aftertaste　金属后味

[记忆窍门]　metal，金属，金属的，以金属覆盖；-lic，形容词后缀；after，在……之后；taste，味道，品尝。

⑦ aspartame　*n.* 阿斯巴甜，又名天冬甜素

[记忆窍门]　aspart，天冬胰岛素。

⑧ monoand diglyceride　甘油单酯和甘油二酯物

[记忆窍门]　mono-，单个，单一；di-，双的，两个；glycine，甘氨酸；glyceride，甘油酯。

⑨ aspartic acid　天冬氨酸

[记忆窍门]　aspart，天冬胰岛素；-ic，构成形容词的后缀；acid，酸，酸的。

⑩ monosodium glutamate　谷氨酸钠，味精

[记忆窍门]　mono-，单个，单一；sodium，钠；gluta，戊二醛；mate，结伴，伙伴。

⑪ autoxidation　*n.* 自动氧化

[记忆窍门]　auto-，自动，汽车；oxid，氧化，氧化物；-tion，构成名词的后缀。

⑫ neotame　*n.* 纽甜；纽甜素

[记忆窍门]　neo，new 的变形；-tame，驯服，使具有。

⑬ coagulant-bittern　盐卤凝固剂

[记忆窍门]　coagu，凝结；coagulation 混凝；lant，陈化尿液；bitter，苦味，苦啤酒；bittern 盐卤。

⑭ non caloric　无热值的

[记忆窍门]　non，非，无；calorie，卡路里。

⑮ bulking agent　填充剂

[记忆窍门]　bulk，体积，使变大；-ing，构成名词的后缀；agent，药剂。

⑯ non-enzymatic　非酶的

[记忆窍门]　non-，非，无；enzyme，酶；-tic，以……方式，构成形容词的后缀。

⑰ chelating agent　螯合剂

[记忆窍门]　chelate，螯合物，使结合成螯合物；-ing，构成名词的后缀；agent，药剂。

⑱ nucleotide　*n.* 核苷酸

[记忆窍门]　nucleus，核；-tide，具备……方式，构成名词的后缀。

⑲ nitrite　*n.* 亚硝酸盐

[记忆窍门]　nitro，硝基。

⑳ nutraceutical　*n.* 保健品

[记忆窍门]　nutrition，营养；nutra，保健品。

㉑ coloring agent　着色剂

[记忆窍门]　color，颜色，着色；-ing，构成名词的后缀；agent，药剂。

㉒ phosphate　*n.* 磷酸盐

[记忆窍门]　phos，无机磷；磷酸盐；-ate，化学名词后缀，盐。

㉓ dipeptide　*n.* 二肽

[记忆窍门] di-，双，二； peptide，缩氨酸，肽。

㉔ processing aid 加工助剂

[记忆窍门] process，过程，加工；-ing，构成名词的后缀；aid，援助，帮助。

㉕ propellant *n.* 推进剂

[记忆窍门] propel，推进，驱使；lant，陈化尿液（用于清洁地板）。

㉖ dough conditioner *n.* 面团改良剂

[记忆窍门] dough，生面团；condition，条件，使适应，使健康；-er，构成名词的后缀。

㉗ proteinaceous material *n.* 蛋白质类物质

[记忆窍门] protein，蛋白质；-aceous，构成形容词的后缀，具有；material，材料，原料，物质。

㉘ fermentation *n.* 发酵

[记忆窍门] ferment，酵素，使发酵；-tion，构成名词的词尾。

㉙ rancidity *n.* 酸败，腐败，臭败

㉚ emulsifier *n.* 乳化剂

[记忆窍门] emulsum，拉丁文“乳剂”；-sion，构成名词的后缀；emulsion，乳剂，乳液； -ify，构成动词的后缀；-er，构成名词的后缀，再变成名词。

㉛ fat replacer *n.* 脂肪替代物

㉜ saccharin *n.* 糖精

[记忆窍门] 形似 saccharide（糖类）。

㉝ flavor enhancer *n.* 风味增强剂

[记忆窍门] enhance，增强；-er，构成名词的后缀。

㉞ snack *n.* 点心，小吃，快餐

[记忆窍门] snack，拉丁文“部分，片”。

㉟ flavor agent 风味剂

[记忆窍门] flavor，风味，滋味；agent，药剂。

㊱ sodium nitrite 亚硝酸钠

㊲ frozen food 冷冻食品

[记忆窍门] froz，速冻；-en，构成形容词的后缀；frozen，冷冻的，结冰。

㊳ fructan *n.* 果聚糖

[记忆窍门] fruit，水果，产物；fructose，果糖。

㊴ sodium sulfite 亚硫酸钠

[记忆窍门] sodium，钠；sulfit，硫化物；sulfite，亚硫酸盐。

㊵ humectant *n.* 湿润剂

[记忆窍门] humid，潮湿的，湿润的。

㊶ soya protein *n.* 大豆蛋白

[记忆窍门] soya，大豆，黄豆；protein，蛋白质。

㊷ ice cream *n.* 冰激凌

[记忆窍门] ice，冰；cream，奶油，乳酪。

㊸ stabilizer *n.* 稳定剂

[记忆窍门] stable，稳定的；-iz，构成动词的后缀；-er，构成名词的后缀。

㊹ non-toxic *adj.* 无毒，无毒的

[记忆窍门] non-，非，不，词的前缀；tox，毒药；-ic，构成形容词的词尾；toxic，有毒的。

㊺ steroyl-2-lactylate *n.* 硬脂酰-2-乳酸盐

[记忆窍门] steroyl，硬脂酰，十八烷酰；lactate，乳酸钠。

㊻ iodine *n.* 碘

㊼ surface finishing agent 表面光滑剂

[记忆窍门] surface，表面；finishing，完成，精加工；agent，药剂。

㊽ lecithin *n.* 卵磷脂

[记忆窍门] lecithic，有卵黄的。

㊾ texturizing agent 调质剂

[记忆窍门] textur，组织，纹理；-ize（-iz），构成动词的后缀；-ing，构成名词的后缀；agent，药剂。

㊿ low-calorie 低热量的

(51) volatile flavor oil 挥发性风味油

[记忆窍门] volatile，易挥发的，不稳定的；flavor，滋味，味道；oil，油，油脂。

(52) lubricant *n.* 润滑剂

[记忆窍门] lubricate，润滑，涂油；cant，斜面。

(53) water-holding capacity 持水性，持水能力

[记忆窍门] holding，保持，支持；capable，有能力的；capacity，能力。

(54) meat product *n.* 肉制品

(55) metabolism *n.* 新陈代谢

[记忆窍门] metabolite，代谢物；-ism，构成名词的词尾。

2.1.2 Texts and Translations

课文及翻译

Food Additives

Food additives can be defined as a class of substances that are used in food production, processing, storage and packaging to extend shelf-life and to meet the processing needs for improving quality, color, flavor and taste. It is important to use food additives correctly to improve food quality, prevent food spoilage.

食品添加剂

食品添加剂可以定义为：食品生产、加工、储存和包装过程中使用的一类物质，用于延长保质期和提高质量，满足改善色泽、风味和口感的加工需要。正确使用食品添加剂对提高食品质量、防止食品变质具有一定的意义。

There is a long history of human use of food additives. The ancient Chinese had fruit and vegetable juice colored rice cake. In 1500 BC, the coloring of candy was depicted on Egyptian tombstones. Chinese began to use food coagulant——bittern to make bean curd from the Eastern Han Dynasty, which is still in use today. In the Southern Song Dynasty, nitrite, as a preservation and color development of meat products, was used in the production of bacon and spread to Europe in the 13th century. With the development of science and technology, especially the progress of chemical industry technology, many chemical additives are produced, which are far better than those of natural substances, such as preservatives, antioxidants, various synthetic perfumes and edible pigments etc. Variety, scope and content of the use of food additives all increased rapidly. Food additives have become an indispensable part of modern food industrial production, even it has developed into an independent industry. There are more than 14,000 kinds of food additives used internationally. Among them, there are more than 4000 kinds for directly using, About 80% are spices. The FAO/WHO has published more than 700 kinds of food additives. The number is more than 400 by the EEC while 700 by the U.S. In our country, there are 1460 kinds that can fit into the international standard and 936 of them are spices, accounting for 64.1%.

人类使用食品添加剂的历史悠久。中国古代就已用果蔬汁着色糕团。公元前 1500 年，埃及墓碑上就描绘了糖果的着色。中国从东汉时期就开始应用食品凝固剂——盐卤来做豆腐，并沿用至今。南宋时将作为肉制品防腐和显色的亚硝酸盐用于腊肉生产，并于 13 世纪传至欧洲。随着科学技术的发展特别是化学工业技术的进步，出现了许多性能远优于天然物质的化学合成添加剂，如防腐剂、抗氧化剂、各种合成香料和食用色素等。食品添加剂的使用种类、范围和用量均在迅速增加。食品添加剂已成为现代食品工业生产中不可缺少的组成部分，其生产已发展为独立的行业。目前国际上使用的食品添加剂种类已达 14000 多种，其中直接使用的有 4000 多种，约 80%为香料。联合国粮农组织/世界卫生组织已公布 700 多种，欧共体 400 多种，美国 700 多种，我国符合国际标准的有 1460 种，其中香料 936 种，占 64.1%。

2.1.2.1 Classification
分类

(1) More classification methods

食品添加剂的诸多分类方法

Food additives include natural food additives and artificial chemical synthetic products. Natural food additives can be divided into animal and plant extraction and fermentation or enzyme preparation by biotechnology. Artificial synthetic chemicals can be divided into two kinds too, general chemical synthesis and artificial synthesis, such as synthetic perfume, synthetic pigment and so on.

食品添加剂分为天然食品添加剂和人工化学合成品两大类。天然食品添加剂又分为由动植物提取制得和由生物技术发酵或酶法制得两种；人工化学合成品又可分为一般化学合成品与人工合成品，如人工合成香料、人工合成色素等。

Food additives can be divided into twenty-one kinds according to their major functions. They are acidity regulator, anti caking agent, defoaming agent, antioxidant, bleaching agent, leavening agent, gum base agent, colorant, coloring agent, emulsifiers, enzyme preparation, flavor enhancer, flour treatment agent, coating agent, water retention agent, nutrition enhancer, preservatives, stability and curing agent, sweetener and thickener, etc. We will introduce seven major categories in the following.

食品添加剂按其主要功能分为 21 种（编者注：我国《食品添加剂使用标准》GB 2760—2024 分为 24 种），包括酸度调节剂、抗结剂、消泡剂、抗氧化剂、漂白剂、膨松剂、胶基剂、着色剂、护色剂、乳化剂、酶制剂、增味剂、面粉处理剂、被膜剂、保水剂、营养强化剂、防腐剂、稳定和凝固剂、甜味剂和增稠剂。以下我们将介绍七类重要的食品添加剂。

(2) Preservative

防腐剂

There are basically three types of preservatives used in foods: antimicrobial agents, antioxidants, and all anti-browning agents. These additives are used to restrict or prevent the growth of microorganisms. Antimicrobial agents play an important role in extending the shelf life of numerous fast food and convenience foods. In addition, with the increase in food microbial safety problems, the use of antimicrobial agents is more widely.

食品中使用的防腐剂大概有三类：抗菌剂、抗氧化剂和所有抗褐变剂。这些添加剂用于限制或防止微生物的生长。抗菌剂在延长许多快餐和方便食品的保质期方面起着重要作用。另外，随着食品微生物安全问题的增加，抗菌剂的使用更加广泛。

The antioxidants are used to prevent oxidation of lipids and vitamins in food products. They are used primarily to prevent oxidation and subsequent development of rancidity and off-flavor. They vary from natural substances such as vitamins C and E to synthetic chemicals such as butylated hydroxyanisole (BHA) and butylated hydroxytoluene (BTH). The antioxidants are especially effective in preserving dry and frozen foods for an extended period of time.

抗氧化剂用于防止食品中的脂质和维生素氧化。它们主要防止氧化以及酸败和异味的发生。抗氧化剂从维生素 C 和维生素 E 等天然物质到丁基羟基甲苯（BHA）和丁基羟基甲苯（BTH）等合成化学品各不相同。抗氧化剂在长时间保存干燥和冷冻食品方面特别有效。

Anti-browning agents are chemicals used to prevent both enzymatic and non-enzymatic browning in food products, especially for dried fruits or vegetables. Vitamin C, citric acid, sodium sulfite are the most commonly used additives in the category.

抗褐变剂是用于防止食品酶促和非酶促褐变的化学用品，特别适用于干果或蔬菜。维生素 C、柠檬酸和亚硝酸钠是该类别中最常用的添加剂。

(3) Nutrition additives

营养添加剂

Nutritional additives have increased in use in recent years as consumers have become more concerned about and interested in nutrition. Vitamins, which are also used in some cases as preservatives, are commonly added to cereals and cereal products to supplement nutrients lost in processing or to enhance the overall nutritive value of the food. The addition of vitamin D to milk and the addition of B type vitamins to bread have been associated with the prevention of major nutritional deficiencies in the United States. Minerals such as iron and iodine have also been of extreme value in preventing nutritional deficiencies. Like vitamins, the primary use of minerals is in cereal products.

近年来随着消费者对营养的日益关注和兴趣增加，营养添加剂的使用有所增加。维生素有时可用作防腐剂，通常是被添加到谷物或者谷物制品中以补充加工过程中损失的营养素或提高食品的整体营养价值。在美国，向乳中添加维生素 D 以及向面包中添加 B 族维生素与预防严重营养缺乏有关。诸如铁、碘之类的矿物质在预防营养缺乏方面也有极大的价值。与维生素一样，矿物质也主要用于谷物制品。

Amino acids and other proteinaceous are not commonly used in foods. However, lysine is sometimes added to cereals to enhance protein quality. Proteins or proteinaceous materials such as soya protein are sometimes used as nutritional additives, although they are most commonly used as nutritional additives.

食品中通常不使用氨基酸和其他蛋白质类物质。但是，赖氨酸有时被添加到谷物中，以强化蛋白质品质。蛋白质或蛋白质类物质，如大豆蛋白，有时被用作营养添加剂，尽管它们是最常用的营养添加剂。

As consumers pay more attention to dietary fibers, the popularity of fiber additives has increased in recent years. Various cellulose, pectin, and starch derivatives have been used for this purpose. Recently, naturally derived fiber from apples and other fruits as well as sugar beets have been introduced as fiber additives. Fiber additives are not well defined ; And in reality, they provide little or no direct nutritional value, although they do have indirect nutritional benefits.

近年来随着消费者对膳食纤维关注度的增加，膳食纤维添加剂越来越受欢迎。为此，人们使用了各种纤维素、果胶和淀粉衍生物。最近，从苹果和其他水果以及甜菜中分离出来的天然衍生纤维也被用作纤维添加剂。纤维添加剂的定义并不明确，实际上它们几乎不提供直接的营养价值，尽管它们确实有间接的营养益处。

The number of food additives used for special dietary purposes has increased significantly in recent years with an emphasis on the replacement of fat to reduce calories. Fat replacers include many texturizing agents and other carbohydrate, protein, and fat-based systems.

近年来用于特殊膳食目的的食品添加剂的数量明显增加，其重点是替代脂肪以降低热量。脂肪替代物包括很多调制剂和其他以碳水化合物、蛋白质和脂肪类为基础的食物体系。

The increased interest in nutrition has also led to the rapid growth of the functional food or nutraceutical industry, resulting in the development of several additives that play an overall role in health enhancement.

对营养问题的关注也导致了功能性食品或保健品产业的迅速发展，从而开发了几种在增强健康方面发挥整体作用的添加剂。

(4) Sweetener

甜味剂

Sweetener refers to the substances that can make food sweet. It can be classified into natural sweeteners and artificial sweeteners according to the source. Natural sweetener refers to the substances with certain sweetness in natural plants, such as sucrose, glucose, fructose, fructose syrup, etc. They are called sugar and seen as food in our country. Only sugar alcohols or non-sugar sweeteners can be supervised in China. Sugar alcohols used in food mainly include xylitol, sorbitol, mannitol and maltitol etc. Some of their sweetness is the same as sucrose, others maybe hundreds of times of sucrose. In addition, liquorice is another kind of sweetener. It's a sort of traditional Chinese medicine which has been widely used. It is mainly used in cans, seasoning, candies and cookies, while its production depends on the usage.

甜味剂是指能给食品以甜味的物质。甜味剂按来源可分为天然甜味剂和人工合成甜味剂。天然甜味剂系指天然植物中含有的具有一定甜味的物质，如蔗糖、葡萄糖、果糖、果葡糖浆等，在我国通常称为糖，并视为食品。在中国，仅糖醇和非糖甜味剂受监管。食品中使用的糖醇，主要有木糖醇、山梨糖醇、甘露糖醇和麦芽糖醇等。它们的甜度有的与蔗糖相当，有的可能是蔗糖的几百倍。另外，甘草也是另一种甜味剂。它是中药，用途广泛。它主要用于罐头、调味料、糖果及饼干中，其产量取决于使用量。

Synthetic sweeteners refer to those non-carbohydrate compounds that taste sweet. Generally, their sweetness is several times to several hundreds times that of sucrose but without any nutritional value. Synthetic sweeteners have a great variety of categories. The most commonly used one is saccharin and its sodium salts which sweetness equals 300~500 times that of sucrose. Due to the low water solubility, it is used with sodium salt (sodium) based on Food Additives Standards of our country. Besides saccharin and its salts, there are other synthetic sweeteners such as sodium cyclamate(cyclamate), potassium acetylsulfonate, methyl aspartate phenylalanine (aspartame), acesulfame potassium and aspartame (nutrasweet).

人工合成甜味剂是指一些具有甜味的非糖类化合物。它们的甜度一般较蔗糖高几倍至几百倍，但没有任何营养价值。人工合成甜味剂种类很多。使用最多的是糖精及其钠盐，其甜度相当于蔗糖的 300~500 倍。由于糖精的水溶性低，故在我国食品添加剂标准中规定使用它的钠盐（糖精钠）。人工合成的甜味剂除了糖精及其钠盐，还有环己基氨基磺酸钠（甜蜜素）、乙酰磺胺酸钾、天门冬酰苯丙氨酸甲酯（阿斯巴甜）、安赛蜜钾和阿斯巴甜（果乐甜）。

(5) Coloring agents

着色剂

Most coloring agents are used to improve the overall attractiveness of the food. A number of natural and synthetic additives are used to color foods. In addition, sodium nitrite is used not only as an antimicrobial, but also to fix the color of meat by interaction with meat pigment. There has been a controversy regarding their use. Although synthetic coloring agents continue to be used extensively, attention to natural colorants has increased significantly.

大多数着色剂用于改善食品的整体吸引力。许多天然和合成的添加剂用于食品着色。此外，亚硝酸钠不但作为抗菌剂使用，而且也通过与肉中的色素反应固定肉的颜色。对于它们的使用一直存在很多争议。虽然合成色素仍然大量使用，但对于天然色素的关注已经明显增加。

(6) Flavoring agent

风味剂

Flavoring agents comprise the greatest number of additives used in foods. There are three major types of flavoring additives: sweeteners, natural and synthetic flavors, and flavor enhancers.

风味剂是食品中使用最多的添加剂。风味剂主要有三类：甜味剂、天然和合成风味剂以及增味剂。

The most commonly used sweeteners are sucrose, glucose, fructose, and lactose, with sucrose being the most popular. These substances, however, are commonly classified as foods rather than as additives. The most common additives used as sweeteners are low-calorie or non caloric sweeteners such as saccharin and aspartame. These sweeteners are the main driving force for the development of new types of food.

最为常用的甜味剂是蔗糖、葡萄糖、果糖和乳糖，其中蔗糖最受欢迎。然而，这些物质通常被归类为食品，而不是添加剂。用作甜味剂的最常见的添加剂是低热值或无热值甜味剂，如糖精和阿斯巴甜。这些甜味剂是开发新型食品的主要推动力。

In addition to sweeteners, there are more than 1700 natural and synthetic substances used to flavor foods. These additives are, in most cases, mixtures of several chemicals and are used to substitute for natural flavors. Flavoring agent is a kind of chemical mixture which has the same chemical composition as a natural flavor substance and can provide the same flavor. The acidulants, which add a sour taste, often serve other purposes, including preservation.

除了甜味剂外，还有 1700 多种天然和合成物质用于食品调味。多数情况下，这些添加剂是若干化合物的混合物，用来替代天然风味剂。风味剂是一种化学混合物，其化学成分与天然风味物质相同，可以提供相同的风味。增加酸味的酸味剂通常还有其他用途，包括防腐。

Flavor enhancers magnify or modify the flavor of foods and do not contribute any flavor of their own. Flavor enhancers, which include chemicals such as monosodium glutamate and various nucleotides, are often used in Asian foods or in soups to enhance the perception of other tastes.

风味剂会放大或改变食物的味道，本身并不提供任何味道。由诸如谷氨酸钠和各种核苷酸在内的化学剂构成的风味强化剂，通常用于亚洲食品或汤料中以强化其他口味。

(7) Texturizer

调质剂

Although flavoring agents comprise the greatest number of chemicals, texturizing agents are the most used additives. These agents are used to improve the overall texture or taste of food. Emulsifiers and stabilizers are the primary additives in this category. Phosphates and dough conditioners are another class of chemical agents that play a major role in improving food texture. Phosphates are some of the most widely used and serve a number of functions in foods.

虽然风味剂是数量最多的添加剂，但调质剂却是用量最多的添加剂。调质剂用于改善食品的整体质地或口感。这类添加剂主要有乳化剂和稳定剂。磷酸盐和面团改良剂是另一类在改善食品质地方面起主要作用的化学剂。磷酸盐属于使用最广的添加剂，并且在食品中能够起到多种作用。

Emulsifiers include natural substances such as lecithin, monoglycerides and diglycerides, and several synthetic additives. The main function of these additives is to allow flavors and oils to be evenly distributed in the food.

乳化剂包括天然物质，如卵磷脂、甘油单酯和甘油二酯，以及若干合成添加剂。这类添加剂的主要作用是能够使风味剂和油脂均匀地分布于食品。

Stabilizers include several natural gums such as carrageenan as well as natural and modified starches. These additives have been used in products such as ice cream for several years to provide the desired texture and are now also used in dry and liquid products. They are also used to prevent evaporation and deterioration of volatile flavor oils.

稳定剂包括几种天然胶，如卡拉胶以及天然和改性淀粉。这些添加剂已经在冰激凌等产品中使用了几年，以提供所需质地，现在也用于干制和液体产品中。它们也用于防止挥发性风味油的蒸发和变质。

Phosphates are often used to modify the texture of protein or starch-containing foods. These chemicals are especially useful in stabilizing various dairy and meat products. Phosphate surfaces react with proteins or starches to improve the water retention of these natural food components.

磷酸盐常用于含蛋白质或淀粉食品的质地改良。这些化学物质在稳定各种乳制品和肉制品方面特别有用。磷酸盐与蛋白质或淀粉反应，从而可以改善这些天然食品成分的持水能力。

Dough conditioners such as steroyl-2-lactylate and various humectants such as sodium silicoaluminate are also used as texturizing agents under very specific conditions.

面团改良剂，如乳酰化硬脂酸钠，以及各种润湿剂，如硅铝酸钠，在非常特殊的条件下也当作调质剂使用。

(8) Food processing aids

食品加工助剂

Food processing aids are those kinds of auxiliary materials for the needs of food processing, including solvent, adsorption agent, filter aid, purifying agent, etc. Processing aids themselves must comply with the food grade and remove from the products that are provided for their residues. The most common solvents are propylene glycol, glycerin, acetone, ethyl acetate, hexane, etc. Others are ion exchange resin, active carbon, diatomite, talc, kaolin, paraffin, stearic acid and D- mannitol which is dedicated to anti sticky candy.

食品加工助剂是指满足食品加工需要的辅助材料，包括溶剂、吸附剂、助滤剂、净化剂等。加工助剂本身必须符合食品级，并最终能够从产品中去除其残留物。常用的溶剂有丙二醇、甘油、丙酮、醋酸乙酯、己烷等，其他如离子交换树脂、活性炭、硅藻土、滑石粉、高岭土、石蜡、硬脂酸及专用于糖果防黏的 D-甘露糖醇等。

2.1.2.2 Using principles of food additives 食品添加剂的使用原则

(1) Food additives should be non-toxic harmless.

食品添加剂应该是无毒无害的

GB 15193.1—2014《食品安全国家标准 食品安全性毒理学评价程序》(National food safety standard food safety toxicology evaluation procedure) to prove that their long-term use within the limit of use is safe and harmless to humans. Or it must be fully proved it is non-toxic and harmless by using a foreign basis. Nor should there be toxic impurities.

各种食品添加剂必须严格按 GB 15193.1—2014《食品安全国家标准 食品安全性毒理学评价程序》，证明其在使用限量范围内长期使用对人体安全无害，或采用国外依据充分证明其无毒无害，也不应有其他有毒杂质。

Non-toxic harmless also means that after processing and cooking, it can be destroyed and decomposed into non-toxic substances or it can participate in the normal metabolism of the body, but no harmful substances are produced or directly discharged from the body.

无毒无害亦是指经加工、烹调后，可被破坏分解成无毒的物质或可以参加机体正常代谢，但不产生有害的物质或直接排出体外。

(2) Food additives should not destroy the nutritional content of food, or affect the sensory properties of food, and they should have no adverse effect on the quality and flavor of food.

食品添加剂不应破坏食品的营养成分，也不影响食品的感官性状，对食品的质量及风味没有不良影响。

(3) Food additives should use the lowest dose to achieve a significant effect on improving food quality.

食品添加剂应使用最低剂量，以达到显著提高食品质量的效果。

(4) Food additives shall not be used to cover up food defects or as a means of forgery to make crude products and deceive consumers. The peculiar smell of cake is made by using yellow pigment instead of eggs, saccharin instead of granulated sugar, chemical fertilizer (ammonium carbonate, ammonium sulfate) instead of baking soda. The resulting cake has a strong ammonia taste, so it is called smelly cake. Sanjing soda (saccharin, essence, pigment flavor) and other products that simulate food ingredients are called fake and inferior food.

不得使用食品添加剂掩盖食品的缺陷或作为造假手段，制作质量差的产品，欺骗消费者。异味蛋糕是以黄色素代替鸡蛋，糖精代替砂糖，化肥（碳酸铵、硫酸铵）代替小苏打制成的。所制蛋糕氨味浓，故称为异味蛋糕。三精（糖精、香精、色素精）汽水等模拟食品原料的产品称为假冒伪劣食品。

(5) Food additives should be able to be analyzed and identified after being added to food, which is conducive to supervision.

食品添加剂添加到食品中后应能进行分析和鉴定，利于监管。

(6) The main and supplementary foods exclusively made for infants should not be added with artificial sweeteners, colors, flavors, sodium glutamate and other unsuitable food additives, except for food nutrition fortifiers according to regulations.

专供婴幼儿食用的主、辅食品除按规定可加入的食品营养强化剂外，不得添加人工甜味剂、色素、香精、谷氨酸钠及其他不适宜的食品添加剂。

(7) When producing or using new food additives, the hygienic evaluation data and the basis of actual use should be submitted in advance, and approved by relevant departments after level-by-level review.

生产或使用新的食品添加剂时，应事先提交卫生评价资料和实际使用依据，经有关部门逐级审议后批准。

2.1.3 Homework

课后作业

2.1.3.1 Sentence Translation

句子翻译

(1) Original Texts

原句

① Food additives are chemical substances artificially added to food to improve quality, extend shelf life, or facilitate processing.

② Common food additives include preservatives, colorants, and sweeteners.

③ Natural additives and synthetic additives must be clearly labeled.

④ Preservatives inhibit microbial growth, while antioxidants delay oxidative spoilage.

⑤ Antimicrobial agents are a type of food additive used to inhibit or kill microorganisms (e.g., bacteria, fungi), commonly applied to extend food shelf life.

⑥ Nutritional additives are used to enhance the nutritional value of food and compensate for nutrient loss during processing.

⑦ Vitamin E and vitamin C, as antioxidant additives, can effectively delay food oxidation and extend shelf life.

⑧ When used appropriately, food additives can improve food quality, but excessive intake may pose potential health risks.

⑨ Flavor enhancers, consisting of chemicals such as sodium glutamate and various nucleotides, are usually used in Asian foods or soups to enhance other flavors.

⑩ Food additives must undergo rigorous toxicological evaluations to ensure safety and establish an Acceptable Daily Intake (ADI).

(2) Translations

翻译

① 食品添加剂是指为改善食品品质、延长保质期或便于加工而人工添加到食品中的化学物质。

② 常见的食品添加剂包括防腐剂、色素和甜味剂。

③ 天然添加剂和合成添加剂需在标签中明确标注。

④ 防腐剂（如苯甲酸钠）用于抑制微生物生长，而抗氧化剂（如维生素 E）可延缓食品氧化变质。

⑤ 抗菌剂是一类用于抑制或杀灭微生物（如细菌、真菌）的食品添加剂，常用于延长食品保质期。

⑥ 营养添加剂用于强化食品的营养价值，弥补加工过程中的营养损失。

⑦ 维生素 E 和维生素 C 作为抗氧化添加剂，能有效延缓食品氧化变质，延长保质期。

⑧ 对于营养问题的关注也导致了功能性食品或保健品产业的迅速成长，结果使一些总体起健康强化作用的添加剂得到发展。

⑨ 食品添加剂在合理使用下可以提升食品品质，但过量摄入可能对健康产生潜在风险。

⑩ 食品添加剂需通过严格的毒理学评估，以确保其安全性并确定每日允许摄入量（ADI）。

(3) 翻译文中划线句子

2.1.3.2 Common Sentence Patterns of Scientific Papers 科技论文常见句型

① The use of enzymes such as rennet in cheese making and barley amylases in brewing is as old as the food and beverage industry itself.

"as + *adj* + as"结构表示"和……一样"，用于同级比较。其中，第一个"as"是副词，修饰形容词或副词；第二个"as"是连词，用于连接比较的对象。其基本结构为"as + *adj./adv.* + as"。

② The quantity and variety of enzymes used in the food and beverage industry has increased dramatically in the past two decades.

③ Throughout the history of bread making, enzymes have always played an important role.

④ Even the ancient Egyptians made use of enzymes present endogenously in flour, although they may not have been aware of the effect.

⑤ Furthermore, these biological catalysts are able to produce value-adding ingredients in situ…

⑥ In many cases, the beneficial effects of using enzymes in the baking industry are also obtainable by using chemical agents…

⑦ This results in a smaller storage volume, cheaper transportation, and better concentrate stability without spoilage.

⑧ In association with new equipment and processing technologies, industrial enzymes allow processors to add value to raw material for food and feed and to reduce waste quantity.

⑨ Nowadays, enzyme producers provide a wide range of pectinases for the processing of fruit to give various products.

⑩ The trend is to process fruit…

⑪ However, because processing technology evolves faster than regulation, it is necessary to define food standard values and process references.

⑫ Malting depends on many factors, including the barley variety and quality, …

⑬ In future, new enzymes for food applications are expected to lead to major developments in the use of industrially produced enzymes.

2.2 Enzymes in Food

2.2 食品中的酶

2.2.1 Glossary

专业词汇分析

① rennet *n.* 凝乳酶

[记忆窍门] 词源同 run，跑，-et，词后缀。即跑到一起，引申词义凝结，后用于指凝乳酶。

② amylase *n.* 淀粉酶

[记忆窍门] 酶常用在作用物的英文名词后面作后缀“- ase”。

③ dextrin *n.* 糊精；葡聚糖

④ cereal *n.* 谷类，谷物；谷类食品；谷类植物

⑤ substrate *n.* 酶作用物，培养基

[记忆窍门] sub（下面的）+strate［形似 structure（结构）］→下面结构，即基质层，培养基。

⑥ thermostability *n.* 热稳定性；耐热性

[记忆窍门] thermo 热的；stability 稳定性，合起来就是热稳定性。

⑦ catalyst *n.* 催化剂

[记忆窍门] 来自 catalyse，催化。

⑧ arabanase *n.* 阿拉伯聚糖酶

[记忆窍门] arab 阿拉伯的，-ase 表示“…酶”。

⑨ araban *n.* 聚阿拉伯糖

⑩ maceration *n.* 泡软；浸渍作用

⑪ lager *n.*（美）贮藏啤酒（味淡，通常多泡沫）

[记忆窍门] 词源 lay，放置。

⑫ dessert *n.* 餐后甜点；甜点心

[记忆窍门] “ser”词根的衍生词为 serve（服务），servant（仆人）等。变形“sert”，再加前缀“des”表取消。那么“dessert”的字面意思是“取消服务，停止上菜”，即：上甜点。

⑬ clot *vt.* 使凝结成块

[记忆窍门] 词源同 cloud，clod，clump，指各种大块状的东西。

⑭ coagulate *vt.* 使…凝结

[记忆窍门] coa 近似，coal，gul 近似 glue，coal+glue→煤是古生物经高温高压凝结而成→coagulate 使…凝结。

⑮ whey *n.* 乳清；乳清蛋白；酪蛋白

⑯ galactosidase *n.* 半乳糖苷酶

[记忆窍门] galactose，半乳糖，-ase 表示"…酶"。

⑰ lactase *n.* 乳糖酶

[记忆窍门] lactose 乳糖， -ase 表示"…酶"。

⑱ bloating *n.* 腹胀

[记忆窍门] bloat 使膨胀。

⑲ diarrhea *n.* 腹泻，痢疾

[记忆窍门] dia 原是个希腊介词，意思相当于 through 或 across，穿过+ rrh 流动+ ea 表疾病，ia 的变体 → 吃的东西未经正常消化，就穿肠而过直接排出来了。

⑳ flatulence *n.* 肠胃气胀

[记忆窍门] -flat-（轮胎）没气的+ulence 多→多气的→肠胃气胀。

2.2.2 Texts and Translations

课文及翻译

Application of Enzymes in Food 酶在食品工业中的应用

Introduction

引言

The use of enzymes such as rennet in cheese making and barley amylases in brewing is as old as the food and beverage industry itself. However, the production of amylase represents the first example of the industrial production of an enzyme for use in the food industry. The quantity and variety of enzymes used in the food and beverage industry has increased dramatically in the past two decades. More than 20 different enzymes are regularly used in the food and beverage industry at present time. The conversion of starch to different commercial products, such as glucose and maltose syrups and dextrin preparations, represents the major application of food enzymes. The use of enzymes in the dairy industry for cheese making and for the production of low lactose dairy products is the second largest market.

酶的使用历史，如奶酪制作中的凝乳酶和酿酒中的大麦淀粉酶，与食品和饮料行业本身一样古老。然而，淀粉酶的生产标志着酶工业化生产在食品工业中的首次出现。在过去二十年里，食品和饮料工业中使用的酶的数量和种类有了极大的增加。目前，食品和饮料工业中有超过 20 种常用酶。将淀粉转化为各种商业产品，比如，葡萄糖浆、麦芽糖浆和糊精制剂，代表着食品酶的主要应用。在乳业中使用酶制造奶酪和生产低乳糖乳制品是酶应用的第二大市场。

(1) Enzymes in Baking

酶在焙烤中的应用

Bread and baked products are among the main nutritional sources today. Over 600×10^6 tons of wheat are grown in the world each year, making it the single most important crop. Europeans are estimated to obtain approximately half their required carbohydrates and about one-third of their protein from bread. Throughout the history of bread making, enzymes have always played an important role. Even the ancient Egyptians made use of enzymes present endogenously in flour, although they may not have been aware of the effect. However, not until the 20th century were enzymes used as flour improvers. The first application of enzymes in baked goods was supplementation of α-amylase by the addition of malt to correct the concentration of endogenous α-amylase in the flour. Later malt was substituted by microbial α-amylases having a more suitable thermostability for baking. This was the first enzyme industrially produced as a tool to compensate for variations in natural flour. Today, a whole range of enzymes is available for end users of flour. These make it possible to correct suboptimal concentrations of endogenous flou enzymes. Furthermore, these biological catalysts are able to produce value-adding ingredients in situ from compounds present in the flour, and thus it is possible to upgrade lower grades of flour.

面包和焙烤食品是当今主要的营养来源。全世界每年种植小麦的产量超过 6 亿吨，小麦成为最主要的单一作物。据估计，欧洲人从面包中摄取了大约一半的碳水化合物和大约三分之一的蛋白质。纵观面包制作的历史，酶一直发挥着重要作用。甚至古埃及人都使用面粉内源性酶，尽管他们对于其功效并不知晓。然而，直到 20 世纪，酶才被用作面粉改良剂。酶在焙烤食品中的首次应用是通过添加麦芽的方式补充 α-淀粉酶，以改善面粉中内源性 α-淀粉酶的浓度。后来麦芽被微生物 α-淀粉酶替代，因其有适宜焙烤的热稳定性。这是工业上第一种用于补偿天然面粉成分变化的酶。如今，面粉的消费者可以使用各种酶。这些酶可以改善内源性面粉酶的次优浓度。此外，这些生物催化剂能够利用面粉中的现有物质产生具有高附加值的成分，因此，可提升低等面粉的等级。

In many cases, the beneficial effects of using enzymes in the baking industry are also obtainable by using chemical agents such as sodium metabisulfite, cysteine, azodicarbonamide (ADA), potassium bromate, etc. However, the food market today shows a clear trend towards more "green" products, and this has clearly favored the use of biological catalyst enzymes.

在很多情况下，烘焙业中使用酶的有益效果也可以通过使用化学制剂来获得，如焦亚硫酸钠、半胱氨酸、偶氮二甲酰胺（ADA）、溴酸钾等。然而，当今食品市场呈现出一种明显的趋势，即产品更加“绿色”，这显然有利于生物催化剂酶的使用。

(2) Enzymes in Fruit Juice Production and Fruit Processing

酶在果汁生产与水果加工中的应用

The first application of enzymes in the fruit juice industry was the use of pectinases for apple juice clarification in the 1930s. The fast clarification of juice after breakdown of pectin by pectinases and the decrease in juice viscosity resulted in a shorter process and greatly improved the quality of industrial apple juice. Later, pectinases were applied to depectinization of red-berry juice. The use of pectinases and amylases to degrade apple pectin and starch during the hot clarification stage prevents post-bottling haze formation, and thus concentration of the juice by a factor of six has become possible. This results in a smaller storage volume, cheaper transportation, and better concentrate stability without spoilage. Treatment of apple pulp with pectinases and hemicellulases was introduced later: by lowering the viscosity of the pulp, the press capacity and the yield were significantly improved. Depectinization of juice with pectinases with high arabanase activity improved product quality further by preventing araban haze formation after concentration of the juice. In the production of clear and stable red-berry juice or concentrate, hot maceration with enzymes ensures a higher juice yield and a better color extraction. Nowadays, enzyme suppliers provide fruit juice producers with tailor-made enzyme preparations optimally blended on the basis of fruit composition for improved quality and stability of the finished products, together with shorter process duration and larger plant capacity. In association with new equipment and processing technologies, industrial enzymes allow processors to add value to raw material for food and feed and to reduce waste quantity.

酶在果汁工业中的首次应用是在 20 世纪 30 年代使用果胶酶澄清苹果汁。果胶酶将果胶分解后，果汁可以快速澄清且黏度降低，从而缩短了工艺流程，显著提高了工业苹果汁的质量。后来，果胶酶应用于红莓果汁的脱果胶处理。在热澄清阶段使用果胶酶和淀粉酶能够降解苹果果胶和淀粉，能够防止在灌装时形成雾气，从而有可能使得果汁的浓度提高 6 倍。这样一来，贮藏体积更小，运输成本更低，浓缩物的稳定性更好，不会变质。后来又开始用果胶酶和半纤维素酶处理苹果果肉：通过降低果浆黏度，榨汁能力和产量都显著提高。采用具有高阿拉伯聚糖酶活性的果胶酶对果汁进行脱果胶处理，可防止果汁浓缩后形成阿拉伯聚糖浑浊物，进一步提高产品质量。在生产澄清稳定的红莓果汁或浓缩汁时，用酶进行热浸可确保果汁产量更高，颜色提取更好。如今，酶制剂供应商为果汁生产商提供量身定制的酶制剂，这些酶制剂根据水果成分进行了优化混合，以提高成品的质量和稳定性，同时缩短生产周期，提高生产能力。工业酶制剂与新设备和加工技术相结合，使生产商提高食品和饲料原料的价值，并减少废弃物生成量。

Nowadays, enzyme producers provide a wide range of pectinases for the processing of fruit to give various products such as pure, cloudy juice, clear juice, and concentrate. The evolution of technology and processes including enzymes allow processors to obtain higher juice yield (productivity) together with higher quality of finished products. The use of specific pectinases adapted to the fruit process improves the shelf life of juices and concentrates (stability of color and freedom from turbidity). Apart from juice processing, the wide range and the high specificity of commercial enzymes open the way to new processes and new types of fruit-derived products. The trend is to process fruit under milder and more strictly controlled conditions to obtain new fruit products with sensory characteristics closer to those of fresh fruit.

如今，酶制剂生产商提供多种果胶酶，用于加工水果，以生产出各种产品，例如纯果汁、混汁、清果汁和浓缩果汁。包括生物酶在内的科技和工艺的进展可以使生产商获得更高的果汁产量（生产率）以及更高质量的成品。在水果处理中使用特定的果胶酶，可以延长果汁和浓缩物的保质期（颜色稳定、避免浑浊）。除加工果汁外，商业用酶的广泛性和高特异性为新工艺和新型水果制品开辟了道路。这种趋势是在更加温和与更加严格的监管下，以获得感官特性与新鲜水果更接近的新型水果产品。

However, because processing technology evolves faster than regulation, it is necessary to define food standard values and process references. In Europe, a Code of Practice has been developed to maintain quality and authenticity standards. Members of the Association of the Industry of Juices and Nectars from fruits and vegetables (AIJN) in parallel with the Association of Microbial Food Enzyme Producers (AMFEP) have established references for fruit juice composition and enzyme specifications, in line with commercial standards and regulations of different countries.

但是，由于监管跟不上制造科技的进步，有必要确定食品标准值和加工参考值。欧洲已经制定了一部操作规则以保持质量和真实性标准。果蔬汁和花蜜行业协会（AIJN）的成员与微生物食品酶生产商协会（AMFEP）的成员根据不同国家的商业标准和法规，制定了果汁成分和酶规格的参考标准。

(3) Enzymes in Brewing

酶在酿酒业中的使用

Brewing is an old and traditional process that uses a variety of raw materials; in centuries past, many brewing processes have evolved, and they show the versatility and craftmanship of historic brewmasters. By far, the most important brewing style is the "lager" type, characterized by the use of very pure water, low-temperature fermentation, and a long maturation period. Even in this relatively young beer style, many variations have developed. The common denominator in the brewing of beer is that part of the starch of a cereal is converted into alcohol. In the first stage, enzymes hydrolyze starch into fermentable sugars. In a second process stage, these sugars are converted to alcohol and carbon dioxide by yeast. (Not all beers use yeast for fermentation; e.g., in the case of gueuze beers and weissen, bacteria are involved.)

酿酒是一种古老而传统的工艺，使用的原料多种多样；几个世纪以来，酿酒工艺不断演变，展现出历史上酿酒大师们的非凡才华和高超技艺。迄今为止最重要的酿酒方法就是“淡啤酒”法，特点是使用十分纯净的水，经过低温发酵和长时间的后熟期。即使是在这相对较新的酿酒法中，也有许多不同的变化。酿造啤酒的共同点是将谷物中的部分淀粉转化为酒精。在第一阶段，酶将淀粉水解为可发酵性糖。在第二阶段，酵母将这些糖转化为酒精和二氧化碳（并非所有啤酒都使用酵母进行发酵，例如格兹啤酒和小麦啤酒中使用细菌）。

The traditional source of enzymes used for the conversion of cereals into beer is malted grain, and malted barley is a key ingredient in brewing. Malting depends on many factors, including the barley variety and quality, the malt kilning regime and the skill of the malter. The extent and success of the malting process depends on the development, distribution, and survival of indigenous barley enzymes, and in the case of the notoriously heat labile malt enzymes, quality varies from season to season and from region to region.

将谷物转化成啤酒的酶的传统来源是麦芽谷物，发芽大麦是酿酒中的关键成分。麦芽糖化依赖于很多因素，包括大麦的品种和品质、发芽窑的制度和发芽师的技术。麦芽加工过程的程度与成功取决于大麦中内源大麦酶的发展、分布和存活情况，而对于众所周知的热不稳定的麦芽酶，其质量随季节和区域的变化而波动。

(4) Enzymes in Dairy Applications

酶在乳业中的应用

Dairy products are among the classic examples of fermentation-derived foodstuffs, and their history of development goes back several millennia. Through the ages, a huge variety of dairy products have been developed based on empirical experimentation. Profound understanding of biochemical, microbiological, and physicochemical processes has mainly been achieved during the second half of the 1900s. Economical interest and scientific progress have led to the development of dairy food science as a special branch within food science, and it is the basis of control in manufacturing a huge variety of dairy products. Emphasis on understanding and controlling taste and texture development has led to a still growing assortment of cheeses and desserts. Enzymes originating from raw materials, microbial starter cultures, or other sources are prime tools in improving existing and creating novel dairy products.

乳制品是发酵食品的经典例子之一，其发展历史可追溯至几千年前。从古至今，人们根据经验实验开发出了种类繁多的乳制品。人类对生物化学、微生物和物理化学过程的深刻理解主要是在 20 世纪下半叶实现的。经济利益和科学进展使得乳品食品科学发展成为食品科学中的一个独特分支，乳品食品科学是生产各种乳制品的控制基础。对口味和质地发展的理解和控制使奶酪和甜点的种类不断增加。源于原料、微生物发酵培养物或其他来源的酶类是改进现有乳制品和创造新型乳制品的主要工具。

A basic element in the process of cheese making is the clotting of the milk. Milk turns into a gel structure through the action of coagulating enzymes, briefly called coagulants. The casein proteins in milk lose their colloidal stability and aggregate to form a gel structure. After cutting the gel, the liquid whey fraction, containing whey proteins, minerals, and lactose, separates from the casein chunks. The casein material, the curd, is collected in molds. After pressing and brining, the cheese is kept under conditioned storage for ripening. Storage time may last from weeks to months, even years, depending on the type of cheese.

奶酪制作过程中的一个基本要素是牛奶的凝固。牛奶通过凝固酶（简称为凝固剂）的作用转化成凝胶结构。牛奶中酪蛋白的胶体稳定性被破坏，聚集在一起形成了胶体结构。凝胶切断后，含有乳清蛋白、矿物质和乳糖的液态乳清部分从酪蛋白中分离出来。酪蛋白材料即凝乳被收集到塑模中。经过挤压和盐浸后，奶酪会在适宜的贮藏条件下成熟。根据奶酪种类的不同，存储的时间从几周到数月，甚至数年不等

β-Galactosidase (E.C. 3.2.1.23) or lactase is an enzyme that has found ample application in the hydrolysis of lactose, a disaccharide consisting of a glucose and a galactose moiety, in cow's milk. The consumption of milk is hampered by some people due to a deficiency of lactase in the digestive system. Lactose intolerance in these people, predominantly in Asian countries but also in Africa and South and Middle America, results in symptoms such as bloating, diarrhea, and flatulence. In many cases, these symptoms occur after consumption of 200~300 ml of milk.

β-半乳糖苷酶（E.C. 3.2.1.23）或乳糖酶是一类广泛应用于牛乳中水解乳糖的酶类，乳糖是由葡萄糖和半乳糖形成的二糖。由于消化系统中缺少乳糖酶，一些人无法饮用牛奶。乳糖不耐受人群主要分布在亚洲，但在非洲和南美洲、中美洲也有分布，其会导致腹胀、腹泻和胀气等症状。在很多实例中，饮用 200~300mL 牛奶后会出现这些症状。

(5) Other Food Applications

酶在其他食品中的应用

The use of enzymes for food applications has increased steadily over the past two decades, not only in traditional application areas such as starch processing, brewing, fruit processing, and dairies. In applications such as baking, the use of enzymes has grown even more.

在过去的二十年里，酶在食品中的应用稳步增长，不仅是在淀粉加工、酿酒、水果加工和乳业等传统行业，在烘焙等应用领域，酶的使用甚至有了更大的增长。

The appearance of new enzyme applications is due to the increasing diversity of the enzymes available, the majority based on GM technology. In future, new enzymes for food applications are expected to lead to major developments in the use of industrially produced enzymes.

新型酶应用的出现是由于现有酶的多样性不断增加，其中大部分基于转基因技术。未来，新的食用酶有望在工业生产的酶的使用方面取得重大进展。

2.2.3 Homework

课后作业

2.2.3.1 Sentence Translation

句子翻译

(1) Original Sentences

原句

① Changes in temperature and pH affect enzyme conformation and catalytic efficiency.

② These biological catalysts are widely used in food, pharmaceuticals, and environmental protection due to their high efficiency and specificity.

③ Pectinase degrades pectin and is widely used in juice clarification and plant fiber processing.

④ Pectinase breaks down pectin in cell walls, improving juice yield.

⑤ Enzymes significantly accelerate biochemical reactions by lowering activation energy.

⑥ Yeast converts sugars into alcoholand carbon dioxide through anaerobic fermentation.

⑦ Dairy fermentation is the process by which lactic acid bacteria convert lactose into lactic acid.

⑧ Fermented dairy products are rich in probiotics, benefiting gut health.

⑨ Cheese fermentation relies on specific molds or bacteria.

⑩ Lactase (β-galactosidase) hydrolyzes lactose into glucose and galactose.

(2) Translations

翻译

① 温度和 pH 值的变化会影响酶的构象和催化效率。

② 这些生物催化剂（如酶）因其高效性和特异性，广泛应用于食品、制药和环保领域。

③ 果胶酶能降解果胶，广泛应用于果汁澄清和植物纤维加工。

④ 果胶酶可分解细胞壁中的果胶，提高果汁出汁率。

⑤ 酶通过降低反应活化能显著加速生化反应。

⑥ 酵母通过无氧发酵将糖类转化为酒精和二氧化碳。

⑦ 乳品发酵是通过乳酸菌将乳糖转化为乳酸的过程。

⑧ 发酵乳制品富含益生菌，有助于肠道健康。

⑨ 奶酪发酵依赖特定霉菌或细菌。

⑩ 乳糖酶（β-半乳糖苷酶）可将乳糖水解为葡萄糖和半乳糖

(3) 翻译文中划线句子

2.2.3.2 Common Sentence Patterns of Scientific Papers 科技论文常见句型

(1) Over 600×10^6 tons of wheat are grown in the world each year, making it …

(2) They may not have been aware of …

(3) These make it possible to…

(4) This has clearly favored…

(5) In association with new equipment and processing technologies, …….

(6) The trend is to……

(7) It is necessary to……

(8) By far, the most important brewing style is the "lager" type, ……

2.3 Food Fermentation

2.3 食品发酵

2.3.1 Glossary

专业词汇分析

① chopping　*n.* 斩拌

[记忆窍门]　词根 chop，切碎，砍。

② stuffing　*n.* 填料，灌肠

[记忆窍门]　词根 stuff，*v.* 装，填+ing 表名词→填料。

③ acidulation　*n.* 酸化；酸化作用

[记忆窍门]　acid *n.* 酸；　acidulate *vt.* 使酸化；　-tion 动词转化成的名词词尾。

④ lactic acid　乳酸

[记忆窍门]　lactic *adj.* 乳的+ acid n. 酸。

⑤ simultaneous　*adj.* 同时的；联立的；同时发生的

[记忆窍门]　词根 simu 与 same 形似，tane 与 time 形似，“-ous”为形容词后缀，因此可以联想记忆为“相同时间的”，“同时的”或“同步的”

⑥ fermentation　*n.* 发酵

[记忆窍门]　词根 ferment *v.*发酵，tion 名词词缀。

⑦ availability　*n.* 可用性；有效性；实用性

[记忆窍门]　avail *vt.* 有利，有用+ability，能力，性质。

⑧ denaturation　*n.* 使变性；改变本性

[记忆窍门]　词根 nature *n.* 自然，本质；　de- 否定前缀，denature *v.* 使变性。

⑨ shelf-life　*n.* 货架期，贮藏寿命

⑩ interrelated　*adj.* 相关的，互相联系的；*v.* 相互联系（interrelate）的过去式

[记忆窍门] inter- 前缀，……之间，相互；related *adj.* 有关系的，有关联的。

⑪ microbiological　*adj.* 微生物学的

[记忆窍门] micro- 前缀，微；biological *adj.* 生物的；生物学的。

⑫ biochemical　*adj.* 生物化学的

[记忆窍门] bio- 前缀，生物的；chemical *adj.* 化学的。

⑬ starter bacteria　*n.* 发酵剂

⑭ antioxidant　*n.* 抗氧化剂

[记忆窍门] anti- 前缀，反，防；oxidant *n.* 氧化剂。

⑮ proteolytic　*adj.* 蛋白质水解的，解蛋白质的

[记忆窍门] proteo- 蛋白质；–lytic 分解的。

⑯ lipolytic　*adj.* 分解脂肪的，脂解的

[记忆窍门] lipo *n.* 脂肪；–lytic 分解的。

⑰ ripening　*n.* 成熟

[记忆窍门] rip 撕开，裂开+-en 使…→ripen　*v.*（使）成熟。

⑱ bacteriological　*adj.* 细菌学的，细菌学上的

[记忆窍门] bacteria *n.* 细菌；-ology 学（科）；-（c）al　*adj.*……的。

⑲ polyunsaturated　*adj.* 多不饱和的

[记忆窍门] poly- 多，聚；un- 否定前缀，不……；saturated *adj.* 饱和的。

⑳ sodium ascorbate　抗坏血酸钠

㉑ semisynthetic　*adj.* 半合成的

[记忆窍门] semi- 半；synthetic *adj.*合成的，人造的。

㉒ permeable　*adj.* 能透过的，有渗透性的

[记忆窍门] 词根 permeate, *v.* 渗透，扩散，传播。

㉓ case hardening　*n.* 表面硬化

㉔ combustion　*n.* 燃烧，氧化

㉕ polycyclic hydrocarbons　*n.* 多环烃

[记忆窍门] poly- 多，聚；cyclic *adj.* 环的，循环的，周期的；hydro- 氢或水+carbon *n.* 碳→烃。

㉖ inoculation　*n.* 接种

㉗ lactobacilli　*n.* 乳酸杆菌

[记忆窍门] lacto- 乳的；bacilli *n.* 杆菌，细菌。

㉘ micrococcaceae　*n.* 微球菌科

[记忆窍门] micro- 微；coccaceae 球菌。

㉙ probiotic　*n.* 益生菌

[记忆窍门] pro *adv.* 站在赞成方面；正面的+biotic *adj.* 生物的；生命的→有益生命的就是益生菌。

㉚ in relation to 关于，涉及

2.3.2 Texts and Translations

课文及翻译

Meat Fermentation 肉的发酵

Introduction

前言

The chopping or mincing of meat and fat with curing salt and/or sugar together with spices, herbs and other plant material, followed by the stuffing of such mixture to form a "sausage" that is left to dry, is a practice dating back to centuries before the Common Era. Since these early beginnings, variations in "meat" species, subjected to various degrees of mixing with other ingredients or additives and subjected to various temperature and humidity conditions have yielded at least 56 different "fermented meat products". The shelf-life and safety, as well as the specific flavour, texture and colour of these products are determined by combinations, varying in relative importance, of acidulation brought about by lactic acid production and the lowering of water activity (a_w) by the addition of salt (curing) and by drying.

将斩拌或斩碎的肉和脂肪用盐和/或糖以及调味料、草药和其他植物性原料进行腌制，并将这些腌制过的混合物灌装到肠衣中形成干制香肠，这种生产方式可以追溯到公元前几个世纪。从早期开始，不同种类的“肉”与其他成分或添加剂进行不同程度的混合，并在不同的温度和湿度条件下发酵，产生了至少 56 种不同的“发酵肉制品”。这些产品的货架期和安全性以及它们各自特殊的风味、质地和色泽等都是由乳酸产生的酸化作用，以及盐的添加（腌制）和干燥而引起的水活度（a_w）的降低等不同相对重要的组合决定的。

The simultaneous or successive combination of these processes is generally referred to as "fermentation". The presence of salt, the lowering of water activity (a_w) by both the addition of salt and drying, and the limited availability of oxygen, intensified in most industrial productions by vacuum stuffing, selects salt-tolerant bacteria from the contaminating and/or added flora, producing lactic acid from carbohydrates added to or naturally present in the mix. This "fermentation" lowers the pH to final values between 4.5 and 5.5, inducing the denaturation of salt-solubilized protein to a gel that can be sliced. The adequate (rapid) reduction of pH and the lowered a_w are the major factors determining both shelf-life and safety.

我们把这些同时发生或者连续进行的过程称作“发酵”。盐的存在、通过添加盐和干燥而降低水活度（a_w）以及氧气的有限供应（在大多数工业生产中通过真空填料加剧），从污染和/或添加的菌群中选择耐盐菌，这些耐盐菌可以将混合物中添加的或者本身存在的碳水化合物转化为乳酸。这种“发酵”可以将 pH 降低至 4.5~5.5，诱导盐溶性蛋白质变性成为可切片的凝胶。充分（快速）地降低 pH 和水活度是决定货架期和安全性的主要因素。

Considerable recent research efforts have generated more detailed knowledge of the interrelated microbiological, biochemical, chemical and physical changes taking place during "meat fermentation", emphasizing two major and apparently contrasting developments:

最近的大量研究工作使人们对“肉类发酵”过程中发生的相互关联的微生物、生物化学、化学和物理变化有了更详细的了解，其中强调了两个主要而又明显相反的发展方向：

• The need for "starter bacteria", well-characterized for acidifying, antioxidant and amino acid degrading acidities.

• The importance of both proteolytic and lipolytic enzymes, present in the meat and/or fat raw materials used.

• 需要具有酸化、抗氧化和氨基酸降解特性的“发酵菌”。

• 所用肉类和/或脂肪原料中蛋白质分解酶和脂肪分解酶的重要性。

The many intricate interactions between microorganisms, meat and fat enzymes and processing conditions determining sausage quality encompass more than the concept of fermentation and are therefore better referred to as "metabolism".

微生物、肉和脂肪酶之间复杂的相互作用和决定香肠质量的加工条件超出了发酵的概念，因此称之为“代谢”更好。

(1) The Processing of Fermented Sausages

发酵香肠的加工

Industrial production, mainly in continental Europe, from where the technology was transferred to the United States and Australia, has narrowed down the many types of fermented meat products. These are classified in several ways, based on moisture content, moisture/protein ratio, weight loss, water activities, surface treatment, texture, fat particle size, and other parameters.

工业生产主要集中在欧洲大陆，技术从那里转移到美国和澳大利亚后，已经缩小了发酵肉制品种类的范围。这些发酵肉制品主要根据水分含量、水/蛋白质比例、质量损失、水活度、表面处理方式、质地、脂肪粒以及其他参数等方式分类。

The industrial production period, referred to as "ripening", is separated into two consecutive periods: fermentation followed by drying. Technologies differ mainly in the length of the total ripening period in relation to that of the fermentation period. High initial rates of lactic acid production resulting from the use of lactic acid-producing "starters" and/or high temperatures during fermentation are associated with short drying periods. The drying period may even be omitted, as in "summer sausage", prevalent in parts of the United States and fermented at 38 °C. In Europe, a major distinction can be made between the so-called Northern type and Mediterranean type sausages. Northern type of sausages (NS) contain both beef and pork as raw meats, are ripened for short periods (up to 3 weeks) and are usually subjected to smoking. In these sausages, shelf-life and safety are mainly due to the fast drop in acid pH (<5.0 after 3 days) at temperatures >20 ℃ and to smoking rather than to drying. Mediterranean sausages (MS) mostly use only pork and are ripened for longer periods (several weeks or even months) and smoke is not so typically applied. Acidulation is slower, takes place at lower temperatures (<20℃) and ends at higher pH values (>5 after 3 days). Shelf-life is mostly due to drying and reduced water activity.

工业生产期被称为“成熟期”，分为两个连续阶段：发酵期和干燥期。其技术的区别主要在于总成熟期与发酵期时间的长短。由于在发酵过程中使用产生乳酸的“发酵剂”

和/或高温，导致乳酸产生的高初始生产率与短干燥期有关。干燥期甚至可以省略，如在美国部分地区盛行的“夏季香肠”其发酵温度为 38℃。在欧洲，所谓的北方香肠和地中海香肠就存在明显差别。北方香肠（NS）主要以牛肉和猪肉作为原料肉，经短期的成熟（最多 3 周）并经常使用烟熏工艺。这种方式生产的香肠货架期和安全性主要取决于 20℃以上时 pH 的迅速降低（3 天后<5.0）和烟熏工艺，而不是干燥工艺。地中海香肠（MS）通常仅以猪肉为原料肉，成熟时间较长（几周甚至几个月），且不经常应用烟熏。酸化速度较慢，一般在较低温度（<20℃）时开始，在 pH 值较高时（3 天后 pH>5）结束，货架期通常取决于干燥过程水活度的降低。

(2) Raw Materials and Additives

原材料和添加剂

Chilled meats (frozen meat tempered to ca. −4℃) and frozen (≤18℃) porcine fats after removal of rind (e.g. lard) are most often mixed at a ratio of 2:1. Lard and sausage meat (ham trimmings, jowls and throats as well as shoulders and bellies) make up 10% and 20%, respectively, of the pork carcass. They are selected mainly on the basis of bacteriological quality, visual fat content, pH (<5.8) and unsaturation (<12% polyunsaturated fatty acids in fat) as well as oxidation status (minimal peroxide value) of the fat. Widely used additives (range of incorporation) are salt (2%~4%) containing sodium nitrite ($NaNO_2$) (added as curing salt containing 0.4%~0.6% $NaNO_2$), glucose (0.5%~1%) sodium ascorbate or ascorbic acid (0.5%~1%) and spices. The use of nitrite is considered essential because of its antibacterial, colour-forming, antioxidant and flavouring properties.

冷冻肉（回火至约-4℃的冷冻肉）和去皮后的冷冻（≤18℃）猪脂肪（如猪油）通常都以 2:1 的比例混合。猪脂肪和香肠肉（腿部修整肉、颚部、喉部、肩部和腹部）分别占猪肉胴体的 10%和 20%。选择它们的主要依据是微生物载量、可见脂肪含量、pH (<5.8)、不饱和度（多不饱和脂肪酸<12%）以及氧化状态（最小过氧化值）。广泛使用的添加剂（添加范围）是含有亚硝酸钠（$NaNO_2$）的盐（2%~4%）（作为含 0.4%~0.6% $NaNO_2$ 的腌制盐添加）、糖（0.5%~1%）、抗坏血酸钠或抗坏血酸（0.5%~1%），还有部分香辛料。因亚硝酸盐具有抗菌、发色、抗氧化以及增味作用，其使用被认为是必要的。

(3) Comminution or Chopping

捣碎或斩拌

Raw materials and additives, including microbial starters, are added for mixing and chopping, often under vacuum, in a mincer or “cutter”. The cutter consists of a set of knives that rotate rapidly (3×10^3 r/min), producing a batter in a bowl that rotates slowly (10~20r/min). The relative speeds of the knives and bowl and the sequence of addition of raw materials and additives determine the fat particle size and are optimized to produce a batter within less than 5 minutes at temperatures ≤2℃, ensuring minimal damage to the fat tissue.

原材料和添加剂，包括微生物发酵剂，通常在真空条件下一起加入绞肉机或者斩拌机中混合斩拌。斩拌机包含一套高速旋转刀具（3000r/min），肉糜在一个旋转缓慢的碗状容器（10~20r/min）中生成。刀片的相对速度、斩拌容器、原料和添加剂的添加顺序决定了脂肪微粒的大小，经过优化后，可在温度≤2℃的条件下在 5min 内制作出最佳肉糜，以确保脂肪组织的损坏最小。

(4) Stuffing

填充

In most industrial processes, the batter is immediately stuffed under vacuum into natural, semisynthetic (collagen) or synthetic casings that are permeable to water and air, and both ends are clipped. The sausage diameter (e.g. 2~15cm) is related positively to the relative importance of fermentation (pH) versus drying (a_w) for stability.

在大多数工业生产过程中，肉糜会在真空条件下被立即充填到天然的、半合成（胶原蛋白）或合成的透气透水的肠衣中，然后将两端修剪整齐。香肠直径（2~15cm）、发酵条件（pH 值）和干燥条件（a_w 值）对稳定性相对重要，呈正相关。

(5) Ripening

成熟

The sausages are hung on racks and placed in natural or, mostly, air-conditioned fermentation chambers at high relative humidity (RH). Sausages are usually left for ripening in two consecutive stages: fermentation for bacterial growth and, mostly after transfer to another chamber, drying for development of sensory characteristics. Temperature–RH–time combinations during fermentation differ between Northern (20~26℃/50%~90%/62h) and Mediterranean (5~24℃/10%~90%/100h) types, whereas drying is carried out under similar conditions (14℃/78%) for anywhere between 2 weeks (Northern) and several months (Mediterranean). <u>It is recommended to have air RH values not more than 0.10 points below the associated a_w values of the sausage, to prevent case hardening, and recommended air speeds are approximately 0.1m · s^{-1}.</u> Controlled fermentation and ripening in air-conditioned surroundings consumes considerable amounts of energy and alternative methods, involving the use of fresh air, have been proposed, inspired by the traditional methods for Mediterranean type sausages and adapted to local climatic conditions.

将香肠悬挂于货架，然后放置在相对湿度（RH）较高的自然发酵室或空调发酵室中。香肠成熟通常要有两个连续阶段：一是适合细菌生长的发酵，二是转移至另一发酵室的继续干燥，以形成合适的感官特征。发酵期间，北方型（20~26℃/50%~90%/62h）和地中海型（5~24℃/10%~90%/100h）香肠采用的发酵温度-相对湿度-时间组合不同，而烘干则是在类似条件（14℃/78%）下进行的，时间从两周（北方型）到数月（地中海型）不等。为了减缓香肠表面硬化，空气的相对湿度应低于香肠水活度值不超过 0.1，空气流速也应控制在约 0.1m/s。在空调环境中进行受控发酵和熟化需要消耗大量能源，受地中海香肠传统制作方法的启发并根据当地气候条件进行调整，人们提出了使用新鲜空气的替代方法。

(6) Smoking

烟熏

At the end of the fermentation period, Northern type sausages are subjected to smoke, generated by controlled combustion of oak wood (300~600℃) to minimize the production of polycyclic hydrocarbons. Smoke contributes to antimicrobial and antioxidant effects, besides generating specific flavour and colour components. Smoking is not used in the production of Mediterranean type sausages, except for Hungarian and Rumanian products, where a light smoking period precedes fermentation.

在发酵期结束后，北方型香肠要进行烟熏。橡木燃烧温度应控制在 300℃至 600℃之间以减少多环烃的产生。烟熏除了产生特定的风味和色泽物质外，还有助于抗菌和抗氧化。除了匈牙利和罗马尼亚的产品在发酵前有一个轻微的烟熏过程，地中海型香肠一般不使用烟熏。

(7) The Use of Microbial Starters

使用微生物发酵剂

Traditionally, fermentation was based on the selective development of the flora contaminating raw materials, sometimes reinforced with "back-slopping", the addition of a previously successfully ripened fermented sausage. Such practices, however, may induce great variability in the ripening changes determining safety and quality. The need for standardized processing and safety assurance led in the 1950s, first in the United States and later in Europe, to the commercial use of starter cultures to ensure rapid acidulation. Although excellent fermented sausages can be produced without starter cultures, the majority of fermented sausage produced nowadays makes use of "combined" starter inoculation (1×10^6~$2\times10^6\ g^{-1}$) as frozen cultures of both lactobacilli and Micrococcaceae to ensure rapid acidulation and optimal flavour development, respectively. The desired properties of "starters" are numerous and obviously include, above all, safety for the consumer and competitive growth compared to that of the contaminating flora of the raw materials under the conditions of sausage processing. Lipolytic and proteolytic activities have long been emphasized for flavour development, but it is now realized that muscle and fat tissue enzymes are by far the most important actors in these processes. Although recent developments consider the use of probiotic starter cultures, the major microorganisms now used as starters are classified into the following groups: lactic acid bacteria, Micrococcaceae, yeasts and moulds.

传统的发酵方法是有选择地培养污染原料的菌群，有时还通过"回种"即添加先前成功熟化的发酵香肠，来加强发酵。然而，这种做法可能在成熟过程中引起很大的变化，从而改变最终产品的安全性和质量。20 世纪 50 年代，自美国至欧洲的引入标准化工艺和安全保障的需求，促使了以确保迅速酸化为目的的发酵剂的商业性使用。尽管不用发酵剂也可以生产出质量优良的发酵香肠，但是，为了确保产品迅速酸化和产生优良风味，现在大多数发酵香肠的生产都会接种作为发酵剂的"复合的"冷冻培养的乳酸杆菌和微球菌（1×10^6~$2\times10^6\ g^{-1}$）。发酵剂所需的特性很多，其中最重要的是对消费者要安全，以及与原料中的污染菌群相比在香肠加工条件下生长具有竞争力。长期以来，人们都在强调脂类分解和蛋白质降解反应对风味形成的作用，但是现在人们开始意识到肌肉和脂肪组织中的酶类是迄今为止风味形成的最重要的角色。虽然最新研究进展中也有考虑用益生菌做发酵剂，但是目前作为发酵剂应用的微生物主要包括以下几种：乳酸菌、微球菌、酵母菌和霉菌。

2.3.3 Homework

课后作业

2.3.3.1 Sentence Translation

句子翻译

(1) Original Sentences

原句

① Sausage production requires fresh pork with a fat-to-lean ratio of 3∶7.

② Pork must be ground to a particle size of 3~5 mm.

③ Lactic acid bacteria (LAB) convert sugars into lactic acid during fermentation, lowering the pH.

④ The shelf life of sausages refers to the period during which they remain safe and edible under specific storage conditions.

⑤ Salt, sugar, and sodium nitrite are evenly mixed into the meat paste.

⑥ Moisture loss is one of the primary causes of sausage hardening.

⑦ Protein and fat degradation generates volatile compounds during fermentation.

⑧ Yogurt, kimchi, and fermented sausages are common probiotic vehicles.

(2) Translations

翻译

① 制作香肠需选用新鲜猪肉，肥瘦比例通常为 3∶7。

② 猪肉须被绞碎至颗粒大小为 3~5mm。

③ 乳酸菌在发酵过程中将糖类转化为乳酸，降低 pH 值。

④ 香肠的货架期是指在特定储存条件下保持安全和可食用性的时间。

⑤ 盐、糖和亚硝酸钠被均匀混合到肉馅中。

⑥ 水分流失是香肠硬化的主要原因之一。

⑦ 发酵过程中，蛋白质和脂肪降解产生挥发性风味物质。

⑧ 酸奶、泡菜和发酵香肠是常见的益生菌载体食品。

(3) 翻译文中划线句子

2.3.3.2 Common Sentence Patterns of Scientific Papers 科技论文常见句型

① 回顾研究背景，常用词汇有：review，summarize，present，outline，describe 等。

We review evidence for this view

This paper outlines some of the basic methods and discusses related…

② 阐述写作目的，常用词汇有：purpose, attempt, aim, objective 等

The aim of this paper is to provide methods to construct such a probability distribution.

In order to achieve these objectives, an xx must meet the following requirements…

③ 介绍论文的重点内容或研究范围，常用词汇有：study, present, include, focus, emphasize, emphasis, attention 等

This paper focuses on the promise of artificial neural networks.

We emphasize the following points…

④ 介绍研究或实验过程，常用词汇有：test, study, investigate, examine, analyse 等

To improve the efficiency of the method, the following approach may be applied.

This approach will be explained and discussed thoroughly in the body of the report.

⑤ 展示研究结果，常用词汇有：show, result, present, demonstrate 等

The experimental results for each time are reported in Table 2.

We show this cell death to be dependent upon expression of …

⑥ 介绍结论，常用词汇有：summary, conclude 等

From the above discussion, the conclusion can be reached that…

In conclusion to this, it becomes obvious that the problem of xx lies not only in...

⑦ 陈述论文的论点和作者的观点，常用词汇有：suggest, report, present, explain, expect, describe 等

A major goal of this report is to extend the utilization of a recently developed procedure for the…

We present representation and uniqueness theorems for the fundamental measurement of fuzziness when the domain of discourse is…

⑧ 阐明论证，常用词汇有：support, provide, indicate, find, confirm, clarify 等

The results indicate that the total benefits are higher than the total costs.

These results demonstrate that ...

⑨ 存在问题，常用词汇：problem，issue，question

...is a difficult problem, yet to be adequately resolved

Some important issues in developing a ...

⑩ 图表描述，常用词汇：Tables and Figures

At the top of Table, ...are shown two blocks of data.

The graphical representation of these functions is shown in Figure.

Chapter 3 Food Technology
第 3 章 食品技术

3.1 Food Processing

3.1 食品加工

3.1.1 Glossary

专业词汇分析

① substantial *adj*. 本质的，实质的，大量的，重大的

[记忆窍门] 可分解成“substant” + “ial”，其中 substant 跟 substance（物质，实质）拼写非常接近，ial 常作为形容词的词尾，表示“……的”，合起来就是“实质的，本质的”。

② geographical *adj*. 地理学的，地理的

[记忆窍门] 该词为 geography 的形容词，geography 由词根 geo（地）+ graph（书写、图画）+ y（名词后缀）组成，意为“关于大地的图画”，即“地理学”。

③ perishable *adj*. 易腐烂的

[记忆窍门] 该词是由动词 perish（腐烂，死亡）+ able（形容词词尾，表示“……的”）组成。perish 与 cherish 组成相近，可联想记忆为：珍惜（cherish）生命，不应随意死亡（perish）。

④ scrutiny *n*. 细看，监视，详细审查

[记忆窍门] 该词可分解为“scru”（理解）+ “tiny”（微小的）两部分，很微小的地方都需要去理解，当然要“详细审查”了。

⑤ simultaneously *adv*. 同时地

[记忆窍门] 该词为形容词 simultaneous + ly 构成的副词。simultaneous 可分解成 simul + taneous 两部分，其中 simul 源自拉丁语（一起，同时），而 taneous 可看成是 spontaneous 的缩写（自动的，自发的），合起来即为“同时地”。

⑥ peel *n.* 果皮；*vt.* 剥，削，剥落

[记忆窍门] 该词发音类似于“皮儿”，很容易想到“果皮”。

⑦ sterilize *vt.* 消毒，杀菌

[记忆窍门] 该词可分解为 steril + ize，其中 sterile 意为“不能生育的，无菌的，消过毒的”，ize 为动词后缀，因此合起来，即为“消毒，杀菌”。

⑧ dehull *vt.* 除去……的壳（或皮等）

[记忆窍门] 由前缀 de-+ hull 构成，其中 de-表示“去除”的意思，而 hull 为“外壳”，合起来即为“除去……的壳（或皮等）”。

⑨ cylindrical *adj.* 圆柱形的；圆柱体的

[记忆窍门] 该词为 cylinder （圆柱体）的形容词。cylinder 谐音为“谁拎的”——圆柱体（cylinder）没有把柄，不好拿，是谁拎的（cylinder）。

⑩ hexane *n.* 己烷

[记忆窍门] 其中 “ane” 为烷烃的后缀。

⑪ evaporate *vt/vi.*（使）蒸发；（使）脱水；（使）消失

[记忆窍门] 该词由 e（出）+ vapor（蒸气）+ ate（和……有关的），合起来为“和蒸气有关的”，即为“蒸发”。

⑫ contaminate *vt.* 污染，玷污；弄脏

[记忆窍门] 该词由 con（共同）+ tamin（来自于拉丁语动词 “taminare”，意思是 “污染，弄脏” ）+ate（和……有关的）组成，表示使某物受到污染，使之变得不纯洁，这个词根结构清晰地传达了污染的过程和结果。

⑬ shelf-life *n.* 贮藏寿命，货架期

⑭ irradiation *n.* 发光，辐照，照射，放射

[记忆窍门] 该单词为 irradiate 的名词形式，可分解为 ir（进入，使……成为）+ radi（发光）+ ate（和……有关的），合起来 “使……发光”，即辐照，照射。

⑮ pathogen *n.* 病原体；病菌

[记忆窍门] 该词由 patho（病理，痛苦，疾病）+ gen（产生），合起来即为疾病之原（源）——病菌。

⑯ intermediate *adj.* 中间的，中级的；*n.* 中间物；媒介

[记忆窍门] 该词可分解为 inter（在……之间，相互）+ medi（中间）+ ate（和……有关的），合起来即为中间的。

⑰ pesticide *n.* 杀虫剂

[记忆窍门] 该词由 pest（害虫）+ icide（杀害者）组成，合起来即为杀虫剂。

⑱ disinfectant *n.* 消毒剂；*adj.* 消毒的

[记忆窍门] 该词由前缀 dis（表否定）+ infect（传染，感染）+ ant（名词后缀）组成，能够阻止传染的东西，即为消毒剂。

3.1.2 Texts and Translations

课文及翻译

Food Processing 食品加工

Overview

综述

The food processing industry transforms the products of agriculture into the foods and drinks we consume daily. The industry is relatively diverse, dealing with some products that need minimal processing, such as fresh fruits and vegetables, and others that require substantial secondary processing to create a final product, such as dry cereal or baked goods.

食品加工业把农产品转变为我们日常消费的食品和饮料。食品加工业种类多样，既涉及一些只需要最小化加工的产品，如新鲜果蔬，又涉及那些需要大量二次加工的制成品，如干麦片或焙烤食品。

The food processing industry has an interesting structure that is determined partly by the geographical distribution of its raw materials, the products of agriculture. In the European Union, 92% of food and drink processors are small or medium sized companies. Some processors are located in rural areas while others are more industrial in scale, e.g., large sugar plants. Some processors, like olive oil producers, have a highly seasonal production cycle that is determined by the harvest, while others, like dairy processors, have a more stable production cycle. Perishable items, like fruits and vegetables, tend to be processed and packed near their source, whereas other products, like soft drinks, are produced closer to population centers and sources of water.

食品加工业具有有趣的结构，某种程度上取决于农产品原料的地理分布。在欧盟国家，92%的食品和饮料加工企业是中小型公司。一些加工企业位于农村地区，而另一些加工企业则规模更大，如大型糖厂。一些加工企业的高度季节性生产周期是由收成决定的，如橄榄油生产商。而其他加工企业的生产周期则更稳定，如乳制品加工业。易腐烂的果蔬类往往在产地附近被加工和包装，而软饮料的生产则更靠近人口密集区和水源区。

The food processing industry is a heavily regulated industry, with regulatory scrutiny focused primarily on the quality and safety of the products delivered to the consumer rather than on environmental aspects of production. In recent years, however, the industry has made progress in improving environmental performance through waste minimization (which also increases production efficiency). Solutions that simultaneously address the quality and safety of the products and the environmental performance of the production process will be particularly attractive to this industry.

食品加工业是受到严格监管的一个行业，监管审查主要集中于消费产品的质量和安全性，而不是生产的环境方面。然而，近年来，该行业通过废弃物最少化（也能提高生产效率）在改善环境绩效方面取得了进步。因此，保证食品质量和安全的同时，提高生产过程环保性的解决方案将会受到该行业的特别关注。

3.1.2.1 Physical and Chemical Operations 物理和化学处理

(1) Physical Operations

物理处理

Many of the operations used in processing foods and drinks are physical in nature. Raw materials are received, sorted, cleaned, cut, blended, ground, formed, or mechanically separated before they are either packaged or sent for further processing or heat treatment. The production of canned juices, for example, consists of the following steps illustrated in Figure 3.1: washing, extracting, straining, container filling, container sealing, cooling, labeling, casing, and storing for shipment. Where vegetables are concerned, peeling, coring, cutting, cooking, and heat sterilizing are included in the process.

在加工食品和饮料时，很多操作本质上都是采用物理方法。在对原料进行包装或运输以进行进一步处理或热处理之前，先对其进行采收、分级、清洗、切分、混合、破碎、成型或机械分离。例如，罐装果汁的生产包括以下步骤（图 3.1）：清洗、提取、压榨、灌装、封罐、冷却、贴标、装箱、储存。对于蔬菜类加工还包括去皮、去核、切分、蒸煮和加热灭菌等操作。

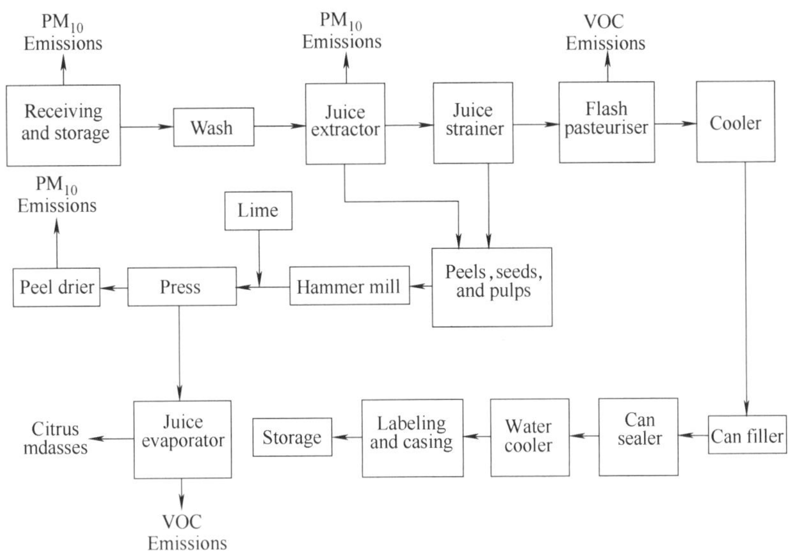

Figure 3.1 The technological sequence diagram for the food processing industry.

The production of soybean oil is slightly more complex, with a number of physical processes used to prepare the beans for the subsequent extraction of the oil. Figure 3.2 shows the typical steps in preparation and extraction. The beans enter a mill on conveyor belts and are weighed, cleaned of metal using magnets, and passed through a roller for "cracking" into several pieces. The hulls are removed from the cracked beans by aspiration, and the cracked beans are heated slightly prior to being pressed through a cylindrical roll which forms them into flakes. The oil is extracted from the flakes by washing them in a hexane solvent. The solvent is then evaporated from the oil and the flakes and steam is used

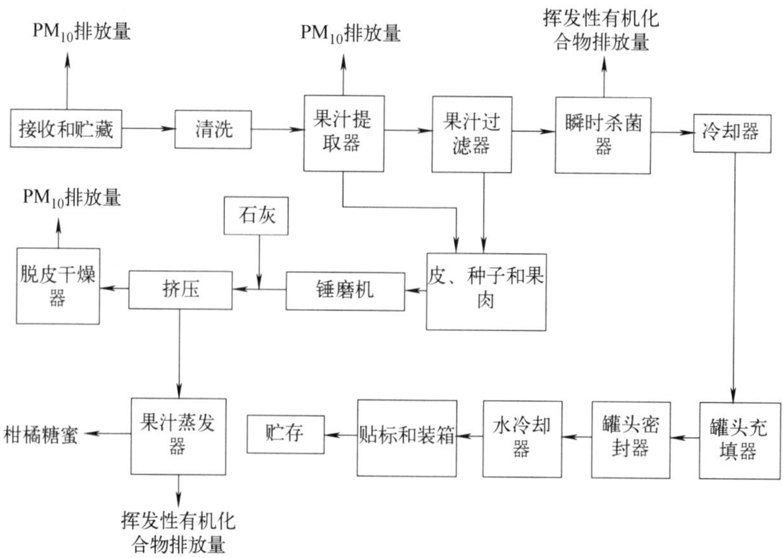

图 3.1 食品加工的工艺流程图

to desolventize the oil further. Residual hexane is removed using mineral oil scrubbers. The oil is then stored for further processing or packaging.

为了便于油脂的后续提取，需要采用大量的物理法对大豆进行预处理，因此大豆油的生产过程更复杂些。图 3.2 为大豆油制备和提取的典型步骤。大豆通过传送带进入粉碎机，

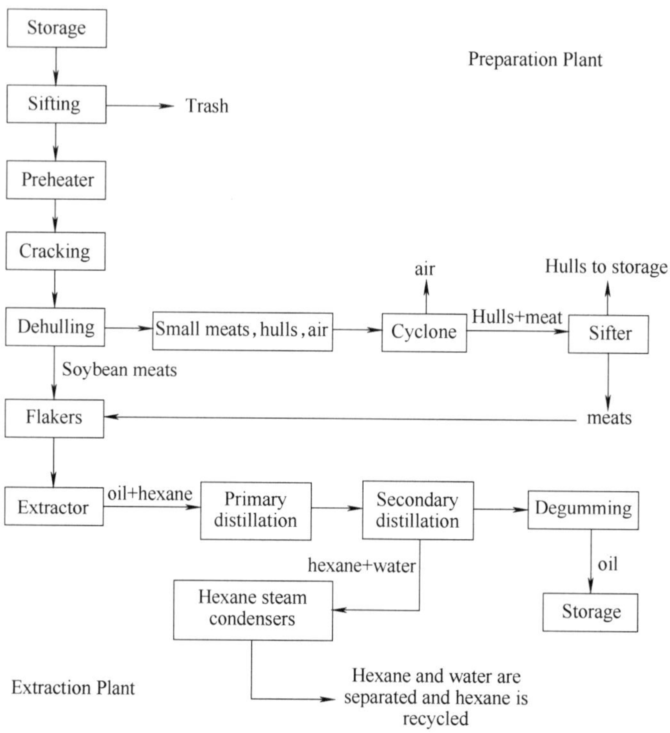

Figure 3.2 Process steps in the preparation of oil from soybeans.

然后经称重、磁选和穿过辊子进行破碎。通过风选除去豆皮，再将破碎的大豆加热并通过圆柱滚筒压成薄片状料坯。之后用正己烷作为溶剂从料坯里浸提豆油，溶剂从油和料坯里被蒸发除去，蒸汽可进一步脱溶油脂。残留的正己烷通过矿物油洗涤器除去。然后，贮存起来用于进一步加工或包装。

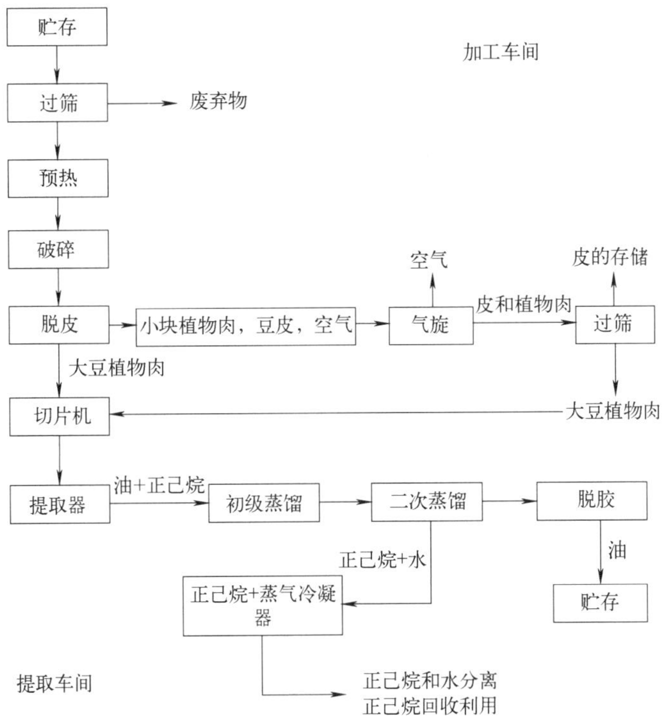

图 3.2 从大豆中制备豆油的处理工艺

(2) Chemical and Biological Operations

化学和生物处理

Chemical and biological operations play an important role in the manufacture of many foods and beverages, including bread, cheese, yogurt, beer, wine, and meats.

化学和生物处理在许多食品和饮料的生产中起着重要作用，包括面包、奶酪、酸奶、啤酒、葡萄酒和肉制品。

Fermentation is used to alter the texture, preserve, or produce certain flavors and aromas in foods and beverages, while curing is used to preserve and alter the flavor of meats.

发酵可以改变食品的组织结构，保留或产生食物和饮料中某些特定的风味和香气，而腌制则用于保留或改变肉的风味。

Fermentation involves the controlled use of biological organisms to break down the sugars in food into either alcohol or lactic acid. To produce beer or wine, yeast is used to break down sugars and produce ethanol and carbon dioxide, as shown in the equation.

发酵是通过控制微生物来将食品中的糖类降解为酒精或乳酸的过程。在生产啤酒或葡萄酒时，酵母被用来分解糖分并产生乙醇和二氧化碳，如下式所示：

$$C_6H_{12}O_6 \longrightarrow 2C_2H_5OH + 2CO_2$$

Breadmaking uses yeast fermentation to leaven the bread (i.e., to generate carbon dioxide to cause the bread to rise) and the ethanol in this case is released to the air.

面包制作常利用酵母菌的发酵作用（即产生二氧化碳使面包膨胀起来），在这种情况下，酒精挥发到空气中。

Cheese and yogurt are produced using various bacterial cultures to break down the lactose in milk and produce lactic acid. Different bacteria give different tastes and aromas, and the conditions under which these cultures are used must be carefully controlled to prevent contamination or spoilage. Fermentation processes also require close regulation of temperature and may require extended periods of storage at specific temperatures, resulting in energy and cooling water consumption.

奶酪和酸奶用各种细菌培养物来降解牛奶中的乳糖并产生乳酸。不同的细菌会产生不同的味道和香气，同时必须要小心控制这些培养物的生长环境以防止污染或变质。发酵过程还需要对温度进行精确调控，以及在特定温度下延长贮藏期，因此需要消耗能源和冷水。

Meat is cured by adding common salt (NaCl) and a source of nitrite from a curing salt (including $NaNO_3$, $NaNO_2$, KNO_3, or KNO_2). A pigment in the meat reacts with nitrite to give the meat a certain color. The presence of the salt and nitrite in the meat inhibits the growth of organisms and increases its shelf-life.

肉的腌制就是向肉中添加食盐（NaCl）和腌制盐（包括 $NaNO_3$、$NaNO_2$、KNO_3 或 KNO_2）。肉中的色素与亚硝酸盐反应赋予肉类特定的色泽。肉中食盐和亚硝酸盐的存在可以抑制微生物的生长并延长其货架期。

A final type of operation that is starting to be employed in the food processing industry is irradiation. Low-dose radiation applied to foods can kill pathogens like *E scherichia coli* and *Salmonella*, and hence increase the shelf-life of the products. It can also inhibit the ripening or sprouting in fruits and vegetables. Foods that are irradiated must be labeled as such in the U.S., a factor that may inhibit the use of this technique as the public is wary of consuming irradiated products. If public perception changes, the irradiation of foods will become more widespread over the next decade or so. Food safety and purification are central concerns in this sector. As a result, much of the water used in the industry is drinking-water quality. This requirement tends to be in opposition to the desire to reduce energy and water use for environmental reasons.

辐照技术是新应用于食品加工业的一种处理方法。对食品进行低剂量的辐照可以杀死大肠杆菌和沙门氏菌等病原体，从而延长食品的货架期。它也可以抑制果蔬的成熟或发芽。在美国，由于公众对消费辐照食品持谨慎态度，因此辐照食品必须进行标识，这或许会限制这一技术的应用。如果公众的认知有所改变的话，在未来的十年中食品辐照可能会得到广泛应用。食品安全和纯化是该领域的核心问题。因此，很多加工用水都是饮用水级别的。这种要求往往与出于环境因素考虑而降低能源和节约用水的愿望背道而驰。

3.1.2.2 The Sector's Use of Resources 部分的资源利用

(1) Energy

能源

The food processing industry is not as energy intensive as the heavy industries, like mining, metal processing, and chemicals. However, the industry ranks relatively high (fifth) on the use of energy by all industrial sectors. The food processing sector uses 5.9% of the total energy consumed by U.S. industry for fuel uses. Similarly, in Germany, the food processing industry uses 6.7% of the total energy consumed by industry, and ranks as the fifth largest energy-consuming sector.

食品加工业不像采矿业、冶金和化工业等重工业那样耗能较大。然而，该行业的能源消耗在所有工业中相对较高(排第五)。在美国，食品加工业占工业能源消费总量的5.9%。同样，在德国，食品加工业占工业能源消耗总量的6.7%，为第五大耗能产业。

Some subsectors of the food and beverage industry are much more energy intensive than others. For example, the manufacture of sugar involves the use of steam and direct heat for evaporation (sugar beets are 75% water). Sugar manufacture ranks highest in energy consumption of the sub-sectors of the German food industry. Other subsectors that rely on heating, cooling, freezing, or the storage and transportation of bulky raw and processed products are also relatively heavy consumers of energy. For example, 77% of the electricity used for the transportation and storage of frozen vegetables is consumed by compressors.

食品和饮料工业的某些子行业比其他行业消耗能源大得多。例如，制糖业需要使用水蒸气和直接加热来蒸发(甜菜中含75%的水)。制糖业在德国食品工业子行业中耗能最大。其他依赖于加热、冷却、冷冻以及大量原料、制成品需要储存和运输的子行业也是耗能大户。例如，在冷冻蔬菜的运输储存过程中压缩机消耗77%的电量。

(2) Water

水

The food and beverage industry has historically been a large consumer of water. Water is used as a primary ingredient (e.g., in the manufacture of beverages), as well as to clean ingredients and equipment, to transport raw materials in a plant, and for heating and cooling. Data for Germany show that, the food and drink industry uses about 5% of the total water consumed by industrial sources, but it uses about 30% of all drinking water consumed by industrial sources. Overall, almost two-thirds of the water used by the industry is of drinking-water quality and some subsectors, like soft drink, beer, and dairy manufacture, use drinking water almost exclusively.

一直以来，食品和饮料行业都是耗水量很大的产业。水是食品加工的主要原料(如饮料生产)，同时在工厂中也被用于清洗原料和设备、运输原料，及参与加热、冷却等过程。德国的数据表明，食品和饮料行业的耗水量大约占整个工业的5%，但占饮用水消耗总量的约30%。总之，在食品业，近2/3的水是饮用水级别的，其他如软饮料、啤酒和牛奶生产的子行业，几乎完全使用饮用水。

The amount of water used for some practices, like washing and rinsing, may be set by regulation. For example, the U.S. Department of Agriculture (USDA) defines minimum standards for the amount of water needed to clean poultry products. While water will always be an important resource for the food and beverage industry, there is scope for conservation and reuse, especially in its non-ingredient uses.

很多单元操作(如清洗和漂洗)所需要的水量可以通过法规来设置。例如，美国农业部(USDA)规定了清洗禽肉产品用水量的最低标准。虽然水一直是食品和饮料行业的重要资源，但是仍有节约和再利用的空间，特别是水不作为主要成分使用的时候。

(3) Materials and Process Chemicals

原料和工艺化学品

The raw materials used in the food and drink industry are primarily products of agriculture. Some subsectors, like fruits and vegetables, rely directly on agricultural products, while others, like breadmaking, rely on intermediate products that have been derived from agricultural products. The abundance or scarcity of these raw materials, or ingredients, is determined by the output of the agricultural sector.

食品和饮料工业中使用的原材料主要是农产品。一些子行业，如水果蔬菜类行业，直接依赖于农产品；而其他子行业如面包制作，依赖于源自农产品的中间产品。这些原材料的充足或稀缺取决于农业部门的产量。

Consumer preference will also, to some degree, dictate the supply of raw materials used in the food and beverage industry. In recent years, for example, sub-sectors of the food industry have developed product lines to serve consumers who wish to avoid consuming foods containing genetically modified organisms (GMOs). At the same time, agricultural biotechnology companies are developing techniques to improve the productivity or alter the properties of seeds and crops, potentially changing both the quantity and quality of the raw materials provided to the food processing industry.

消费者的喜好也会在一定程度上决定食品和饮料工业所使用的原材料的供应。例如，近年来，食品工业的一些子行业专门为不喜欢转基因食品的消费者开发了产品线。同时，农业生物技术公司正在开发提高生产率或者改变种子和作物特性的技术，从而改变食品加工原料的数量和品质。

Whether and how extensively agricultural biotechnology will change the supply of raw materials to the food processing industry remains to be seen. A complex set of issues surrounding consumer preference, government regulation, technology, and international trade are involved. U.S. consumers seem generally more receptive to agricultural biotechnology than their counterparts in Europe and Japan. U.S. farmers have adopted the technology most widely; 70% of the biotech crops planted worldwide are planted in the U.S. On the other hand, major food processors and retailers, including McDonalds and Frito-Lay, have declared that they will not use ingredients produced using biotechnology. Regardless of the rate of change in the industry in terms of adopting or abandoning agricultural biotechnology, fundamental scarcity of raw materials seems unlikely to pose a major problem for the food and beverage industry. Scarcity of agricultural products is typically a question of distribution rather than quantity.

农业生物技术能否以及将在何种程度上改变食品加工业的原料供应尚未可知，这涉及消费者的喜好、政府监管、科学技术和国际贸易等一系列复杂的问题。与欧洲和日本相比，美国消费者更能接受农业生物技术。美国农民已经广泛采用了这些技术，全球 70%的转基因作物种植在美国。另一方面，包括麦当劳和菲多利在内的主要食品生产商及零售商已经宣布将不会使用通过生物技术生产的原料。无论是否采用农业生物技术、它的变化速度如何，原材料的根本缺乏似乎都不可能对食品和饮料行业构成重大问题。农产品的短缺通常是分配问题，而不是数量问题。

3.1.2.3 Potential Environmental Concerns 潜在的环境问题

(1) Releases to Land

土壤排放物

Solid wastes released by the food processing industry consist largely of organic waste derived from food waste such as trimmings and peelings. While they are typically very high in nitrogen and phosphorous, these organic wastes are not of very high volume relative to the waste generated by other industrial sectors. Some organic wastes are reused as components of fertilizer or animal feed. However, much of the solid waste from food processing is disposed of by conventional means, to landfill, by incineration, or by composting.

食品加工业释放的固体废弃物大部分是由像一些辅料、果皮等食品废料产生的有机废料组成的。尽管这些废弃物中氮和磷含量很高，但相对于其他行业产生的废料，它们的含量并不是很高。一些有机废料作为肥料或者动物饲料的组成成分被重新利用。然而，多数的食品加工固体废料是通过填埋、焚化或堆肥等传统方式处理的。

A second source of solid waste is the packaging of foods and beverages. This includes both end-consumer packaging, and the packaging used to handle and transport the products within a plant and to retail locations. Use of reusable plastic totes in a plant or substitution of packaging materials for more environmentally favorable ones are examples of attention to this solid waste issue. Some packages are used almost exclusively by this industry; 95% of all steel cans produced are used by the food and beverage industry, for example.

固体废料的第二个来源是食品和饮料的包装。这包括终端消费者的包装，以及产品在工厂内和零售地处理、运输时的包装。在工厂里可重复使用的塑料手提袋，以及对环境更加友好型的包装替代材料，都是人们开始关注固体废物问题的例子。一些行业使用专门的包装，例如，95%的钢罐都被用于食品和饮料工业。

(2) Releases Water

水排放物

Just as the food processing industry is a large consumer of water; it is a large producer of wastewater. Cleaning of the raw materials is the biggest user of water in the industry. The quality of wastewater emitted is of as much, or more, concern than the quantity. Waste water from food processing is unique among industrial wastewater in that it is relatively low in metals and inorganics, but very high in organic contaminants.

正因为食品加工业是水的消耗大户，它也是废水的大型生产商。在工厂里，原材料的清洗用水最多。相比于废水的排放量，它的质量同样甚至更令人担忧。食品加工产生的废水非常独特，因为它的金属和无机物含量相对较低，但有机污染物含量很高。

Food processing waste water is highly variable, but it is typically very high in biochemical oxygen demand (BOD) and chemical oxygen demand (COD). A high BOD level is associated with high levels of dissolved and/or suspended solids, minerals, and organic nutrients containing nitrogen and phosphorus. Wastewaters with high BOD cannot be released directly into the aquatic environment or POTW (publicly owned treatment works) and will typically be pretreated to lower the BOD. The pH of food processing wastewater can also vary a great deal depending on the natural pH of the raw material, and the process steps used (e.g., dairy operations can produce acid waste streams). Wastewater from the fruit and vegetable subsector may contain residual pesticides, while that from the meat subsector will contain fats and oils.

食品加工废水变化很大，但是生化需氧量（BOD）和化学需氧量（COD）通常很高。高生化需氧量与溶解和/或悬浮的固体、矿物质以及含氮磷的有机营养物质的量呈正相关。这类废水不能直接排放到环境中或者公共污水处理厂，通常需要预处理以降低生化需氧量。食品加工废水的 pH 值也会有很大差异，具体取决于原材料的天然 pH 值以及所使用的处理步骤（例如，乳制品操作会产生酸性废液）。水果和蔬菜加工产生的废水可能残留农药，而肉制品加工产生的废水中则含有油脂。

A final component of the wastewater that is of concern in this industry is pathogens. Such organisms may be present in the water used to clean and process meats, poultry and seafood. Chlorine is typically used to disinfect the wastewaters prior to their discharge, but alternative techniques using UV light or ozone as disinfectants are starting to be used to reduce the use of chlorine.

另外，病原体也是工厂废水中值得关注的问题。这些生物可能存在于用于清洗和加工肉、家禽和海鲜的废水中。在废水排放之前通常用氯对其消毒，但是使用紫外线或者臭氧作为替代技术已开始减少消毒剂氯的使用。

(3) Releases to Air

大气排放物

Air emissions from the food processing industry contain few hazardous compounds. The release of volatile organic compounds (VOCs, involved in smog production) is common, however. Air emissions from brewery operations are among the more significant among the industry's subsectors, and they largely consist of CO_2, ethanol, particulates, and by-products of combustion. Odors can be a significant concern from many food processing plants, but they are difficult to control by regulation and are typically treated as a nuisance rather than an environmental concern. Many food processing plants have some form of odor controls in place.

食品加工业的空气排放物中几乎不含有害化合物。但是，挥发性有机化合物（VOCs，参与烟雾产生）的释放是很常见的。在该行业的子行业中，啤酒厂的空气污染物排放更为严重，主要包括 CO_2、乙醇、颗粒物和燃烧副产物。异味可能是很多食品加工厂所面临的重要问题，但它们很难通过监管进行控制，通常被视为一个麻烦事，但不上升为环境问题。许多食品加工工厂都采取了适当的措施控制气味。

3.1.2.4 Possible Future Scenarios 未来情景展望

(1) Trend World

世界趋势

The trend world for the food processing sector is a world of gradually increasing efficiency in manufacturing, packaging, and distribution. Energy and water will be used with gradually improving attention to conservation (and reuse where possible). Better refrigeration and management will decrease food wastage. Escalating pressures for more convenient foods will result in increased packaging per unit of food, however, and an accompanying increase in the costs of shipment and storage will be realized.

食品加工业的趋势是在加工制造、包装和分配方面效率逐渐提高。能源和水的使用将逐步把注意力放到节约上面（并尽可能地再利用）。更好的冷藏和管理能减少食品浪费。对于更加方便的食品的需求日益增加，这将会增加单位食物的包装成本。但是，随之而来的是运输和贮藏成本的上升。

(2) Green World

绿色环保的世界

In an environmentally superior world, emphasis will be placed on locally derived foods to the degree possible, cutting transport and packaging challenges substantially. Spoilage will be reduced to very low levels by improved control of processing and refrigeration, and by the safe irradiation of a number of food products. Packaging will be reduced, and may be either biodegradable or edible. The world will grow enough food for all its citizens, and will process, package, and distribute it so that hunger is no longer a problem, even in relatively poor countries.

在一个环境优越的世界里，应尽可能强调从当地获取食品，充分减少运输和包装带来的挑战。食品腐败将会通过改善工艺和冷藏以及安全辐照等方式降到非常低的水平。减少包装并采用可生物降解或者可食用的材料。世界将会为人类提供足够的食物，并对其进行加工、包装和分配，因此，即使是在相对贫穷的国家里，饥饿也不再是问题。

(3) Brown World

贫瘠的世界

In a brown world, scarcity of energy and water in many parts of the world will increase the rate of spoilage of whatever food is available. Food distribution will be hampered by a shortage of transportation fuels, and at the same time, the increasing desire for convenience will make locally-sourced food less viable. Continued problems with food safety will raise its cost and force tradeoffs with environmental goals. Rapid climate changes will have resulted in rapidly changing mixes of available food products, and processing facilities and machinery have been unable to adjust in an efficient manner.

在一个贫瘠的世界里，许多地方能源和水的稀缺将会增加所有可用食品的腐败率。食品的分配会因运输燃料的短缺而受到阻碍，与此同时，人们对便利性日益增加的需求将会降低本地食品的生产。持续出现的食品安全问题提高了食品的成本，并迫使产品生产与环境要求相适应。快速的气候变化将导致现有食品的快速变化组合，并且加工设备和机械将无法有效地进行调整。

3.1.3 Homework

课后作业

3.1.3.1 Sentences Translation

句子翻译

(1) Original Sentences

原句

① Food processing is the transformation of raw materials into safe, stable, and edible products via physical, chemical, or biological methods.

② Processing aims to extend shelf life, enhance texture, and improve nutritional value.

③ Fermentation temperature directly affects microbial activity, metabolite production, and fermentation rate.

④ Sustainable food processing aims to minimize environmental impact by reducing energy consumption, waste generation, and water usage.

⑤ Enzymatic hydrolysis is widely used in protein breakdownto produce more digestible food ingredients.

⑥ Biodegradable plasticbags can decompose in nature, minimizing ecological harm.

⑦ UV and ozone disinfection can reduce reliance on chlorine and avoid byproduct contamination.

⑧ Reducing packaging costs requires balancing food safety risks and economic benefits.

⑨ Locally sourced food productionemphasizes utilizing regionalresources to reduce supply chain dependence.

⑩ Extreme heat increases refrigeration energy consumption in food processing plants by 15%~25%.

(2) Translations

翻译

① 食品加工是通过物理、化学或生物方法处理原料，制成安全、稳定且可食用的产品。

② 食品加工旨在延长保质期、改善口感并提高营养价值。

③ 发酵温度直接影响微生物活性、代谢产物及发酵速率。

④ 可持续食品加工旨在通过减少能源消耗、废弃物产生和用水量来降低对环境的影响。

⑤ 酶解技术被广泛应用于蛋白质水解，以生产更易消化的食品配料。

⑥ 生物降解塑料袋能在自然环境中分解，减少生态危害。

⑦ 紫外线（UV）和臭氧消毒可减少对氯的依赖，避免副产物污染。

⑧ 降低包装成本需平衡食品安全风险与经济效益。

⑨ 就地取材的食品生产强调利用本地资源，减少供应链依赖。

⑩ 极端高温导致食品加工厂制冷能耗增加 15%~25%。

(3) 翻译文中划线句子

3.1.3.2 Common Sentence Patterns of Scientific Papers 科技论文常见句型

① The purpose of the present study was to …
② …were characterized by …
③ It was found that…
④ This result is compatible with the…
⑤ Considering that…
⑥ It is worth pointing out that…
⑦ As can be seen…
⑧ The present study demonstrated that…
⑨ This study deals with…
⑩ This result was in opposition to…

3.2 Food Preservation

3.2 食品保存

3.2.1 Glossary

专业词汇分析

① inactivating *n.* 钝化；*v.*使钝化(inactivate 的 ing 形式)

[记忆窍门] active 意为积极的，活跃的；前缀 in 表示否定，inactivating 即为不活跃的，使之不活跃，即钝化。

② biopreservative *n.*生物防腐剂

[记忆窍门] 该词由“bio(生物)+ preservative(防腐剂)”组成，合在一起即为生物防腐剂。

③ decontaminate *v.* 净化

[记忆窍门] 前缀 de 表示离开，去除；contaminate 意为污染，除去污染即为净化。

④ artificially *adv.* 人为地，人工地

[记忆窍门] art 指艺术，而艺术多由人创作，词尾 ly 多表示词性为副词，综上可以联想到词意“人为地”。

⑤ ferment *v.* 发酵 *n.* 发酵，酵素

[记忆窍门] ferment 谐音似“馒头”，而馒头属于发酵食品。

⑥ textural *adj.* 组织的，结构的

[记忆窍门] text 意为课文，文本，即是课文一定有其逻辑结构和一定的思路，语言也是经过组织的，由此可以记住 textural 意为“组织的，结构的”。

⑦ radiation *n.* 辐射，放射物

[记忆窍门] radia 与 radio 形似，tion 发音谐音射，radiation 即能类似广播一样发射信号，即可联想到“辐射”。

⑧ modified atmosphere packaging (MAP) 气调贮藏包装

⑨ preservation *n.* 保存；保藏

⑩ dehydration *n.* 脱水，去湿，干燥

[记忆窍门] 前缀 de-意为除去，hydration 意为水合作用，组合即是“脱水，干燥”。

⑪ superchilling *n.* 过冷

[记忆窍门] 前缀 super-意为过度的，chilling 意为冷却，寒冷，组合即是“过冷”。

⑫ hurdle technology (HT) 栅栏技术

⑬ recrystallisation *n.* 重结晶；再结晶

[记忆窍门] 前缀 re-意为“再，重新”，crystallisation 意为“结晶，结晶作用”，组合即“重结晶，再结晶”。

⑭ Food and Agricultural Organization (FAO) *n.* 联合国粮食与农业组织

⑮ World Health Organization (WHO) *n.* 世界卫生组织

⑯ polyvinylidene *n.* 聚乙二烯

[记忆窍门] 前缀 poly-意为“多，聚”，vinylidene 意为“亚乙烯基”，组合即是“聚乙二烯”。

3.2.2 Texts and Translations

课文及翻译

A Review on Fresh Meat Preservation Technologies 鲜肉保藏技术综述

Abstract

摘要

Fresh meat is a highly perishable product due to its biological composition. Many interrelated factors influence the shelf life and freshness of meat such as holding temperature, atmospheric oxygen (O_2), endogenous enzymes, moisture, light and most importantly, micro-organisms. With the increased demand for high quality, convenience, safety, fresh appearance and an extended shelf life in fresh meat products, alternative non-thermal preservation technologies such as high hydrostatic pressure, superchilling, natural biopreservatives and active packaging have been proposed and investigated. Whilst some of these technologies are efficient at inactivating the micro-organisms most commonly related to food-borne diseases, they are not effective against spores. To increase their efficacy against vegetative cells, a combination of several preservation technologies under the so-called hurdle concept has also been investigated. The objective of this review is to describe current methods and developing technologies for preserving fresh meat. The benefits of some new technologies and their industrial limitations are presented and discussed.

Keywords: Fresh meat, Preservation technologies, Superchilling, HHP, Natural biological preservation, Packaging

由于生物组成的原因，鲜肉是高度易腐败产品。许多相互关联的因素，如保藏温度和大气氧浓度（O_2）、内源酶、水分、光照以及最重要的微生物，都会影响肉的货架期和新鲜度。随着对高品质、方便性、安全性、外观新鲜度和延长货架期鲜肉产品需求的增加，替代传统方法的非热保藏技术，例如高静水压、过冷、天然生物保鲜剂和活性包装技术，已经被提出和探究。尽管这些技术可以有效钝化多数与食源性疾病相关的微生物的活性，但是它们对微生物孢子的作用效果甚微。为了提高它们对营养体细胞的保藏效果，学者们探究了一种基于几种保藏技术相结合的栅栏概念。本文总结和叙述了当前和正在发展中的鲜肉保藏方法，也介绍和讨论了一些新技术的优势及其在工业化应用中的局限性。

关键词：鲜肉，保藏技术，过冷，高静水压，天然生物保鲜，包装

3.2.2.1 Introduction 引言

Meat is defined as the flesh of animals used as food. The term “fresh meat” includes meat from recently processed animals as well as vacuum-packed meat or meat packed in controlled-atmospheric gases, which has not undergone any treatment other than chilling to ensure preservation. The diverse nutrient composition of meat makes it an ideal environment for the growth and propagation of meat spoilage micro-organisms and common food-borne pathogens. It is therefore essential that adequate preservation technologies are applied to maintain its safety and quality. The processes used in meat preservation are principally concerned with inhibiting microbial spoilage, although other methods of preservation are sought to minimise other deteriorative changes such as colour and oxidative changes.

肉是供食用的动物的肉的统称。“鲜肉”一词包括最近加工的动物肉，以及真空包装或气调包装的肉，它们除了经过冷藏外不经其他任何处理。肉的各种营养成分为腐败微生物和常见的食源性致病菌的生长、繁殖提供了理想环境。因此，应用适当的保藏技术以保证肉制品的安全性和品质是至关重要的。尽管一些方法试图减少肉制品在颜色和氧化反应等方面的变化，但其保藏的主要目的是抑制微生物引起的腐败。

A number of interrelated factors influence the shelf life and keeping quality of meat, specifically holding temperature, atmospheric oxygen (O_2), endogenous enzymes, moisture (dehydration), light and, most importantly, micro-organisms. All of these factors, either alone or in combination, can result in detrimental changes in the colour, odour, texture and flavour of meat. Although deterioration of meat can occur in the absence of micro-organisms (e.g., proteolysis, lipolysis and oxidation), microbial growth is by far the most important factor in relation to the keeping quality of fresh meat. Traditionally, methods of meat preservation may be grouped into three broad categories based on control by temperature, by moisture and, more directly, by inhibitory processes (bactericidal and bacteriostatic, such as ionising radiation, packaging, etc.), although a particular method of preservation may involve several antimicrobial principles. Each control step may be regarded as a “hurdle” against microbial proliferation and combinations of processes (so-called hurdle technology (HT)) can be devised to achieve particular objectives in terms of both microbial and organoleptic quality.

许多相关的因素会影响肉的货架期和贮藏品质，尤其是贮藏温度、大气中的氧气（O_2）、

内源酶、水分（脱水）、光照，以及尤为重要的微生物。所有这些因素，无论是单一的还是复合的，都能够导致肉制品的颜色、气味、质地和风味的劣变。尽管肉在缺少微生物的条件下能够发生劣变（如：蛋白质水解作用，脂解和氧化），但是目前为止微生物仍然是关系到肉贮藏品质的最重要因素。个别保藏方法可能涉及几种抑菌原理，传统肉制品的贮藏方法根据控制温度、湿度和更直接地通过抑菌工艺（杀菌和抑菌，如电离辐射、包装等）可以分为三大类。每个控制步骤可以看成是阻止微生物繁殖的一个“栅栏因子”，组合处理（称为栅栏技术，HT）能够实现控制微生物和感官品质上的特定目标。

The latest investigated preservation technologies for fresh meat are non-thermal inactivation technologies such as high hydrostatic pressure (HHP), new packaging systems such as modified atmosphere packaging (MAP) and active packaging (AP), natural antimicrobial compounds and biological preservation. All these alternative technologies attempt to be mild, energy saving, environment friendly and to guarantee a natural appearance while eliminating pathogens and spoilage micro-organisms. The aim of this article is to review these technologies for the preservation of fresh meat.

鲜肉保藏技术的最新研究主要是非热杀菌技术，例如，高静水压（HHP）、气调包装（MAP）和活性包装（AP）等新包装系统、天然抑菌剂和生物保藏。所有这些替代技术都试图在温和、节能、环保和保持原生态外观的条件下，消除致病菌和腐败微生物。本文目的是综述鲜肉保藏技术。

3.2.2.2 Refrigeration 冷藏

Temperatures below or above the optimum range for microbial growth will have a preventative action on the latter. For fresh meat, refrigeration, including storage above or below the freezing point, has been the traditional preservation method. Superchilling technology, which stores meat just above the freezing point, has been used with success.

低于或高于微生物最适生长范围的温度都会对其生长产生抑制作用。对于鲜肉，高于或低于冰点的冷藏一直是传统的保藏方法。在鲜肉保藏中，温度高于冰点的过冷保藏技术，已经取得成功。

(1) Chilling

冷却

Recognition by early civilizations of the preservative effects of cool temperature storage of perishable products such as meat led to storage of such products in natural caves where temperatures were relatively low throughout the year. The principles of artificial ice formation and of mechanical refrigeration date from about 1750 and commercial-scale operations based on mechanical refrigeration were in use 100 years later.

人类文明早期便认识到低温存储易腐产品如肉类的保藏效果较好，于是将其贮藏于全年温度相对较低的天然洞穴中。人工制冰和机械制冷原理的提出可追溯到 1750 年，机械制冷的规模化商业应用也有 100 年的历史。

Chilling is critical for meat hygiene, safety, shelf life, appearance and eating quality. Chilling in air reduces carcass surface temperature and enhances carcass drying; both of which reduce the growth of bacteria. An increase in air velocity and/or a decrease in temperature (both controllable) decrease chilling time. A limiting factor, however, is the difficulty in removing heat quickly from the deeper tissue of carcasses.

冷却对于肉类的卫生、安全、货架期、外观和食用品质来说至关重要。空气冷却能够降低胴体表面的温度和提高胴体的干燥程度，二者均能减少细菌的生长。增加空气流速或降低温度（均可控）能够减少冷却时间。然而对于胴体深层组织的快速降温是一个难度较大的限制因素。

Natural-convection air chilling, where refrigerant is pumped through cooling tubes, is slow and largely uncontrollable, whereas forced-convection air chilling, coupled with fans for air movement is much more efficient. Rapid carcass chilling increases product yield due to lower evaporation from the surface, while rapid drying of the carcass surface helps to reduce bacterial growth. Ultra-rapid chilling of pre-rigour meat may, on the other hand, lead to cold-shortening and toughening. Spray-chilling can enhance the oxygenation of surface myoglobin without increasing metmyoglobin, thus maintaining a bright appearance and eliminating weight loss.

自然对流空气冷却，通过冷却管泵送制冷剂，速度慢且不可控，而配备空气流动风机的强制对流空气冷却则更有效。胴体的快速冷却由于减少了表面蒸发而提高了产品产量，同时快速干燥的胴体表面有助于减少细菌的生长。另一方面，预冻处理过的肉再进行快速冷却会缩短冷却时间和增加韧度。喷雾冷却能够在不增加高铁肌红蛋白的同时，增加表面肌红蛋白的氧合，从而维持肉制品表面颜色鲜艳同时避免质量损失。

(2) Freezing

冷冻

In Britain, large scales of meat preservation by freezing commenced about 1880, when the first shipments of frozen beef and mutton arrived from Australia. At that time, there was a surplus of meat animals in the southern hemisphere, especially in New Zealand and Australia, and freezing offered a means of preserving meat during the long voyages involved between the two areas. The advantages of temperatures below the freezing point were in prolonging the useful storage life of meat and in discouraging microbial and chemical changes.

大约从 1880 年第一批冷冻牛羊肉从澳大利亚运往英国开始，大规模肉制品保藏都是通过冷冻实现的。在那时，南半球存在肉用家畜过剩的现象，尤其是在新西兰和澳大利亚，冷却提供了一种在两地间长途运输过程中肉制品保藏的方法。温度在冰点以下能延长肉制品的货架期并且抑制微生物和化学变化。

Fast freezing produces minute intracellular ice crystals and thus diminishes the drip on thawing. The rate of freezing is dependent not only on the bulk of the meat and its thermal properties (e.g., specific heat and thermal conductivity), but also on the temperature of the refrigerating environment, on the method of applying the refrigeration and, with smaller cuts of meat, on the nature of the wrapping material used.

速冻能够产生微小的细胞内冰晶，从而减少解冻时的水分流失。冻结速度不仅取决于肉的体积和其热性能（如：比热和电导率），还取决于制冷环境的温度和冷却方法，同时，对那些切成小块的肉，取决于所使用的包装材料。

A temperature of –55℃ has been suggested as ideal storage conditions for frozen meat to completely prevent quality changes. At these low temperatures, enzyme reactions, oxidative rancidity and ice recrystallisation are likely to be minimal and thus few deteriorative changes will occur during storage.

冷冻肉品能达到完全防止品质变化的理想贮藏温度是–55℃。在此低温条件下酶促反应、氧化酸败和冰重结晶的可能性最小，因而在贮藏阶段发生变质的概率也很小。

Cryogenic freezing offers faster freezing times compared with conventional air freezing because of the large temperature differences between the cryogen and the meat product and the high rate of surface heat transfer resulting from the boiling of the cryogen. Cryogenic freezing requires no mechanical refrigeration equipment; simply a cryogen tank and suitable spray equipment. However, there may be some distortion of the shape of the product caused by the cryogenic process that might impact on the commercial application. Furthermore, the cost of cryogenic liquid is relatively high and therefore may limit its commercial application.

与传统的空气冷冻相比，低温冷冻的时间更短，这是由于冷冻剂和肉制品之间的温差很大，并且冷冻剂的沸腾导致表面热传递率很高。低温冷冻不需要机械制冷设备，只需简单的制冷剂罐和适当的喷淋设备即可。然而，低温处理可能会导致产品形状变形，影响其商业化应用。此外，低温冷却液的成本相对较高，也可能会限制其商业化应用。

(3) Superchilling

过冷

The process of superchilling was described as early as 1920 by Le Danois, even though he did not actually use the terms “superchilling”, “deep-chilling” or “partial ice formation”. The terms “superchilling” and “partial freezing” are used to describe a process where a minor part of the product's water content is frozen. During superchilling, the temperature of the product is lowered, often 1–2℃, below the initial freezing point of the product. After initial surface freezing, the ice distribution equilibrates and the product obtains a uniform temperature at which it is maintained during storage and distribution. This has been effectively used for seafood and there is now increasing interest in this process for extension of chilled storage life of meat.

Le Danois 早在 1920 年就描述了过冷的过程，尽管他并没有使用“过冷”“深度冷却”或者“部分结冰”等术语。术语“过冷”和“部分冷冻”是用来描述一个过程中产品的小部分的水冻结。在过冷过程中，产品温度通常会下降 1~2℃，低于产品的初始冰点。初始表面冻结后，冰分布平衡且产品获得均匀的温度，可以在贮藏和配送过程中维持该温度。该技术已被有效地用于海鲜，现在人们对延长肉的冷藏货架期这一过程也越来越感兴趣。

① Advantages and Application

优势和应用

At superchilling temperatures, most microbial activity is inhibited or terminated. Chemical and physical changes may progress and, in some cases, even accelerate. Superchilling, as a commercial practice, can reduce the use of freezing/thawing for production buffers and thereby reduce labour, energy costs and product weight losses. The ice present in superchilled products protects the meat from temperature rises in poor cold chains; however, some increase in product drip loss may occur during storage.

在过冷温度下，大多数微生物活性被抑制或终止。在某些情况下化学和物理变化可能仍在进行甚至加速进行。过冷，作为一种商业实践，能够减少冷冻或解冻过程对产品的影响，从而减少劳动力、能源成本和产品质量损失。过冷产品中的冰能够保护肉制品免受冷链温度升高的影响，但在贮藏期间产品水分损失可能会增加。

"Super" or "deep" chilling has been commonly used in the USA, although the product is seldom referred to as "super-chilled" since, legally, in the USA poultry meat kept above –3.3℃ can be marketed as "fresh" (US Poultry Products Inspection Regulations 9CFR381). The process involves water chilling the carcasses and then putting them through an air freezer operating at –15℃ for approximately 30 min. After packaging, they are again placed in an air freezer to achieve the required meat temperature. The carcasses are then stored and distributed at –1℃ to –2℃.

"超级"或"深度"冷却已经在美国广泛使用，尽管产品很少被称为"超级冷却"。因为在美国，保藏在-3.3℃以上的禽肉都能合法地以"新鲜"食品售卖（美国家禽产品检验规范9CFR318）。这一过程包括使用水冷却胴体，然后将其置于-15℃的空气冷冻机中放置约30min。包装后，将其再次置于空气冷冻机中以达到所需温度。之后将胴体在-1℃至-2℃条件下贮藏和运输。

The main reason for implementing this technology is its ability to prolong the shelf life of meat for at least 1.4~4 times the life of traditional meat-chilling methods. Ice-forming and recrystallisation can cause microstructural changes to food tissue during freezing, resulting in cell dehydration, and drip loss and tissue shrinkage during thawing. Food characteristics such as pH, ionic strength, and concentration of dissolved gases, viscosity, oxidation-reduction potential and surface tension may also be altered, leading to changes in enzymatic activity and protein denaturation.

过冷技术能够被使用的主要原因是，相对于传统肉制品的冷藏方法，至少能延长肉制品的货架期 1.4~4 倍。在冻结期间，结冰和重结晶会导致食品组织的显微结构改变，造成细胞脱水，融化过程中水分损失和组织收缩。食品的特性（例如 pH 值、离子强度、气体浓度、黏度、氧化还原电位和表面张力等）也可能改变，最终导致酶活性变化或者蛋白质变性。

Reports on superchilling have mainly involved fish and poultry. Gallart-Jornet *et al.* (2007) evaluated the effect of superchilled storage compared with ice and frozen storage on the quality of raw Atlantic salmon (*Salmo salar*) fillets and found superchilled storage was beneficial for the preservation of freshness of the raw material before processing. Duun, Hemmingsen, Haugland, & Rustad (2008) also found the storage time of vacuum-packed salmon fillets could be doubled by superchilled storage at –1.4℃ and –3.6℃ compared to ice chilled storage. Drip loss was not a major problem in superchilled salmon. Textural hardness was significantly higher in superchilled salmon fillets stored at –3.6℃ compared to those stored at –1.4℃, ice chilled and frozen. Cathepsins B and B+L remained active at the selected storage temperatures, which may therefore lead to softening during subsequent chilled storage.

关于过冷技术的报道主要涉及鱼类和禽类。Gallart-Jornet 通过与冰冻贮藏进行比较，评价了过冷技术对大西洋鲑鱼片（*Salmo salar*）品质的影响。他发现过冷技术对未经处理的生鲜原料的保藏是有利的。Duun、Hemmingsen、Haugland 和 Rustad 也发现与冷冻保藏相比，真空包装鲑鱼片在-1.4℃至-3.6℃的过冷条件下贮藏，其保藏时间能够加倍。过冷处理过的鲑鱼水分损失并不是最主要的问题。与-1.4℃条件下的冰冻保藏相比，在-3.6℃条件下的过冷保藏能够显著增加鲑鱼片的组织硬度。在选定温度条件下，组织蛋白酶 B 和 B+L 仍然保持活性，这可能会使产品在随后冷却过程中更柔软。

Duun et al. (2008) found superchilling of pork roasts at –2.0℃ improved the shelf life significantly compared with traditional chilling at +3.5℃. The superchilled roasts maintained good sensory quality and low microbiological counts during the whole storage period (16 weeks), while the shelf life of chilled samples was just 14 days. Sensory tests indicated that the quality of the superchilled roasts was not reduced by high numbers of psychrotrophic bacteria. The drip loss in superchilled samples was low and showed less variation than in the chilled references and the temperature-abused samples. The temperature-abused and chilled samples had lower liquid losses, measured by centrifugation, than the superchilled samples.

Duun 等（2008）曾发现与传统的+3.5℃冷却相比，在-2.0℃的温度下过冷贮藏的猪肉货架期显著提高。在整个储存期（16 周）内，过冷贮藏的猪肉保持了良好的感官品质和较低的微生物数量，而冷却样品的货架期仅为 14 天。感官试验表明，过冷贮藏烤肉的质量不会因大量嗜冷细菌而降低。过冷样品中的水分损失较低，与低温对照和温度滥用样品相比变化较小。通过离心测量，温度滥用和冷却样品的液体损失低于过冷样品。

② Challenges in Superchilling

过冷技术的挑战

Calculating the required superchilling times and estimating the temperature distributions in a chilling and freezing process is a challenging exercise. It is also difficult to define the degree of superchilling required to sufficiently improve shelf life and fulfil the demands of the process to achieve the quality attributes desired (Magnussen et al., 2008).

在冷却和冻结过程中，计算过冷所需的时间和估算温度分布是一个挑战。很难定义充分延长货架期和完成产品生产过程并保证品质的情况下所需要的过冷度。

The media used to achieve superchilling will affect the possibilities for implementing it in an industrial process. A change from “traditional technologies” such as chilling, freezing, thawing to the more complex superchilling technology is difficult. Superchilling demands more accurate information on product variation and flow. Special care needs to be taken prior to, and after, the superchilling process itself. Most equipment producers today do not have the required energy and thermodynamic competence to design and control superchilling processes.

用于实现过冷的介质将影响其在工业生产上应用的可能性。从冷却、冷冻、解冻等“传统技术”到更复杂的过冷技术的转变很难。过冷技术需要更精确的品质差异的信息和流动特性。过冷过程本身和处理前后都需要特别注意。如今，大多数设备生产商都还没有设计和控制过冷过程所需的能量和热力学能力。

Clearly, industry will need support to develop basic data for graphs and software, of chilling times, chilling temperatures, air-flow and refrigeration loads. This also includes principles for control regulates monitor (CRM) systems for the superchilling process and refrigeration system.

显然，行业需要支持开发图形和软件的基本数据，包括冷却时间、冷却温度、气流和制冷负荷。还包括用于过冷过程和制冷系统的控制调节监视器（CRM）的原理。

3.2.2.3 Ionising Radiation 电离辐射

Ionising radiation has been a method of direct microbial inhibition for preserving meat since around 1940. In 1980, participating bodies (including the Food and Agricultural Organization (FAO) and World Health Organization (WHO)) proposed that irradiation with a dose less than 10 kGy (1 Mrad) should be accepted as a process for preserving all major categories of food. In the UK, "The Food (Control of Irradiation) Regulations (1990)" allows certain classes of food to be irradiated up to a maximum dosage (e.g., 7 kGy for poultry) and under "The Food Labelling (Amendment)(Irradiated Food) Regulations (1990)" all irradiated foods are required to have a label indicating that they have received such treatment. Irradiation technology was promoted by the FAO in the Codex Alimentarius in 2003 and has been well accepted in 50 countries, especially in the USA, Egypt, and China and across Latin America.

自 1940 年以来，电离辐射成为一种直接抑制微生物来保藏肉制品的方法。1980 年，参与的机构［包括联合国粮农组织（FAO）和世界卫生组织（WHO）］提出针对所有主要食品类别保藏的可接受最低辐射计量是 10kGy(1Mrad)。在英国，食品管理条例（辐射控制 1990 年）允许某些种类的食品可能达到最大辐照剂量（比如家禽是 7kGy），在食品标签（修订）（辐照食品）条例（1990 年）中规定，所有辐照食品必须有标签说明它们是否进行过辐照处理。联合国粮农组织于 2003 年在食品法典中推广了辐照技术，并已被 50 多个国家所接受，特别是在美国、埃及、中国和整个拉丁美洲。

The radionuclides approved for food irradiation include ^{137}Cs and ^{60}Co. radioactive cobalt (^{60}Co) decays to non-radioactive nickel by emitting high-energy particles and X-rays. The X-rays kill rapidly growing cells (microbes) but do not leave the product radioactive. Because it is highly penetrating, it can be used to treat packaged food.

允许用于食品辐照的放射性同位素包括 ^{137}Cs 和 ^{60}Co。放射性 ^{60}Co 通过发射高能粒子和 X 射线衰变成非放射性的镍。X 射线能杀死迅速生长的细胞（微生物）但不会使产品具有放射性。因为它的高穿透性，可以用来处理包装食品。

The advantages of ionising radiation for food preservation include its highly efficient inactivation of bacteria, the fact that the product is essentially chemically unaltered and the appreciable thickness of material, which can be treated after packing in containers. A maximum dosage of 10 kGy represents a low amount of energy (equivalent to that needed to raise the temperature of 1 g water 2.4 ℃), which is why the technology is considered non-thermal, thus preserving the freshness and nutritional quality of the meat and meat products when compared with thermal methods.

电离辐射用于食物保藏的优点包括：能够高效地灭活细菌、产品的化学组成基本不变，而且在包装材料有一定厚度时，产品仍可以在包装后进行处理。最大剂量 10 kGy 代表低能量(相当于 1g 水升温 2.4℃需要的能量)，这就解释了为什么称此项技术是非热的。与热处理方法相比，能够保持肉制品的新鲜度和营养品质。

Colour changes in irradiated fresh meat occur because of the inherent susceptibility of the myoglobin molecule to energy input and alterations in the chemical environment; haem iron being particularly susceptible. Brewer (2004) summarised the effects of ionising radiation on meat colour, and concluded that maintenance of ideal meat colour during the process of irradiation could be enhanced by various combinations of pre-slaughter feeding of antioxidants to livestock, condition of the meat prior to irradiation (pH, oxymyoglobin vs. metmyoglobin), addition of antioxidants directly to the product, gas atmosphere (MAP) or lack thereof, packaging and temperature control. Radiation treatment resulted in essentially no loss of thiamine (one of the least stable vitamins), therefore suggesting that such radiation has no detrimental effects on these nutrients.

辐照会引起鲜肉变色，因为鲜肉中肌红蛋白分子对能量供给和化学环境改变具有敏感性。血红素铁最容易受到影响。Brewer（2004）总结了电离辐射对肉制品颜色的影响，并得出结论，若想在辐照过程中保持肉的理想颜色，可以在宰杀前对牲畜喂食适当的抗氧化剂、控制辐照前肉制品的条件（pH 值、氧合肌红蛋白与高铁肌红蛋白）、在产品中直接添加抗氧化剂、气调或真空包装以及控制温度。辐照处理基本上不会损失硫胺素（一种稳定的维生素），由此表明这种辐照不会对这些营养素有不利影响。

3.2.2.4 Chemical Preservation and Biological Preservation 化学保藏和生物保藏

(1) Chemical Preservation

化学保鲜剂

Carbon dioxide and ozone have been used to discourage the growth of surface micro-organisms on beef carcasses during prolonged storage at chilling temperatures. Although ozone leaves no toxic residues in meat, its use in a production environment can be dangerous for personnel. Moreover, it accelerates the oxidation of fat and is more effective against air-borne micro-organisms than against those on meat.

在寒冷温度下长时期贮藏期间，二氧化碳和臭氧已被用于阻止牛肉胴体表面微生物的生长。虽然臭氧残留在肉制品中没有毒性，但在生产环境中对使用的人员有危害。此外，它也加速了脂肪氧化，以及相对于胴体表面，更能有效抑制空气中传播的微生物。

Various micro-organisms produce organic acids and alcohols by anaerobic fermentation of food substrates and these, by inhibiting other organisms that are concomitantly present and which could spoil the food or make it toxic, can act in its preservation. Lactic acid, for example, is a frequently effective inhibitory agent used in fresh meat preservation; however, other organic acids have also been found to be responsible for discolouration and production of pungent odours.

各种微生物以食物为基质进行厌氧发酵产生有机酸和醇类，通过抑制同时存在的其他可能破坏食物或产生毒素的生物，从而起到保藏作用。以乳酸为例，通常将其作为有效的抑菌剂用于鲜肉保藏，但是其他有机酸也能导致变色并且产生刺激性气味。

Salts such as sodium lactate have been used in the meat industry because of their ability to increase flavour, prolong shelf life, and improve the microbiological safety of products. The antimicrobial effects of lactates are due to their ability to lower water activity and the direct inhibitory effect of the lactate ion. Several researchers have successfully extended the shelf life of fresh meat products by adding sodium lactate. Nadeem et al. (2003) extended freshly slaughtered sheep and goat carcasses stored at 5~7℃ for 3 and 2 days, respectively, after spraying the carcasses with solution "B" containing potassium sorbate, sodium acetate, sodium citrate, sodium lactate each at 2.5% and sodium chloride at 5%, when compared with solution "A" (without potassium sorbate) and control.

盐类如乳酸钠能够增加风味、延长货架期、提高产品微生物安全性，所以被用于肉制品工业。乳酸盐的抑菌作用是能够降低水活度，同时直接抑制乳酸离子。一些研究人员已经通过添加乳酸钠成功地延长了鲜肉产品的保质期。Nadeem 等人（2003）发现与"A"溶液（未添加山梨酸钾）及空白溶液处理对比，在新屠宰的绵羊和山羊胴体表面喷涂 2.5% 山梨酸钾、醋酸钠、柠檬酸钠、乳酸钠和 5%氯化钠的"B"溶液后，在 5~7℃条件下，保藏时间可分别延长 3 天和 2 天。

(2) Biological Preservation and Natural Antimicrobials

生物保藏和天然抗菌剂

Natural compounds, such as essential oils, chitosan, nisin and lysozyme, have been investigated to replace chemical preservatives and to obtain "green label" products. Storage life is extended and safety is increased by using natural or controlled microflora, of which lactic acid bacteria (LAB) and their antimicrobial products such as lactic acid and bacteriocins have been studied extensively. Bacteriocins are a heterogeneous group of antibacterial proteins that vary in spectrum of activity, mode of action, molecular weight, genetic origin and biochemical properties.

天然化合物，如精油、壳聚糖、乳酸链球菌素和溶菌酶，已被用来研究替代化学防腐剂，并获得"绿色标签"产品。通过使用天然的或受控的菌群，可以延长保存期并提高安全性，其中乳酸菌（LAB）及其抗菌剂产品如乳酸和细菌素已被广泛研究。细菌素是一组不同种类的抗菌蛋白，其活性谱、作用方式、分子量、遗传来源和生化特性各不相同。

Various spices and essential oils have preservative properties and have been used to extend the storage life of meat products. These include eugenol in cloves and allyl isothiocyanate in mustard seed. Roller et al. (2002) and Sagoo, Board and Roller (2002) reviewed the antifungal and antimicrobial properties of the polysaccharide chitosan. Its efficacy, especially in combination with other antimicrobial agents, warrants further investigation.

各种有防腐特性的香料和精油已经用于延长肉制品的货架期。其中包括丁香中的丁香酚和芥菜籽中的异硫氰酸烯丙酯。Roller 等人（2002）和 Sagoo、Board、Roller（2002）综述了多糖壳聚糖的抗菌特性。它的功效，特别是与其他抗生素联合使用，值得进一步研究。

Nisin is the only commercial bacteriocin and has been used to decontaminate artificially contaminated pieces of raw pork and in combination with 2% of sodium chloride as an anti-listerial agent in minced raw buffalo meat.

乳酸链球菌素是唯一商业抗生素，已经被用于净化人为污染的生肉块，并与 2%的氯化钠结合作为切碎的生水牛肉中的抗李斯特菌剂。

Recently, pentocin 31-1, which was produced by Lactobacillus pentosus 31-1 and isolated from the traditional Chinese fermented Xuanwei ham, was studied as a biopreservative in storage of tray-packaged chilled pork. Results showed that pentocin 31-1 could substantially inhibit the accumulation of volatile basic nitrogen (VBN) and generally suppress the growth of microflora, especially Listeria and Pseudomonas, during chilled pork storage.

近年来，从中国传统发酵的宣威火腿中分离得到的戊糖乳杆菌 31-1 产生的戊糖乳杆菌素 31-1，已有学者研究了其作为生物防腐剂在包装冷却猪肉贮藏中的应用。结果表明，戊糖乳杆菌素 31-1 基本上能够抑制冷鲜猪肉贮藏期间挥发性盐基氮（VBN）的积累，同时广泛抑制微生物群落的生长，尤其是李斯特菌和假单胞菌。

3.2.2.5 High Hydrostatic Pressure (HHP)
高静水压（HHP）

Derived from material sciences (ceramics, superalloys, artificial diamonds, etc.), high-pressure technology (100 –1000 MPa, i.e., 1000 –10 000 bar) is of increasing interest to biological and food systems. High hydrostatic pressure (HHP), a non-thermal technology, is of primary interest because it can inactivate product-spoiling micro-organisms and enzymes at low temperatures without changing the sensory or nutritional characteristics of the product. Pressure processing is usually carried out in a steel cylinder containing a liquid pressure-transmitting medium such as water, with the sample being protected from direct contact by using sealed flexible packaging. Maintaining the sample under pressure for an extended period of time does not require any additional energy apart from that required to maintain the chosen temperature.

对来源于材料科学（陶瓷、超合金、人工钻石等）的高压技术（100~1000 MPa，即1000~10000 bar）在生物和食品体系中的研究兴趣日渐增加。高静水压（HHP）是一个十分热门的非热技术，因为它能够在低温不改变产品感官及营养特性的条件下钝化失活引起产品腐败的微生物和酶类。压力处理通常是在像水为液体压力介质的钢瓶中进行，将样品用密封的软包装保护起来以避免直接接触。样品在压力条件下保持一段时间，除恒温之外并不需要额外的能量。

HHP renders food more stable due to its ability to reduce the number of spoilage and pathogenic micro-organisms, and to inactivate certain food enzymes. HHP is a powerful tool to control risks associated with Salmonella spp. and Listeria monocyto-genes in raw or marinated meats. The effectiveness of HHP for microbial control depends on factors such as the process parameters, pressure level, temperature and exposure time, as well as by intrinsic factors of the food itself, such as pH, strain and growth stage of micro-organisms, and food matrix.

高静水压能够减少腐败及致病微生物的数量，使食品中某些酶灭活，从而使食物更加稳定。在生肉或腌肉中，高静水压是一个控制沙门氏菌和单核增生李斯特菌的强大工具。高静水压对微生物控制的有效性取决于各种因素，比如工艺参数、压力、温度和暴露时间，以及食品本身的内在因素，如 pH 值、张力、微生物生长阶段和食品基质。

HHP, combined with moderate temperature, has been shown to result in changes in the mechanical properties leading to improved tenderness of meat. However, HHP even at low temperatures may have an undesirable effect on fresh meat colour. <u>Colour of fresh beef changes with pressure as a result of denaturation of globin in myoglobin and haem displacement or release, and ferrous oxidation.</u> Denaturation of other proteins such as myosin and actin results in a greater opacity and therefore minimises the red appearance. In contrast to beef and pork, poultry muscles are not drastically discoloured because of their lower myoglobin content. Lipid stability of pressure-treated foods of animal origin has rarely been investigated, and results are contradictory. Rivas-Cañedo, Fernández-García and Nuñez (2009) used high pressure (400MPa, 10 min at 12℃) to treat minced beef and chicken breast, which was packaged with or without aluminium foil in a multilayer polymeric bag. They found pressurisation produced significant changes in the levels of some volatile compounds presumably originating from microbial activity and the plastic material. In the USA, several meat companies have made this methodology available (e.g., Hormel Foods and Purdue Farms) for the extension of shelf life of processed, sliced meats.

高静水压结合适当的温度，已经被证明能够改变机械性能，提高肉的嫩度。然而，高静水压即使在低温条件下也会对鲜肉的颜色产生不良影响。由于肌红蛋白中的珠蛋白变性、血红素的置换或释放以及亚铁氧化，鲜牛肉颜色会随压力而变化。其他蛋白质变性，如肌球蛋白和肌动蛋白将导致更大的不透明性，从而使红色外观最小化。与牛肉和猪肉相比，家禽肌肉的肌红蛋白含量较低，因此不会急剧变色。对于动物源性加压食品的脂质稳定性相关的研究很少，并且得出的结论相互矛盾。Rivas-Cañedo、Fernández-García 和 Nuñez（2009）用高压（400 MPa，12℃、10 min）处理了多层聚合物包装袋中含有或者不含有铝箔的切碎的牛肉和鸡胸。他们发现加压作用使某些挥发性化合物的含量发生了显著变化，这大概是由微生物活性和塑料材质引起的。在美国，一些肉类公司已经使用这种方法（例如，荷美尔食品和普杜农场），以延长加工后的切片肉的保质期。

Although the initial investment is high, the processing cost has been estimated at about 14 eurocent per kilogram of product when treated at 600 MPa, including investment and operation costs, and the technology is well accepted in Europe as an alternative technology.

虽然初期投资很高，但估计 600MPa 条件下的处理成本约为每千克产品 14 欧分，包括投资和运营成本，该技术在欧洲已经作为替代技术被接受。

3.2.2.6 Packaging 包装

Packaging protects products against deteriorative effects, which may include discolouration, off-flavour and off-odour development, nutrient loss, texture changes, pathogenicity and other measurable factors. Variables are product type, gas mixture, package and headspace, packaging equipment, storage temperature and additives.

包装能够保护产品免受变质的影响，包括变色、变味、营养损失、质地改变、致病性和其他可测量的因素。变量包括产品类型、气体组成、包装和顶部空间、包装设备、贮藏温度和添加剂。

Fresh meat packaging is only minimally permeable to moisture and so surface desiccation is prevented, while gas permeability varies with the particular film type used. Packaging options for raw chilled meat are air-permeable packaging, low O_2 vacuum, low O_2 MAP with anoxic gases and high O_2 MAP. While air-permeable packaging is not MAP, use of overwrapped packaging materials within master pack or tray-in-sleeve systems allows for this packaging option to be a component of MAP.

新鲜肉制品包装仅能最低限度地渗透水分，因此可以防止表面干燥，而气体的渗透性随所使用的特定膜类型而变化。冷冻肉的包装包括透气包装、低氧真空包装、低氧气调包装和高氧气调包装。透气包装不是气调包装，托盘包装系统中使用过度包装的包装材料使该包装选项成为气调包装的组成部分。

(1) Vacuum Packaging (VP)

真空包装（VP）

Vacuum packaging materials for primal cuts are usually three layered co-extrusions of ethyl vinyl acetate/polyvinylidenechloride/ethyl vinyl acetate, which generally have an O_2 permeability of less than 15.5 ml $m^{-2}(24\ h)^{-1}$ at 1 atmosphere as a result of the polyvinylidene chloride layer. The lack of O_2 in packages may minimise the oxidative deteriorative reactions, and reduce aerobic bacteria growth, which usually causes pigments to be in the deoxymyoglobin state. Low O_2 vacuum packages for retail meat cuts are usually vacuum skin packaging (VSP) systems for placing the retail cut in a barrier styrene or polypropylene tray and vacuum sealing barrier films that are heat shrunk to conform to the shape of the product. VSP packaging equipment removes atmospheric air or flushes the air from the package with gaseous mixtures such as N_2, CO_2 or mixtures of N_2 and CO_2 before heat sealing the film layers. The common construction for the top and bottom package webs is nylon barrier polymer of polyvinylidene chloride or ethylene vinyl alcohol, tie layer and ionomer. Nylon provides bulk, toughness and low melting point, while the barrier layer prevents vapour permeation and the ionomer gives necessary seal characteristics. A variation of VSP is for the lidding film to have outer barrier and inner air-permeable layers so that before retail display, the outer barrier film layer is peeled away from the permeable layer so that air can then contact the meat product and result in a bloomed colour.

原始切割的真空包装材料通常是乙基醋酸乙烯酯/聚偏二氯乙烯/乙基醋酸乙烯的三层共挤出物，通常，聚偏二氯乙烯层会导致在一个大气压下测得的氧气透过率小于15.5 ml·m^{-2}·$(24h)^{-1}$。在缺氧条件下包装可能会减少氧化变质反应，并减少需氧细菌的生长，这通常会导致色素处于脱氧肌血红蛋白状态。对于零售的肉块低氧真空包装通常是真空贴体包装（VSP），将零售的肉块放置在苯乙烯或聚丙烯托盘上并且用热收缩阻隔性薄膜来密封，以符合产品的形状。真空贴体包装的包装设备在热封膜前要去除空气或者用气体混合物如氮气、二氧化碳或者二者混合物冲洗掉原气体。顶部和底部包装网采用聚偏二氯乙烯或乙烯醇组成的尼龙聚合物阻挡层、连接层和离聚物。尼龙体积大、韧性强、熔点低，且阻挡层能防止蒸汽渗透，离聚物赋予必要的密闭性。真空贴体包装的一种变型是具有外部阻隔层和内部透气层的覆膜。零售展示前，将外部阻隔膜层从透气层上剥离下来，这样空气就可以接触到肉制品，并产生鲜艳的颜色。

(2) Modified Atmosphere Packaging (MAP)

气调包装（MAP）

MAP for meat requires a barrier of either of moisture and gas permeation through packaging materials to maintain a constant package environment during storage. For any type of MAP, it is necessary to remove or change the normal composition of atmospheric air, and encompass both aerobic and anaerobic types of packaging for meat. The major gases in dry air by volume at sea level are N_2 (78%), O_2 (20.99%), argon (0.94%) and CO_2 (0.03%), but the percentages vary when calculated by weight.

肉制品的气调包装，要求通过包装材料阻挡水分和空气的渗透来保持贮藏过程中包装环境的稳定。对于任何类型的气调包装，包括两种肉制品的有氧和无氧包装方式，必须移除或调整正常的大气组分。海平面上干燥空气中的主要气体为氮气（体积比，78%），氧气（20.99%），氩气（0.94%），二氧化碳（0.03%），但是按照质量计算的时候百分比是不同的。

Non-barrier overwrapped packages of meat may be enclosed in a barrier pouch appropriately sized for each individual overwrapped tray package (tray-in-sleeve configuration), or in a larger barrier film master pack that contains multiple packages in the anoxic gas. The meat pigments become oxygenated when the overwrapped permeable film package is removed from the master pack for retail display. Another variation is the use of anoxic MAP that has an inner air-permeable film and outer barrier film sealed to the barrier tray or bottom web containing the meat. When the outer film is peeled before display, the meat is exposed to O_2 in the atmospheric air and subsequently blooms. Where air-permeable films may not allow sufficient O_2 passage for adequate oxymyoglobin formation, microperforated shrink films with additional holes or perforations have been manufactured and used to promote faster meat blooming after removal of barrier film or removal of overwrapped trays from master packs.

肉的非阻隔外包装可以装入独立托盘包装对应的适当尺寸的包装小袋中（托盘在内的结构），或在一个包含多个缺氧气体的小包装的较大的阻隔性膜的主包装中。当零售展示时，可透气的包装膜，从主包装中除去之后，肉制品发生了氧化。另一种变化是使用具有透气性的内膜和阻隔性的外膜密封的放置肉的阻隔托盘或底部网状物的厌氧气调包装。当展示前脱去外层薄膜时，肉暴露在空气中的 O_2 中，随后颜色变鲜艳。透气性薄膜可能不允许足够的氧气进入以形成足够的氧合肌蛋白，而可以生产有额外的孔或穿孔的微孔收缩膜，用于促进与加快肉在拆除阻隔性膜或外包装托盘后的颜色变鲜艳。

3.2.2.7 Hurdle Technology (HT) 栅栏技术（HT）

HT (also called combined methods, combined processes, combination preservation, combination techniques or barrier technology) advocates the deliberate combination of existing and novel preservation techniques to establish a series of preservative factors (hurdles) to improve the microbial stability and the sensory quality of foods as well as their nutritional and economic properties.

栅栏技术（也称联合法、组合过程、联合保藏、组合技术或屏障技术）提倡将现有的和新颖的保藏技术合理结合，建立一系列防腐因子（栅栏技术）来提高食品的微生物稳定性和感官品质以及食品的营养和经济特性。

The most important hurdles used in food preservation are temperature (high or low), water activity (aw), acidity (pH), redox potential (Eh), preservatives (e.g., nitrite, sorbate, sulphite), and competitive micro-organisms (e.g., lactic acid bacteria). However, more than 60 potential hurdles for foods, which improve the stability and/or quality of the products, have been described, and the list of possible hurdles for food preservation is by no means complete. The influence of food preservation methods on the physiology and behavior of micro-organisms in foods, that is, their homeostasis, metabolic exhaustion and stress reactions, should be taken into account.

食品保藏中最重要的栅栏是温度（高低）、水分活度（a_w）、酸度（pH）、氧化还原电位（Eh）、防腐剂（如亚硝酸盐、山梨酸盐、亚硫酸盐）和竞争性微生物（如乳酸菌）。虽然能够提高食品稳定性和产品质量的 60 多种潜在的栅栏已经有过描述，但对食品保藏的可能栅栏列表仍然是不完整的。应考虑食品保存方法对食品中微生物生理和行为的影响，即微生物的体内平衡、代谢衰竭和应激反应。

Generally, biological preservation and natural antimicrobials provide an excellent opportunity for such combined preservation systems. For example, oregano essential oil, combined with MAP, was studied as hurdles in the storage of fresh meat and a longer shelf life was observed over that of the same packaging alone. In Atlantic salmon (S. salar) fillets, the greatest extension of shelf life was obtained by a combination of superchilling and MAP. The samples with the highest CO_2 concentration (90%) and gas-to-product volume (g/p) ratio of 2.5 showed the highest shelf life: 22 days versus 11 days for the control sample.

一般来说，生物保护和天然抗菌剂为这种联合保藏系统提供了一个绝佳的机会。例如，牛至精油与气调包装相结合，被认为是鲜肉贮藏中的栅栏，而且与单独使用相同包装相比，保质期更长。对大西洋鲑鱼的研究中发现，通过将过冷和气调包装相结合的方法可以最大限度地延长保质期。利用高二氧化碳浓度（90%）和气体/产品体积比 2.5 的结合条件下，样品的最长保质期可达 22 天，而空白样品的保质期只有 11 天。

Many studies indicate that it is possible to reduce bacterial spores through combinations of mild heat or nisin and HHP. The combined effect of gamma irradiation in the presence of ascorbic acid on the microbiological characteristics and lipid oxidation of ground beef coated with an edible coating were evaluated. Results showed that lactic acid bacteria and *Brochothrix thermosphacta* were more resistant to irradiation than Enterobacteriaceae and Pseudomonas. Shelf-life extension periods estimated on the basis of a limit level of 6 log CFU g^{-1} for APCs were 4, 7 and 10 days for samples irradiated at 1, 2 and 3 kGy, respectively. However, the incorporation of ascorbic acid in ground beef did not improve significantly (P>0.05) the inhibitory effect of gamma irradiation.

许多研究表明，通过轻度加热、添加乳酸链球菌素和高静水压技术的结合来减少细菌孢子是可行的。研究者对 γ 射线辐照和抗坏血酸结合对涂有可食性涂层的绞碎牛肉中的微生物特征和脂肪氧化进行了研究。结果表明，乳酸菌和热死环丝菌要比肠杆菌科和假单胞菌更耐辐照。在基于抗原提呈细胞（APCs）为 6 log CFU g^{-1} 的极限水平下，对产品的保质期进行估算。样品分别经过 1kGy、2kGy 和 3kGy 的辐照条件下，产品的保质期分别为 4 天、7 天和 10 天。但是，结合了抗坏血酸（P>0.05）处理的碎牛肉，并没有发现对辐照抑制效果的增强作用。

3.2.2.8 Conclusion
结论

This review aimed to describe current methods and technologies for fresh meat preservation and their developments. In addition to the relatively mature technologies, such as chilling, freezing and ionizing radiation, new preservation techniques for fresh meat were introduced. We conclude this review by presenting important opportunities and some drawbacks of the following new techniques.

本文旨在介绍目前鲜肉保鲜的方法和技术及其发展。除了相对成熟的技术，如冷却、冷冻和电离辐射，还介绍了新的鲜肉保鲜技术。我们对新技术的一些重要的机遇和缺点进行了总结，得出如下结论。

(1) Superchilling can reduce the use of freezing/thawing for production buffers and thereby reduce labour, energy costs and product weight losses. The other two advantages of the technique are its

capability for prolonging shelf life and improving meat safety. However, the major drawback is that complex calculations and measurements of heat transfer and temperatures are required for each product. More research is required before the wide application of this new technology. Furthermore, this process will only function effectively with improved cold chains, as many current meat supply chains are comprised of fragmented components rather than logical cold chain systems.

过冷可以减少冻结/解冻过程对产品的影响，从而减少劳动力、能源成本和产品质量损失。过冷技术的其他两个优势是能延长货架期和增强肉的安全性。然而，最主要的缺点是计算复杂、要求测量每个产品的传热量和温度。这个新技术的广泛应用还需要进行更多的研究。此外，这个过程只能利用冷链高效运行，目前很多肉的供应链是由分散的组件组成的，而不是符合逻辑的完全冷链系统。

(2) As a mild, non-thermal technology, HHP can inactivate some product spoilage microorganisms and enzymes at low temperatures without changing the majority of the sensory or nutritional properties. However, spores are not sensitive to these pressures and they can only be inactivated when pressure is combined with heat or another system such as lactoperoxidase or lysozyme treatment. Although HHP has certain advantages, it does however have some drawbacks in that high pressures may result in discolouration through protein denaturation. Further, commercially it involves a batch process, which is not convenient for product handling.

作为一个温和的、非热的技术，高静水压技术可以在较低的温度下抑制一些产品中的腐败微生物和酶的活性，而不改变大多数的感官及营养特性。但是，孢子对这些压力并不敏感，它们仅能在高静水压与热处理，或其他系统如乳过氧化物酶和溶菌酶处理相结合的条件下，才能得到抑制。尽管高静水压技术具有特定的优势，但仍然存在一些缺点，高压下可能导致由蛋白质变性引起的褪色。而且，商业上可能涉及一些间歇加工过程，导致这些产品不方便处理。

(3) Natural antimicrobial compounds: Essential oils, chitosan, nisin and lysozyme are natural compounds. As they can replace chemical preservatives, they provide the opportunity for "Green labelling" to which consumers are attracted by their "natural image". This is imperative in the current world environment in which food quality and safety food are of prime importance. Nevertheless, they are often less attractive commercially due to their ability to react with other food ingredients and some may have low water solubility. They can also change the organoleptical properties and have a narrow activity spectrum.

天然抗菌化合物：精油、壳聚糖、乳酸链球菌素、溶解酶都是天然化合物。因为它们可以代替化学防腐剂，为"绿色标签"提供了机会，使消费者被它们的"自然影像"所吸引。这些在当前认为食品质量和安全非常重要的世界环境中是必要的。但是，它们缺乏足够的商业吸引力，主要是因为它们往往具有与其他食品成分反应的能力且某些具有较低的水溶性。同时，它们也能改变肉制品的感官特性，具有相对狭窄的活性范围。

In conclusion, by applying these new technologies to meet increased demand, the storage life of fresh chilled meat can be largely extended to many weeks by proper control of the hygienic condition and temperatures of the product, and by the appropriate selection and use of preservative methods. Factors restricting the commercial extension of shelf life are the current processing and distribution systems.

总之，通过应用这些新的技术来满足日益增长的需求，对产品卫生条件和温度进行适当的控制，以及选择和使用适当的保藏方法，新鲜冷冻肉的保存期限可以延长数周。商业上货架期延长的限制因素，是当前的加工和流通系统。

3.2.3 Homework

课后作业

3.2.3.1 Sentence Translation

句子翻译

(1) Original Sentences

原句

① The paper aims to investigate the effect of storage period on the chemical, microbiological and sensory characteristics of frozen dumplings.

② The effects of variety preservation methods were compared, and the experiments show that using the freeze dry method to long-term preserve caproic acid bacteria is better.

③ Good hygienic slaughtering practices reduce the contamination of carcasses by faeces, but will not guarantee the absence of Campylobacter from meat and meat products.

④ The study found that higher intakes of red and processed meat were associated with modest increases in total mortality, including death associated with cancer and heart disease.

⑤ In the absence of cold chains, such conditions favoured further processing of meat and temporary storage of processed meat products.

⑥ The gas proportion mixing, packaging material required and shelf life on 0~4℃ for some fresh products of modified atmosphere packaging can be obtained by testing.

⑦ Active packaging is in line with the new direction of food packaging. The antimicrobial packaging has attracted much attention and has undergone extensive investigation.

⑧ In this paper, the safety in irradiation food and the application of irradiation technology in food preservation were discussed. The developmental future of food irradiation preservation was expected.

⑨ The concentration of ethanol and acetaldehyde in Meiguixiang grape after 120 days storage was studied.

⑩ Fresh beef was treated with different methods for the surface sterilizing, dipped for a short time in coating fresh-keeping solvent of different proportion and stored at 0~4℃.

(2) Translations

翻译

① 本文主要目的是研究冷冻保藏时间对于速冻水饺的理化性质、微生物指标及感官特性的影响。

② 实验比较了己酸菌不同保存方式的保藏效果，表明采用冷冻干燥保藏法长期保藏菌种效果良好。

③ 良好的卫生屠宰规范可减少粪便对动物胴体造成的污染，但并不会保证在肉类和肉制品中完全没有弯曲杆菌。

④ 该研究发现摄入较多的牛羊肉或加工的肉制品，死亡率会相应增长，包括因癌症或心脏病而引发的死亡。

⑤ 在缺乏冷链的情况下，这种气候条件有利于肉品的进一步加工以及肉制品的临时性贮藏。

⑥ 试验得到了新鲜农产品的改良气调包装所需的气体混合配比、包装材料要求以及0~4℃下的保鲜期限。

⑦ 活性包装是食品包装发展的新方向，其中的抗菌包装得到了人们的高度重视和广泛研究。

⑧ 本文对辐照食品的安全性和辐照技术在食品保藏上的应用进行了综述，并对辐照食品技术的发展前景进行了展望。

⑨ 本文研究了贮藏 120d 后玫瑰香葡萄果实内乙醇和乙醛浓度的变化。

⑩ 采取不同灭菌方式对鲜牛肉进行表面灭菌，在不同配比的涂膜保鲜剂中浸渍一定时间，在 0~4℃下贮存。

(3) 翻译文中划线句子

3.2.3.2 Common Sentence Patterns of Scientific Papers 科技论文常见句型

① 研究目的（purpose of the study）

The work presented in this paper focuses on…

② 背景和历史（background and history）

The new findings from the experiment agree well with the results obtained in …

Compared with the current research, the previous work was in connection with …

③ 问题的难易程度（difficulty of the problem）

It is easy to present (reveal, analyze, discuss) the problem in all its complexity (in every detail).

It is no easy task to gain an insight into the intricate detail of …

④ 问题的范围（scope of the problem）

Studies of these effects cover various aspects of …

⑤ 理论说明（theoretical explanations）

The validity of the theory has become obvious in the light of recent findings.

The basic (essential, fundamental) feature of this theory is …

⑥ 方法介绍（method introduction）

The procedure we followed has certain advantages over the existing method

The above procedure makes it possible to evaluate …

Another good feature of this method is …

⑦ 实验描述（experiment description）

The experiments reported here demonstrate a variety of changes in (a correlation between, a much resistance to) …

Further experiments in this area lead us to conclude (believe, suggest) that …

From these experiments we can conclude that …

⑧ 结果的意义（meaning of the results）

These preliminary findings are very reliable (encouraging, promising. Convincing, ambiguous)

We can consider (interpret, look at) these results as fully reliable (consistent with) …

⑨ 推断的结论（conclusion deduced）

Further progress can be provided by this experiment.

3.3 Beer Brewing

3.3 啤酒酿造

3.3.1 Glossary

专业词汇分析

① abstaining　*n.* 原意为弃权，此处课文中意为戒酒。

[记忆窍门]　戒除、禁绝（abstain），-ing 表示动名词，此处课文中意为戒酒。

② worty　*adj.* 麦芽汁的

③ off-flavor　*n.* 异味

[记忆窍门]　off- 不在……上，离开，flavor 为味道。

④ tailor-made　*adj.* 特制的

[记忆窍门]　tailor 意为裁缝，则该词可记成：裁缝（tailor）制作的（made），即特制的。

⑤ dealcoholization　*n.* 脱醇

[记忆窍门]　该词可分解为“de+alcohol+ization”的组合，前缀“de-”意为去除，alcohol 意为酒精（乙醇），-ization 意为“……的行为”，则该词可记成：去掉乙醇的行为，即脱醇。

⑥ vacuum rectification　真空精馏

[记忆窍门]　vacuum 为真空，rectification 为精馏。

⑦ dialysis　*n.* 透析

⑧ reverse osmosis　反渗透

[记忆窍门]　re-作为前缀意为“又、再”，reverse 为“反面的”，osmosis 为“渗透性”。

⑨ liveliness　*n.*（指酒或饮料的）口味，典型性

[记忆窍门]　lively 意为快活、鲜明生动的，-ness 为名词性词缀。原意为活泼、热烈，这里指酒的典型性、风格特征。

⑩ in terms of　根据；用……的话；就……而言；以……为单位。

⑪ volatile　*n.* 挥发物　*adj.* 易变的，易挥发的

⑫ carbonized beer *n.* 充气[碳酸气饱和]啤酒

⑬ mashing *n.* 捣烂；糊状物；糖化

⑭ spent grains *n.* 酒糟，（啤酒）废麦糟

[记忆窍门] spent 为废的，grain 为粮食。

⑮ lager yeast *n.* 拉格啤酒酵母，发酵时间较长。到发酵末期，酵母菌下沉于酒桶底部，由于此啤酒酒色较为透明，属下面发酵酵母。

⑯ maturation *n.*（葡萄酒、奶酪等的）成熟过程

[记忆窍门] 该词可分解为“matura+tion”的组合，-tion 为名词词根，可记忆成：（葡萄酒、奶酪等的）成熟（mature）。

⑰ krausen *n.* 麦芽汁发酵时所产生的泡沫；发酵醪。

3.3.2 Texts and Translations

课文及翻译

A Review of Methods of Low Alcohol and Alcohol-Free Beer Production
低酒精度啤酒与无酒精啤酒生产方法的综述

Introduction

简介

In most of the EU countries beers with low alcohol content are divided into alcohol free beers (AFBs) containing≤0.5% alcohol by volume (ABV), and to low-alcohol beers (LABs) with no more than 1.2% ABV. In the United States alcohol-free beer means that there is no alcohol present, while the upper limit of 0.5% ABV corresponds to so-called non-alcoholic beer or “near-beer” (Montanari et al., 2009). In countries that enforce religious prohibition, the alcohol content in beverages must not exceed 0.05% by volume.

在大多数的欧盟国家，低酒精度啤酒可分为无酒精啤酒［AFB，酒精含量小于 0.5%（按体积计，ABV）］和低酒精度啤酒（LAB，酒精含量不超过 1.2%ABV）。在美国，无酒精啤酒意味不含酒精，然而，达到上限 0.5%ABV 的啤酒相当于所谓的“无醇啤酒”或“淡啤酒”。在一些实施宗教禁酒令的国家中，饮料中的酒精含量必须不超过其体积的 0.05%。

The terminology of this article in the following chapters will be governed by the aforementioned European legislation. However, while the methods to produce both LAB and AFB are from practical point of view identical, the AFBs market share prevails over the LABs one. Hence, in this article the beverages with low alcohol content produced from malt will be generally termed alcohol-free beers (AFBs).

本文以下章节中的术语将遵从前述的欧洲立法。但是，尽管从实际角度看，生产低酒精度啤酒和无酒精啤酒的方法是一致的，但 AFB 的市场份额高于 LAB。因此，在本文中，由麦芽生产的低酒精度的饮料通常称为无酒精啤酒。

(1) Beer and Health

啤酒与健康

Alcohol abuse has been on the public agenda for many years since it carries risks of violent crime, traffic accidents, public disorder, and health damage. Ethanol is one of the most commonly used recreational drugs worldwide and it is often ingested as a component of beer. When beer is consumed, ethanol is absorbed from the gastrointestinal tract by diffusion and is swiftly distributed in the blood before entering tissues. Ethanol is metabolized to acetaldehyde mainly in the stomach and liver. Acetaldehyde is highly toxic and binds cellular constituents generating harmful acetaldehyde adducts.

由于酒精可能会带来暴力犯罪、交通事故、聚众骚乱及健康威胁等危险，酒精滥用成为公众议题已经很多年了。酒精是世界范围内最普遍使用的娱乐性药物之一，经常作为啤酒的一种成分被摄取。当啤酒被饮入体内后，酒精通过扩散方式被胃肠道吸收，在进入组织之前迅速地分散到血液中。酒精在胃和肝脏中主要被代谢成乙醛，乙醛具有高毒性并且会与细胞成分结合形成有害的乙醛加合物。

Simultaneously, there are strong evidences that moderate alcohol consumption has not only a better long-term health outcome than excessive alcohol consumption, but even better than abstaining. Moderate beer drinking has been shown to be, at least, as effective as wine drinking at reducing risks of coronary diseases, heart attack, diabetes, and overall mortality. Besides alcohol, which is probably the most important component of beer that counters atherosclerosis, these positive effects may be attributed to a whole range of other properties and valuable cereal and hop-related substances found in beer such as no fat or cholesterol content, low energy and free sugar content, high antioxidant (e.g. polyphenols, flavonoids), magnesium and soluble fiber content. In addition, beer provides essential vitamins and minerals and is thus contributing to a healthy balanced diet. The alcohol-free beers also claim beneficial effects of healthy beer components with a simultaneous effect of the lower energy intake and complete absence of negative impacts of alcohol consumption.

同时，强有力的证据显示，适度的酒精消费比过度饮酒甚至比戒酒更有助于长期的健康。有数据显示适量地饮用啤酒与葡萄酒一样能有效降低冠心病、心脏病发作，糖尿病风险及总体的死亡率。酒精可能是啤酒中抗动脉硬化的最重要成分，同时，啤酒中各种各样的其他特性以及谷物有效成分、啤酒花的相关物质，例如无脂肪或无胆固醇、低热量和无糖、高抗氧化剂（如多酚、类黄酮）、镁和可溶性纤维都具有积极作用。此外，啤酒还提供必要的维生素与矿物质，因此有益于健康均衡的膳食。无酒精啤酒同样具有健康啤酒成分和低能量摄入的有益效果，完全没有酒精消耗的负面作用。

(2) Methods of the Alcohol-free Beer Production

无酒精啤酒的生产方法

The strategies to produce AFBs can be divided into two main groups (physical and biological processes), which can be further broken down as shown here (Fig. 3.3). The so called physical methods are based on gentle removal of alcohol from regular beer and require considerable investments into the special equipment for alcohol removal. After the removal process has been optimized, the sensorial quality of produced AFBs is usually good. Their further advantage is that they can remove ethanol from beers to vanishingly low levels. The most widespread biological approaches are based on limited ethanol formation during the beer fermentation. They are usually performed in traditional brewery equipment and hence do not require additional investments, but their products are often characterized by worty off-flavors. Improvements taking advantage of special yeast increase the costs by the purchase, selection, or construction of the production organisms as well as by the need for their propagation have to be separated. However, suitable tailor-made or selected microorganisms can contribute significantly to the product sensorial quality improvement. There are also AFB production processes (continuous fermentation with immobilized yeast) based on limited alcohol formation, which require special equipment and material (continuously operating bioreactor, carrier for cell immobilization). In this case, the higher investment costs have to be justified by the higher productivity of continuous processes. In general, the ethanol formation, which is intrinsic to the biological methods, makes impossible the production of AFBs with alcohol content close to zero.

无酒精啤酒的生产方法可以分成两个主要部分（物理过程和生物过程），它可以进一步细分，如图 3.3 所示：所谓的物理方法建立在温和去除普通啤酒中酒精的基础之上，需要相当大的投资，购入专用设备来去除酒精。酒精去除工艺优化之后，所生产的无酒精啤酒的感官品质普遍是良好的。物理方法的更大优点是，可以把啤酒中的酒精去除到难以检测的水平。最广泛使用的生物学方法是抑制啤酒发酵过程中产生酒精。这种方法通常在传统啤酒厂中应用，因此，它们不需要额外的投资，但是，这种方法所生产出来的产品往往具有麦芽汁的异味。利用特殊酵母的改进提高了购买、选择和构建生产用微生物的成本，而且，这些微生物必须相互隔离繁殖。然而，特制的或经过筛选的微生物有助于显著提高产品的感官质量。也有些基于抑制酒精生成的无酒精啤酒的生产工艺（用固定化酵母连续发酵）需要特殊的设备和材料（连续操作的生物反应器，细胞的固定化载体）。在这种情况下，毫无疑问地证实了，投资成本越高，连续生产的生产率越高。一般来说，乙醇的形成是生物学方法所固有的，不可能使无酒精啤酒产品的酒精度接近零度。

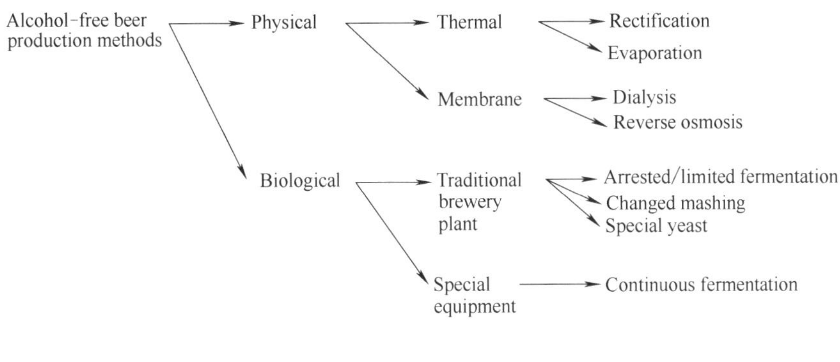

Fig.3.3 The scheme of most common alcohol-free beer production methods.

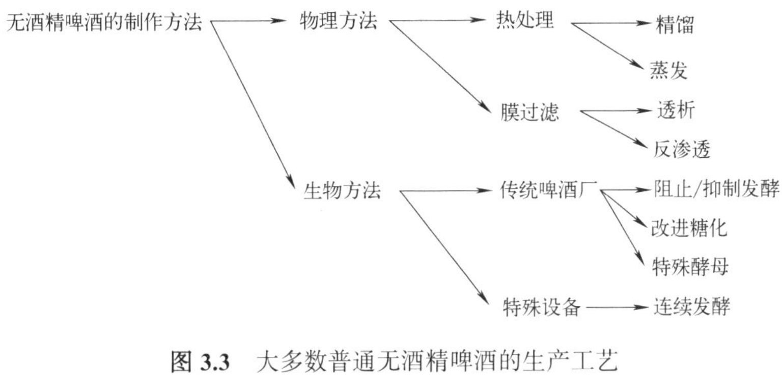

图 3.3 大多数普通无酒精啤酒的生产工艺

(3) Production of Alcohol-free Beer by Ethanol Removal Methods

乙醇去除法的无酒精啤酒生产

The technologies applied for complete or partial ethanol removal from regular beers can be classified into two groups based on the principle of the separation process such as thermal and membrane processes (Fig. 3.3). Besides the industrially applied methods of beer dealcoholization (vacuum rectification and evaporation, dialysis, and reverse osmosis) there have been several other methods studied under laboratory conditions such as membrane extraction, supercritical CO_2 extraction, pervaporation, adsorption on hydrophobic zeolites, and freeze concentration.

这项完全或部分去除普通啤酒中乙醇的技术，依据分离工艺如加热和膜处理的原理可以将其分为两类（图 3.3）。除工业应用的啤酒脱醇的方法以外（真空精馏、蒸发、透析、反渗透），实验室条件下还研究了一些其他的方法，诸如膜萃取、二氧化碳超临界萃取、渗透蒸发、疏水性沸石吸附和冷冻浓缩。

① Thermal Processes

热加工过程

The early attempts to dealcoholize beer by evaporation or distillation under atmospheric pressure, which revealed significant temperature damage to the beer taste, were soon replaced by vacuum distillation. If the pressure is reduced, alcohol can be drawn off at much lower temperature. All thermal processes to produce AFBs are therefore performed at an absolute pressure of 4-20 kPa, whereby evaporation temperatures of 30-60℃ are achieved. Even so, a great loss of beer flavor and liveliness can occur during thermal processes. The deterioration of beer quality by thermal dealcoholization depends mainly on the evaporation temperature and the period of exposure, which depends on the thermal separator construction. AFB production at industrial scale has been implemented using vacuum distillation (rectification) plants or vacuum evaporators (single or multistage) of two main construction variants i.e. centrifugal and falling film evaporators.

常压下通过蒸发或蒸馏对啤酒脱醇的早期尝试结果显示，温度严重破坏啤酒的味道，所以其很快被真空蒸馏取代。如果压力降低，酒精可以在更低的温度下流出。所有生产无酒精啤酒的加热过程是在绝对压力为 4~20 kPa、蒸发温度为 30~60℃的条件下完成的。即便如此，在加热过程中仍然会对啤酒的风味和口味造成很大的损失。加热脱醇所导致的啤酒品质下降，主要因为热分离器结构所需要的蒸发温度和时间。工业化生产无酒精啤酒上已经实现了利用真空蒸馏（精馏）设备或真空蒸发器（单一或多级）中两个主要结构变型即离心和降膜式蒸发器。

Generally, advantages of thermal processes are: the potential to remove alcohol from beer completely, the possibility to commercialize the separated alcohol, the continuous and automatic operation with a short start-up period, and the flexibility in terms of volumetric performance and the input beer composition. Conversely, the purchase of these systems requires significant investment as well as there are considerable running costs (energy consumption) and some risks of thermal damage or loss of volatiles from beer. At the end of all thermal processes the concentrated alcohol-free beer has to be diluted with oxygen-free water and carbonized.

一般来说，加热过程的优点是：具有完全去除啤酒中酒精的能力、分离酒精商品化的可能性、短周期的连续和自动操作、根据体积动态和投入的啤酒成分可以灵活控制。相反地，购买这些系统需要大量的投资以及相当大的运行成本（能量消耗），有热损害的风险和啤酒挥发的损失。所有的加热过程结束之后浓缩的无醇啤酒必须用无氧水稀释并充气。

② Membrane Processes

膜处理

These alcohol removal methods are based on the semipermeable character of membranes, which separate only small molecules like ethanol and water from the beer to the permeate liquid. Two types of membrane processes used for beer dealcoholization can be distinguished on the industrial scale: dialysis and reverse osmosis. They differ in applied pressures and temperatures, membrane materials and their structures. It is known that all of the membrane processes have less thermal impact on beer, they can be operated automatically and in flexible manner, but at the same time they require significant capital and running costs. The economic feasibility of membrane processes for the production of beverages with an alcohol percentage lower than 0.45 vol.% was by some authors challenged, while others stated that the energy requirement of a membrane system for alcohol purification (reverse osmosis) would be significantly lower than that of a conventional distillation system. Membrane processes were also suggested as a part of a system for the continuous production of delacoholized beverages. And dialysis and reverse osmosis are used in common.

这类酒精去除方法是基于膜的半渗透性，能分离啤酒的小分子物质像乙醇和水到渗透液中。用于工业规模啤酒脱醇的膜处理可以分为两种类型：透析和反向渗透。它们的不同在于应用的压力和温度、膜材料及其结构。众所周知，所有的膜处理对啤酒没有热影响，可以自动和灵活操作，但同时也需要大量的资本和运营成本。膜处理生产酒精百分比低于0.45%（体积分数）饮料的经济可行性遭到一些学者的质疑，而其他一些阐述指出，用于酒精纯化的膜系统（反渗透）对能源的需求会远远低于传统的蒸馏系统。膜处理也被认为是连续生产脱醇饮料系统的一个部分。常用的膜处理方法有透析和反渗透等。

(4) Production of Alcohol-Free Beer by Methods of Restricted Ethanol Formation

限制乙醇形成生产无酒精啤酒的方法

The methods of the alcohol-free beer (AFB) production based on limited alcohol formation can be divided according to the production equipment they require and further subdivided according to alterations in technology or use of special yeast. The most exploited technologies are those requiring the equipment of a traditional brewery plant, while the continuous limited fermentation is a promising but marginal technology. The respective procedures applied on the industrial scale are often combinations of strategies, which belong to technologies using traditional brewery facilities.

基于限制乙醇形成生产无酒精啤酒的方法，可以按照所需产品设备分类，还可以根据技术的变化或使用的特殊酵母来进一步细分。最常用的技术是那些只需要传统啤酒厂中使用的设备，而连续抑制发酵是一个很有前景但处于边缘的技术。各自的工艺过程应用于工业化生产中常常是策略的组合，属于使用传统酿酒设备的技术。

① Changed Mashing Process

糖化过程的改变

Mashing consists of complex physical, chemical, and biochemical (enzymatic) processes, the main purpose of which is to completely degrade starch to fermentable sugars and soluble dextrins. The spectrum of sugars formed depends on the actual enzyme activities present. β-Amylase (temperature optimum of 62~65℃) produces the fermentable sugar of maltose, whereas α-amylase (temperature optimum of 72~75℃) generates first non-fermentable sugars (dextrins) and at prolonged action also fermentable sugars. The final content of fermentable sugars in wort then determines the alcohol level in beer. Therefore, by changing the mashing process, it is possible to modulate the profile of wort sugars in a way that their fermentability is limited and results in low alcohol content. A low wort sugar content can be achieved by different strategies as follows:

- Inactivation of saccharifying β-amylase by high temperature mashing (75~80℃).
- Cold water malt extraction.
- Re-mashing of spent grains to produce a second extract with very little fermentable sugar.

糖化是由复杂的物理的、化学的和生化的（酶的）过程组成的，主要目的是使淀粉完全降解变成可发酵糖和可溶性糊精。糖色谱的形成取决于实际呈现的酶活力。β-淀粉酶（最适温度 62~65℃）产生可发酵的麦芽糖，而 α-淀粉酶（最适温度 72~75℃）首先生成不可发酵的糖类（糊精），延长反应也生成可发酵糖。麦芽汁中的可发酵糖的终浓度决定了啤酒中酒精的含量。因此，通过改变糖化过程，在某种程度上可以改变麦芽汁中糖的情况，抑制其发酵能力，致使酒精含量降低。可以通过如下不同策略使麦芽汁的糖含量达到一个较低的水平：

- 高温（75~80℃）糖化使 β-淀粉酶失活。
- 冷水麦芽提取。
- 用酒糟再糖化来制备只含有少量可发酵糖的二次提取物。

Used on their own, methods relying solely on the modified mashing are seldom successful for the production of AFBs and they have to be combined with further measures such as vigorous wort boiling (lowering the level of aldehydes), wort acidification, limited fermentation, color and bitterness adjustment, etc.

单独使用上述方法，或者仅仅依赖于改进糖化都很难成功地生产出无酒精啤酒，必须结合更多的措施如麦芽汁煮沸（降低醛的含量）、麦芽汁酸化、抑制发酵、调整颜色和苦味值等。

② Arrested or Limited Fermentation Process

阻止或抑制发酵过程

In general, the major disadvantage of both stopped and limited fermentation approach is that it is hardly feasible to achieve low alcohol levels with adequate conversion of wort to beer. Therefore, the objective of these methods is to keep the ethanol content low by removal of yeast before excessive attenuation (stopped fermentation) or creating conditions for restrained yeast metabolism (limited fermentation) and simultaneously reducing the worty flavor impression or limit it from the beginning. These production methods operate with traditional brewery equipment and unit operations, but they require accurate and swift analytical control. These approaches represent the most usual way to produce alcohol-free or low-alcohol beers. When these techniques were carried out with worts of original gravity from 9% to 13%, the smell and taste of AFBs were characterized by a strong worty flavor impression due to the non-reduced wort aldehydes. It has been verified that for stopped or limited fermentation processes, an original gravity from 4.0% to 7.5% is desirable. However, brewing at high gravity (20%) increases the formation of higher alcohols and esters. This phenomenon can be exploited to strengthen the flavor of reduced alcohol beers obtained after dilution of a higher gravity beer. Further adjustments of volatiles can be achieved by higher fermentation temperature (greater effects on lager yeasts) or reduced oxygen content of wort, which increased dramatically the ester formation by ale yeasts.

一般来说，停止和抑制发酵的方法主要的缺点是麦芽汁充分转换成啤酒时很难实现低酒精含量。因此，这些方法的目标是在发酵糖过度减少之前，通过去除酵母保持低乙醇含量（停止发酵）或为抑制酵母代谢创造条件（限制发酵），同时减轻麦芽汁味道或从一开始就抑制它的味道。这些生产方法采用传统酿酒设备和单元操作运转，但是需要精准快速的分析控制。这些方法是生产不含酒精或低度啤酒最常用的方法。当麦芽汁的初始浓度在 9%~13%范围时使用这些技术，因非还原麦芽醛的作用会使无酒精啤酒的气味和口感具有强烈的麦芽味。已经证实了对于阻止或抑制发酵工艺，初始浓度在 4.0%~7.5%（wt.）之间是比较理想的。然而，高浓度（20%）下酿造增加了高级醇和酯的形成。这种现象可以应用于高浓度啤酒稀释后获得的低酒精啤酒，增强其风味。对挥发物的进一步调整可以通过提高发酵温度（对下面啤酒酵母影响较大）或降低麦芽汁中的氧含量来实现，这样能通过爱尔酵母大幅增加酯的形成。

The fermentation activity can be arrested (stopped or checked) quickly by temperature inactivation (rapid cooling to 0℃, pasteurization) and/or by removal of yeast from fermenting wort (filtration, centrifugation). The fermentation initial phase can be carried out at a relatively wide range of temperatures without a significant impact on the formation of volatiles and the reduction of aldehydes (Table 3.1). However, at higher temperatures the fermentation has to be arrested, either by yeast separation or cooling, rather shortly after the wort was pitched, which requires a prompt analytical control and intervention. The increasing fermentation temperature deepened the attenuation and simultaneously enhanced the formation of volatiles and diacetyl by bottom fermenting yeast. A comparison of yeast types showed that the top fermenting yeast achieved a significantly higher aliphatic alcohol formation at lower attenuation, but the top fermented AFBs had also rather high diacetyl content (Table 3.1). After interrupting the fermentation at an alcohol content less than 0.5 vol.%, the AFB is usually matured for at least 10 days at 0 to 1℃ to avoid an overpowering sulfur flavor. Then the AFB is filtered, carbonated, stabilized, and sterilized.

发酵活性可以通过温度失活（快速冷却到 0℃、巴氏杀菌）和/或从发酵麦芽汁中（过滤、离心）去除酵母而被迅速地抑制（停止或受阻）。发酵初始阶段可以在一个相对宽泛的温度范围下进行，这对挥发物的形成及醛类的减少没有什么大的影响（表 3.1）。然而，在较高的温度下，发酵会因酵母分离或是冷却被抑制，需要在麦芽汁投入后马上进行快捷的分析控制和调节。发酵温度的上升加剧了糖的消耗，同时由下面发酵酵母增强了挥发物和双乙酰的形成。酵母类型的比较显示：在糖消耗较低时，上面发酵酵母能形成相当多脂肪醇，但上面发酵的无酒精啤酒也含有相当多的双乙酰（表 3.1）。在酒精含量（体积分数）小于 0.5%时中止发酵后，无酒精啤酒通常需要在 0~1℃成熟至少 10 天，以避免强烈的硫黄味。然后无酒精啤酒被过滤、碳酸化充气、稳定和除菌。

Table 3.1 The influence of yeast type and fermentation temperature on the composition of alcohol-free beers.

Fermentation yeast	Bottom	Bottom	Bottom	Bottom	Top	Top
Temperature /℃	0	4	8	12	8	12
Original gravity/ %	11.4	7.5	7.5	7.5	7.4	7.4
Ethanol/%	0.27	0.37	0.37	0.42	0.32	0.27
Real extract/%	10.64	6.79	6.79	6.52	6.87	6.94
Attenuation/%	8	12	12	16	9	8
Fermentation time/h	48	24	7/24①	7/24①	24	7/24①
pH	5.01	4.87	4.92	4.89	4.87	4.89
Bitterness (EBC)	25.4	17.5	17.7	17.4	17.7	17.8
DMS/ (μg/L)	30	22	30	32	35	45
Total diacetyl/(mg/L)	0.06	0.09	0.08	0.14	0.51	0.35
Total HAA/(mg/L)	2.2	6.8	6.7	8.6	15.8	14.2
Total EAA/(mg/L)	0.55	0.69	0.6	0.84	0.9	0.9
Reduction of aldehydes/%	85.8	77.6	80.2	83	88.2	77.5

① After 7h at the initial temperature, the wort was cooled to 0℃ until 24h were completed, source: Narziss et al. (1992). HAA, higher aliphatic alcohols; EAA, esters of acetic acids.

表 3.1 酵母类型和发酵温度对无酒精啤酒组成物质的影响

发酵酵母	下面发酵	下面发酵	下面发酵	下面发酵	上面发酵	上面发酵
温度/℃	0	4	8	12	8	12
原浓度/%	11.4	7.5	7.5	7.5	7.4	7.4
乙醇浓度/%	0.27	0.37	0.37	0.42	0.32	0.27
实际提取物/%	10.64	6.79	6.79	6.52	6.87	6.94
发酵浓度/%	8	12	12	16	9	8
发酵时间/h	48	24	7/24①	7/24①	24	7/24①
pH 值	5.01	4.87	4.92	4.89	4.87	4.89
苦味值(EBC)	25.4	17.5	17.7	17.4	17.7	17.8
二甲基硫醚/(μg/L)	30	22	30	32	35	45
双乙酰总量/(mg/L)	0.06	0.09	0.08	0.14	0.51	0.35
HAA 总量/(mg/L)	2.2	6.8	6.7	8.6	15.8	14.2
EAA 总量/(mg/L)	0.55	0.69	0.6	0.84	0.9	0.9
乙醛还原量/%	85.8	77.6	80.2	83	88.2	77.5

① 初始温度发酵 7h 后，将麦芽汁 24h 冷却到 0℃。HAA，高脂肪醇；EAA，乙酸酯。

③ Use of Special Yeast

使用特殊的酵母

This approach to the AFB production is associated with the use of special yeast performing a limited fermentation process. The dissimilarity of these “special” yeasts compared to traditional brewing yeast lies mainly in their tendency to produce lower amounts of ethanol or no ethanol at all. This can be achieved by strategies such as selection of a proper microbial genus (strain) with specific properties or intentional modification of brewing yeast by random mutation or genetic engineering.

这种无酒精啤酒的生产方法是关于使用特殊酵母限制发酵的工艺。这些“特殊”酵母与传统酿造酵母相比，主要差别在于它们倾向于产生少量的乙醇或不产乙醇。这可以通过一些方法来完成，如选择合适的具有特定属性微生物种属（菌株）或选择通过随机突变或基因工程有意改造的酿造酵母。

The most common approach relies on the fact that the major fermentable sugar of all malt worts is maltose (ca. 75%) and some strains of the genus *Saccharomyces* (e.g. used in the wine fermentation) are unable to ferment this sugar. Thus the beer resultant from conversion of glucose, fructose, and sucrose will contain less than<0.5% ethanol. Except the application of a special yeast strain, this method of the AFB production is identical with the manufacturing of standard beer. However, due to limited yeast activity and high residual extract content, this manufacturing process is vulnerable to microbial contamination. Therefore, high standards of cleanliness and microbiological control are required.

最常见的方法依赖于这样的情况，所有麦芽汁中主要的可发酵糖是麦芽糖（大约 75%），酵母属的一些菌株（例如用于葡萄酒发酵）是无法发酵这种糖的。因此通过葡萄糖、果糖、蔗糖的转换得到的啤酒，其乙醇含量少于 0.5%。除去使用特殊酵母菌株，这种生产无酒精啤酒的方法与标准啤酒的生产是相同的。然而，由于有限的酵母活性和提取物的高残留量，这种制造工艺容易受到微生物污染。因此需要高标准的清洁度和微生物控制。

The most successful genus, other that *Saccharomyces*, used for the industrial production of alcohol-free beer is *Saccharomycodes ludwigii*. The controlled fermentation can be carried out by this yeast thanks to its disability to ferment maltose and maltotriose, the prevailing fermentable sugars of all malt worts. Although according to some authors, the beer fermented by *S. ludwigii* tends to be sweet due to its high residual maltose and maltotriose content, the relative sweetness of these sugars is significantly lower than that of sucrose and glucose (Attenborough, 1988). The fermentation with *S. ludwigii* is characterized by slow attenuation even at 20℃ which implies that the process does not require continuous monitoring. A comparison of traditional bottom fermenting yeast with *S. ludwigii* with/without wort acidification showed a significantly higher formation of sensorially active by-products (higher alcohols and esters) by special yeast (Table 3.2). These volatiles, together with wort acidification, were found to mask the typical worty flavor of AFBs and contributed positively to fullness and pleasant liveliness of AFBs. However, in spite of the high volatile content there was a remaining slight worty off-flavor, which can be ascribed to lower aldehyde reduction by *S. ludwigii*. The AFBs produced with *S. ludwigii* contained diacetyl slightly above the taste threshold level, which was picked up in the tasting (Narziss et al., 1992).

酵母属的其他菌种中，路德酵母是工业化生产无酒精啤酒最成功的。这种酵母的控制发酵得以实现是由于它缺乏发酵麦芽糖和麦芽三糖的能力，而这两种糖是所有麦芽汁中占优势的可发酵糖。尽管一些学者认为由路德酵母发酵的啤酒因为麦芽糖和麦芽三糖的残余量高而使口感偏甜，但是这些糖的相对甜度远远低于蔗糖和葡萄糖。路德酵母发酵的特点是即使在 20℃耗糖也很缓慢，意味着发酵过程不需要连续监测。传统的下面发酵酵母与路德酵母关于有/没有麦芽汁酸化的比较结果显示，通过特殊的酵母形成的感官活性副产品（高级醇和酯类）的量明显更高（表 3.2）。已发现这些与麦芽汁一起被酸化的挥发物能掩盖无酒精啤酒典型的麦芽汁味，有利于促成无酒精啤酒的饱满性和令人愉快的爽口性。然而，尽管挥发物含量高，但仍然有轻微的麦芽汁异味，这归结于路德酵母对醛的还原能力较低。把路德酵母生产的无酒精啤酒拿来品尝，其所含双乙酰略微超过品评的阈值。

Table 3.2 The influence of yeast type and wort acidification on the composition of alcohol-free beers.

Fermentation yeast	Bottom	*S. ludwigii*	*S. ludwigii* + acidification
Temperature/℃	0	20	20
Original gravity/%	11.5	11.5	11.5
Ethanol/%	0.3	0.68①	0.68①
Real extract/%	10.7	10.34	10.34
Attenuation/%	9	13	13
Fermentation time/h	48	120	120
pH	5.15	4.98	4.18
Bitter substances (EBC)	28.0	27.2	22.2
Total diacetyl/(mg/L)	0.04	0.14	0.13
Total HAA/(mg/L)	3.0	31.8	30.3
Total EAA/(mg/L)	0.79	1.88	2.31
Reduction of aldehydes/%	81.0	56.8	32.6

① Ethanol content higher than the legal limit for AFB. Source: Narziss et al. (1992.)HAA, higher aliphatic alcohols; EAA, esters of acetic acids.

表 3.2 酵母类型及麦芽汁酸化对无酒精啤酒组成的影响

发酵酵母	下面发酵	路德酵母	路德酵母+酸化
温度/℃	0	20	20
原浓度/%	11.5	11.5	11.5
乙醇/%	0.3	0.68*	0.68*
实际提取物/%	10.7	10.34	10.34
发酵度/%	9	13	13
发酵时间/h	48	120	120
pH 值	5.15	4.98	4.18
苦味值（EBC）	28	27.2	22.2
双乙酰总量/(mg/L)	0.04	0.14	0.13
HAA 总量/(mg/L)	3	31.8	30.3
EAA 总量/(mg/L)	0.79	1.88	2.31
乙醛还原量/%	81	56.8	32.6

① 酒精含量高于无酒精啤酒的规定限值。HAA，高脂肪醇；EAA，乙酸酯。

Another invention suggests leading steam saturated air through alcoholic beer in a sieve bottom column in order to desorb the alcohol. The involved loss of sensorially active compounds by desorption was suggested to be compensated either by addition of a fermenting wort or by using the species *Saccharomyces rouxii* able to consume ethanol under aerobic conditions and at the same time to produce flavor active substances. However, the author does not suggest how to deal with the possible negative effect of oxygen from stripping air on flavor and colloidal stability of produced AFB.

另一个发明建议在一个有筛底柱的容器中使饱和蒸汽的空气通过含酒精啤酒，以便其释出酒精。在解吸过程中感官活性化合物的相关损失，建议通过添加发酵麦芽汁补偿或使用鲁氏酵母，它能在有氧条件下消耗乙醇，同时产生风味活性物质。然而，如何应对脱除空气中的氧对所生产的无酒精啤酒的风味和胶体稳定性可能带来的负面效应，作者并没有给出建议。

A method for producing an alcohol-free beer-like fermented beverage employing a slow fermentation process by fungi from the genus *Monascus* has been proposed, too. According to the authors, the final product looks like beer, has a refreshing taste, glittering red color, low alcohol content, and has high anti-oxidation activity. However, it is questionable whether this beverage can be considered beer.

还有一种推荐的方法是利用源自红曲霉的真菌缓慢发酵生产无醇的类啤酒发酵饮料。根据作者的描述，最终的产品看起来像啤酒，有一种清爽的味道，颜色亮红，酒精含量低且具有较高的抗氧化活性。然而值得怀疑的是，这种饮料是否可以被认为是啤酒。

④ Continuous Fermentation

连续发酵

Although the continuous beer fermentation has been studied for several decades, the number of industrial applications is still limited. The major obstacle hindering the industrial exploitation of this technology is the difficulty in achieving the correct balance of sensory compounds in the final product. Given the shifts in metabolism of cells grown in continuous culture, it has proven difficult to "translate" the traditional batch process into a continuous and immobilized process. The production of AFBs using immobilized yeast cell systems rank among limited fermentation methods using short contact (1~12h residence time) between immobilized yeasts and wort. The continuous AFB fermentation can outperform the rival technologies in productivity; however, it is essential that it produces a final product competitive in terms of sensorial quality.

尽管连续啤酒发酵已经研究了几十年，但是工业上的应用仍然有限。阻碍这项技术工业化开发的主要障碍是最终的产品很难实现感官化合物的正确平衡。鉴于连续培养中生长细胞新陈代谢的变化，已经证实很难将传统的分批发酵工艺"转换"成连续的和固定化的工艺。利用固定化酵母细胞系统生产无酒精啤酒属于限制发酵方法中固定化酵母与麦芽汁之间的短时接触法（1~12 h 停留时间）。在生产效率上，这种无酒精啤酒的连续发酵是可以超越许多竞争技术的；然而，最终产品在感官品质上的竞争力也是十分必要的。

Alcohol-free beers are usually characterized by worty off-flavors and lack of pleasant fruity (estery) aroma found in regular beers. Although the formation of higher alcohols and esters during continuous AFB production has already been studied, very few papers comparing flavor formation in the traditional batch fermentation and the continuous one are available. One reported a significantly lower formation of higher alcohol and acetic acid esters, while more recent papers concluded the importance of process parameters and yeast strains for the formation of volatiles. Among process parameters it is aeration, which has perhaps the most important impact on the formation of volatiles in continuous systems. An optimal and constant flavor profile of the AFB can be achieved by the accurate oxygen supply. The concentration of total higher alcohols (HA) and ester (ES) as well as the HA/ES ratio found in continuously fermented model medium under optimized oxygen supply was comparable with those found in three commercial alcohol-free beers.

无酒精啤酒的特点通常是具有麦芽汁异味，缺乏普通啤酒中令人愉快的水果（酯）香气。尽管在连续的无酒精啤酒生产中高级醇和酯的形成已经有过研究，但是只有很少的比较传统分批发酵和连续发酵中风味形成的论文是可用的。有一篇报道了高级醇和乙酸酯的形成显著降低，而最近更多的论文得出了工艺参数和酵母菌株对挥发物形成起重要作用的结论。工艺参数中，充气可能是连续系统中影响挥发物形成的最重要因素。精准的氧气供应可以使无酒精啤酒的风味最佳且恒定。在优化的供氧条件下，连续发酵的模型培养基中，总高级醇（HA）和酯（ES）的浓度以及 HA / ES 的比率可以与三种商业无酒精啤酒媲美。

Several studies have been carried out on the alcohol-free beer production by the limited fermentation with immobilized cells of *S. cerevisiae* at low temperature (0~4℃) and nearly anaerobic conditions. Similarly to the cold contact process (CCP) these conditions lead to the suppressed cell growth, low ethanol formation, and stimulated production of higher alcohols and esters. The authors hypothesized that the increased production of volatiles can be ascribed to the effort of cells to maintain the redox balance under anaerobic conditions by reoxidation of NADH coupled with the reduction of carbonyl compounds to higher alcohols. However, some oxygen is essential for several yeast biosynthetic pathways and thus for the long-term production of AFB with balanced flavor.

一些研究在低温（0~4℃）和几乎厌氧的条件下，利用固定化的酿酒酵母细胞通过限制发酵进行了无酒精啤酒的生产。类似于冷接触法（CCP），这些条件导致细胞生长受到抑制、乙醇形成量低，并能刺激生产高级醇类和酯类。作者推测，产品中挥发物的增加可以归结于细胞在厌氧条件下为保持氧化还原平衡，通过还原型辅酶 I 的再氧化，同时伴随着羰基化合物还原成高级醇。然而，一定的氧气对于一些酵母生物合成途径、长期生产具有和谐风味的无酒精啤酒都是必要的。

Wort carbonyls were proposed to contribute to the unpleasant worty taste of AFBs. Although the reduction of wort aldehydes by yeast is relatively fast during batch fermentations, there was concern it may not be sufficient at the speed of the continuous AFB production. However, the carbonyl reducing capacity of continuous immobilized cells systems for the AFB production has been reported to be satisfactory. This can be ascribed to either an increased alcohol dehydrogenase activity in immobilized yeast and/or a wise compromise between the alcohol formation and the carbonyl reduction by optimizing the process parameters (biomass load, residence time, temperature, and aeration) of the continuous systems.

无酒精啤酒中不愉快的麦芽汁异味被认为是麦芽汁中羰基化合物造成的。虽然在分批发酵期间麦芽汁中的醛能够相对快速地被酵母还原，但令人担忧的是，连续无酒精啤酒的生产中可能没有足够的还原速度。然而，已有报道表明，生产无酒精啤酒的连续固定化细胞系统中羰基的还原能力令人满意。这可以归因于固定化酵母乙醇脱氢酶活性的增加和/或通过优化连续系统的工艺参数（生物质装载、停留时间、温度和换气）对酒精形成和羰基还原良好的协调。

As in the processes involving the limited fermentation, the pH drop during the continuous AFB production does not take place in the required extent, a continuous biological acidification for the direct adjustment of pH of mash and wort by immobilized lactic acid bacteria (DEAE cellulose) has been studied during test periods of a few months. The continuous acidification would suitably match with the subsequent continuous fermentation.

当涉及有限的发酵过程，连续无酒精啤酒的生产中 pH 值的降低并不在所需的范围程度内进行，在几个月的试验期间，研究了固定化乳酸菌（DEAE 纤维素）连续酸化以直接调节麦芽糖浆和麦芽汁的 pH 值。

Several industrial examples of testing and implementation, of the continuous AFB production, have been reported. However, information on the current industrial application of the continuous limited fermentation of AFBs is not available to the authors. It can be assumed that the continuous fermentation systems have not found widespread utilization in the AFB production mainly due to the need of special equipment (bioreactor and tools for its continuous feed and control), eventually additional methods (immobilization) and materials (carrier).

已经有一些连续生产无酒精啤酒工业上测试和实施样例的报道。然而，在当前的工业应用信息下，用连续抑制发酵方法来生产无酒精啤酒是不可能实现的。可以假设连续发酵系统没有广泛运用在无酒精啤酒的生产上，主要是由于特殊设备的需求（生物反应器和连续进料及控制装置)、额外的方法（固定化）及材料（载体）。

(5) Sensorial Properties and Additional Improvements of Alcohol- free Beer

无酒精啤酒的感官性状及进一步改进

The aroma and taste of an AFB is usually rather different from its fully fermented counterpart. The AFBs often suffer from various flavor imperfections. For instance, the AFBs produced by the membrane processes have usually less body and a low aromatic profile, the thermally dealcoholized AFBs may suffer heat damages, while the beers obtained by biological methods have often a sweet and worty off-flavor. It has been proved that ethanol significantly increases aldehyde retention, leading to lower perception of the worty character. In a usual 5% ABV beer the retention of aldehydes was 32%~39% in comparison to 8%~12% retention at 0.5% ABV. Similarly, higher levels of mono- and disaccharides in AFBs intensify such off-favors. Headspace extraction and sensorial analysis further showed that the aldehyde retention in AFBs can be enhanced by increasing the level of dextrins or glycerol. These findings suggest that the flavor perception of a regular beer cannot be mimicked simply by trying to get the volatile distribution in AFBs as close as possible to that one in a regular beer. Instead, promising results can be achieved by changing the degree of volatile retention in AFBs and/or by creating a balance of volatiles, different from that present in beers containing ethanol, but with similar flavor impression. Particular flavor balance can be produced by process adjustments as well as by adding flavor active compounds into the final product.

无酒精啤酒的气味和味道与完全发酵的对照啤酒相比通常会有相当大的差别。无酒精啤酒在风味上常常会有各种欠缺。例如，通过膜处理生产出的无酒精啤酒通常酒体轻、风味物质减少，热脱醇处理的无酒精啤酒可能遭受热损伤，而通过生物学方法所获得的啤酒通常含有甜味和麦芽汁异味。已经证实乙醇能显著提高对乙醛的保留能力，从而降低对麦芽汁特征的感知。在酒精含量5%ABV的普通啤酒中乙醛的保留量为32%~39%，相比之下酒精含量为0.5%ABV的啤酒中乙醛保留量为8%~12%。类似地，无酒精啤酒中较高浓度的单糖和二糖增强了异味感。顶空萃取和感官分析进一步表明可以通过增加糊精或甘油的含量来提高无酒精啤酒对乙醛的保留。这些发现表明，在无酒精啤酒中，不能简单地试图通过所获挥发物尽可能接近于普通啤酒的调配来模仿对普通啤酒风味的感知。反之，理想的结果可以通过改变无酒精啤酒中挥发物的保留程度和/或创立一个挥发物质的平衡来实现，不同于含乙醇的啤酒，但有类似的风味印象。特殊风味的平衡可以通过工艺调整以及向最终的产品中添加香味活性成分来实现。

① Post-treatments and Blending

后处理与调配

Both the thermal and membrane processes often use different post-treatment and blending techniques in order to improve the sensorial quality and colloidal stability of dealcoholized beers. Improvements can be achieved by the addition of fresh yeast followed by maturation or by blending with the original beer, aromatic beer (beer fermented at elevated temperatures), or krausen. Another possibility is to adopt the Barrell patent to gently dealcoholize beer by treating it with CO_2 from fermenting green beer and finally add krausen followed by maturation and filtration process. The addition of 6 vol% of krausen into a beer dealcoholized to 0.1 ABV returned about 15% and 31% of the higher alcohols and esters originally present in the alcoholic beer, respectively. Other studies have shown that the thresholds of the important aroma components in the AFBs are significantly lower than in the alcohol-containing beer. This means that even a partial replacement of aroma compounds by one of the above suggested methods can improve significantly the AFB flavor.

为了提高脱醇啤酒的口感和胶体稳定性，热处理法和膜处理法通常采用不同的后处理与调配技术。还可以在随后酿熟的过程中添加鲜酵母或者用原啤酒、香气浓郁的啤酒（高温发酵的啤酒）或是发酵醪来调配以实现改进。另一种可能性是采用Barrel专利，即用生啤中的CO_2处理，温和地将啤酒脱醇，最后添加发酵醪并酿熟、过滤。添加6%（体积分数）发酵醪至0.1ABV的脱醇啤酒中，可使高级醇和酯类分别回归到含酒精啤酒中的15%和31%。其他的研究表明，无酒精啤酒中重要芳香成分的阈值明显低于含酒精啤酒。这就意味着即使采用上述任何一种方法替代部分香气成分，都能够显著改善无酒精啤酒的风味。

② Additives

添加剂

The use of additives will be explained on the example of Czech alcohol-free beers. Currently, there are 30 AFB brands commercialized in the Czech Republic (AFBs represented 2.92% of the Czech beer market in 2008). Among them, 26 brands are produced by the arrested/limited fermentation (at least one also uses a changed mashing process), two are fermented with special yeast and one is produced by vacuum rectification. According to information on the labels, 10 brands from the whole group of AFBs are produced only using traditional brewing raw materials, 9 contain one additive, 9 contain two additives, and 2 contain three or more additives.

添加剂的使用将以捷克的无酒精啤酒为例来说明。目前，有 30 个无酒精啤酒的品牌在捷克共和国市场上销售（2008 年在捷克，无酒精啤酒占据了 2.92%的啤酒市场）。其中 26 个品牌是通过阻止/抑制发酵法生产的（至少有一种品牌也使用了改变糖化的工艺），两个品牌采用了特殊酵母发酵，还有一个品牌采用真空精馏的生产方式。根据标签上的信息，在整个无酒精啤酒生产中，只有 10 个品牌使用传统的酿酒原料，9 个品牌含有一种添加剂，9 个品牌含有两种添加剂，2 个品牌含有三种或更多的添加剂。

(6) Cost Evaluation and Conclusions

成本评估与结论

The available literature is poor in comparisons of processes and their impact on the product quality, but the comparison of economic aspects of processes producing LABs of AFBs is even scarcer. Nevertheless, it is clear that the arrested/limited fermentation process can be performed in a common brewery equipment but shorter production time and fewer raw materials are needed. Therefore, the production costs for such LAB/AFBs are the same or lower, than for the regular beer. Conversely, processes of the alcohol removal do require an extra equipment, relevant utilities and space, which mean additional investments and operating costs above the production costs of the regular beer to be dealcoholized. The advantage of alcohol separation processes is their flexibility (start-up within hours, high productivity) and possibility to produce zero alcohol beers, which is hardly achievable by fermentative processes, given by their nature. Some authors also state that the taste of the dealcoholized AFBs is dryer and closer to regular beer. Somewhat contradictory to this is the fact the only Czech AFB produced by vacuum rectification was ranked 21st among 30 samples by the taste panel. Additional profit can be also created from the separated alcohol, which is obtained at different concentrations. The diluted alcohol solution can be further concentrated to a marketable content, used in the brewing process as blending water or sold for acetification to produce vinegar. From one rare cost comparison of four different processes it was the falling film system, which emerged victorious followed by the thin film evaporator, reverse osmosis, and, finally, dialysis. However, a reliable and comprehensive economic comparison of various methods of the LAB/AFB production is not available and therefore it is impossible to define the best process. Moreover, choosing the most appropriate process is further influenced by the available production capacity, expected sales, and marketing strategy of the product and hence it requires a detailed balance sheet reflecting the existing technology and the specifics of the local market.

可查的文献中，比较生产工艺及其对产品质量影响的很少，而对无酒精啤酒中低酒精度啤酒生产工艺在经济方面的比较更是凤毛麟角。尽管如此，很明显，阻止/抑制发酵工艺可以用普通的酿造设备完成，但所需生产时间更短和原材料的使用更少。因此，对于这样的低酒精度啤酒/无酒精啤酒的生产成本与普通啤酒相比是一样的，甚至更低。相反，去除酒精的工艺需要额外的设备，以及相关的器械和空间，这就意味着去除酒精额外的投资和，高于普通啤酒的生产费用。酒精分离工艺的优势在于灵活性（在几个小时之内运转、生产效率高）和生产零酒精啤酒的可能性，这是自然发酵工艺很难实现的。一些学者指出，去除酒精的无酒精啤酒的味道更浓郁，更接近于普通啤酒。对于这一点，某种程度上也有矛盾之处，真空精馏生产的捷克无酒精啤酒在 30 个样品中由品尝小组给出的排名仅为第 21。从不同浓度的分离酒精中还可以创造额外的利润。稀释的酒精溶液可进一步浓缩到可销售的浓度、用于酿造过程中作为勾兑水或出售用于醋化制醋。在一份罕见的对四种不同工艺的成本比较中，降膜系统胜出，其次是薄膜蒸发、反渗透，最后是透析。然而，对于不同方法生产低/无酒精啤酒还没有一个可靠的综合性的经济比较，因此它不可能确定出最佳工艺。此外，选择最合适的方法，更进一步地受产品的现有生产能力，预计销售额以及市场策略的影响，因此需要一个详细的资产负债表来反映现有的技术和当地市场的具体情况。

3.3.3 Homework

课后作业

3.3.3.1 Sentence Translation

句子翻译

(1) Original Sentences

原句

① Concentrated lime juice with 20% total soluble solids was dried using three levels of maltodextrin (40%, 50%, and 60% solid base) and a BÜCHI B-190 spray dryer.

② The results of this study are beneficial for scaling up the spray drying of lime juice to the food industry.

③ Effect of freezing and thawing on bread quality can be studied objectively to develop relationships between temperatures, durations of holding and shelf life after baking.

④ The same clarifying agent with the same concentration along with sterile filtration has decreased the tannins by 41.75% with improved visual clarity of 96%.

⑤ Acrylamide inhibition through reducing the acrylamide precursors including asparagine and reducing sugars, by the use of asparaginase and/or substituting some of the added sugar using stevioside were investigated for their effects on dynamic rheology, hardness of dough, and for baking and sensory properties of the prepared cookies.

⑥ Addition of bacterial α-amylase, specially to blends of enzymes also containing lipase and pentosanase, improved white, lidded-pan bread quality by increasing elasticity and lowering firmness of crumb, and enhanced the keeping quality over time by providing a significant 2-day increase in the shelf life.

⑦ Response surface methodology (RSM) was used to optimise jelly formulation using as independent variables: total sugar content, ranging from 14 to 46°Brix; and total gum concentration ranging from 0.30 to 0.70% (w/v), with the proportion of gums in the mixture xanthan:LBG:gellan ranging from 5∶5∶90 up to 45∶45∶10.

⑧ This paper describes semi-continuous acetic acid fermentations for wine vinegar production performed isothermally and using temperature gradients in order to determine the influence of temperature on this industrial biotransformation.

⑨ The texture characteristics, i.e. gel hardness, cohesiveness and springiness, were found to be similar to those of a reference product, a previously developed reduced-calorie grape juice jelly with low methoxyl pectin.

⑩ Powders hygroscopicity decreased with increasing maltodextrin concentration, decreasing temperature and increasing feed flow rate.

(2) Translations

翻译

① 用三个浓度(40%, 50%, and 60% 固体基质)的麦芽糊精和 BÜCHI B-190 型喷雾干燥机来干燥含有 20%总可溶性固形物的浓缩酸橙汁。

② 研究结果有助于在食品工业中按比例大规模进行浓缩酸橙汁的喷雾干燥。

③ 冻融对面包品质的影响可以通过构建温度、保温时间及焙烤后保质期之间的关系来客观地研究。

④ 相同浓度的澄清剂经无菌过滤后，单宁含量降低 41.75%，视觉清晰度提高 96%。

⑤ 通过使用天冬酰胺酶和/或用甜菊糖苷替代部分添加的糖来减少丙烯酰胺前体(包括天冬酰胺和还原糖)对丙烯酰胺的抑制作用，研究了它们对动态流变学、面团硬度以及所制备的饼干的烘烤和感官性能的影响。

⑥ 细菌 α-淀粉酶的添加，特别是在含有脂肪酶和戊聚糖酶的混合酶中，通过增加面包屑的弹性和降低面包屑的硬度来提高白面包和模具成型面包的品质，并通过将保质期显著延长 2 天来提高保藏质量。

⑦ 采用响应面法(RSM)通过自变量优化果冻配方：总糖含量范围 14~46°Brix（白利糖度）、胶浓度范围 0.30~0.70% (w/v)、混合胶黄原胶：刺槐豆胶：结冷胶的比例从 5∶5∶90 升至 45∶45∶10。

⑧ 本文描述了生产酒醋的半连续醋酸发酵，为了确定温度对这种工业生物转化的影响，发酵在等温和不同温度梯度下进行。

⑨ 与对照产品，一种先前开发的含有低甲氧基果胶的低热量葡萄汁果冻相比，其质构特性如凝胶硬度、内聚性和弹性是相似的。

⑩ 随着麦芽糊精浓度的增加、温度的降低及进料速度的加快，粉末的吸湿性降低。

(3) 翻译文中划线句子

3.3.3.2 Common Sentence Patterns of Scientific Papers 科技论文常见句型

(1) Title format

标题的写作

① 标题的书写格式

a. 一是标题的第一个词和每一个实词的第一个字母都用大写，虚词则采用小写。

【例句】 Effects of Heating Media and Operating Conditions on Drying Kinetics and Quality of Germinated Brown Rice

加热介质、操作条件对发芽糙米干燥动力学及品质的影响

b. 二是标题的第一个词的第一个字母用大写，其余全部小写。

【例句】 Enzymatic polishing of rice ——A new processing technology

大米酶法抛光——一种新型加工技术

c.三是标题的每个词的字母全部采用大写。

【例句】THE RAPID DETERMINATION OF γ-AMINOBUTYRIC ACID

γ-氨基丁酸的快速测定

② 标题的结构

英文标题以名词短语为主要形式，由一个或几个名词连同定语构成。一般只有名词、形容词、连词、冠词和介词，动词只以现在分词或过去分词形式出现。标题要有中心词，并放在突出的位置上，如：Effects of heating media and operating conditions on drying kinetics and quality of germinated brown rice 中 Effects 是中心词。英文标题中心词提前，这与汉语是不同的，如上例："……的影响"。另外，标题不是句子，在标题中不采用句子的形式，不用不定式短语，也不出现从句。

③ 标题中的冠词

论文标题中一般冠词较多，近年来趋于简化，冠词多可以省略。

【例句】(The) Accumulation of γ-Aminobutyric Acid in Rice Germ Using Protease

利用蛋白酶富集大米胚芽中的 γ-氨基丁酸

④ 词的增减

标题的中英文在原则上应该一致，但也常有省略的情况，如汉语中的"……的研究"，在英语中通常都省略。例如： "A Study on..." "The Study of..."等均应省略才更简洁，更符合英语标题的写作习惯。

【例句】"Comparative Studies on Rheological Properties of Mayonnaise Samples"改为"Comparison of Rheological Properties of Four Mayonnaise Samples"

4 种蛋黄酱的流变特性比较研究

(2) Main body

正文写作

① 常放在摘要开头的主题句，一般是研究的目的，要研究和解决的问题。如： be aimed to...; The aim of this study was to...; be analysed; be discussed; ...be described; ...be evaluated.

【例句】This study was aimed to analyse the impact of the debittering process (DP) on the overall sensory properties of orange juice.

本研究旨在分析脱苦工艺对橘子汁总体感官性质的影响。

② 介绍研究途径，分析方法或介绍实验条件等，可以采用的句型有：Measurements were carried out to...; Conditions were considered for/of...; the approach was based on...

【例句】All measurements were made in triplicate for each sample.

每份样品重复测定三次。

③ 经过试验和研究所得出的新数据、观点和结果，要进行评价，常见的句式有：Results show that...; Facts express that...; Study proves that...

（结果显示……）

【例句】The results for the physico-chemical analysis are shown in Table 2.

理化分析结果见表 2。

【例句】The results showed that the juices obtained after the microfiltration and pasteurisation processes had low microbial counts.

结果表明果汁经过微孔过滤和巴氏杀菌之后微生物含量较低。

④ 处理结果或工艺处理之间的比较，常见的句式有：Compare with…; There was no change; There was significant difference.

【例句】Compared with traditional juice processing methods, membrane processes are associated with low investment costs and athermal separation techniques which involve no phase change (low temperatures) or chemical agents (clarification).

与传统果汁加工方法相比，膜处理投资成本低，属于不涉及相变（低温）或化学药剂（澄清剂）的非热分离技术。

【例句】There was no change in the parameters analysed in relation to different temperatures used in the thermal treatment.

不同温度热处理的相关分析参数没有变化。

⑤ 以 it 作为形式主语的情况，在科技英语中经常出现。下面是最常见的句型：It is easy to; It is a simple matter to find; It should be noted that; It is obvious that.

【例句】It is clearly seen that with increased SMC, wort viscosity decreased.

显然，随着浸提度的增加，麦芽汁的黏度降低。

⑥ 结论句式，反映研究的成果与水平，以及应用范围。

【例句】Finally, it was concluded that microfiltration is a viable alternative to thermal processes in sugar cane juice conservation.

最后得出结论，相对于热加工而言，微孔过滤对甘蔗汁的保存更为可行。

【例句】More research should be performed in order to satisfy consumer demands for fresh-tasting products while retaining safety.

保证食品安全的同时，为满足消费者对新鲜食品的需求，还应该进行更多的研究。

Chapter 4 Food Safety and Management

第4章 食品安全和管理

4.1 Transgenic Food

4.1 转基因食品

4.1.1 Glossary

专业词汇分析

① GMOs= Genetically modified organism 转基因生物

② pharmaceutical *adj*. 制药（学）的 *n*. 药物

[记忆窍门] 词根 pharma 意为药物、制药公司。

③ nutraceutical *n*. 营养食品；功能食物

[记忆窍门] 词根 nutri 指营养。

④ prevalence *n*. 流行；盛行；普遍；广泛

⑤ polygenic *adj*. 多基因的

[记忆窍门] poly 聚合；复合；genic *adj*. 基因的。

⑥ hypertension *n*. 高血压

[记忆窍门] hyper 高度紧张的；亢奋的；tension 拉力，张力。

⑦ CAD= coronary artery disease 冠状动脉疾病

[记忆窍门] coronar *n*. 冠状物。

⑧ susceptibility *n*. 敏感性；易感性；感情；磁化系数

[记忆窍门] sus 表示“在……下面”；suscept“感病体”；-ibility 后缀表示“性质；能力”。

⑨ precursor *n.* 前体

[记忆窍门] pre- 前缀表示“提前”。

⑩ heritability *n.* 遗传力；遗传率

[记忆窍门] heritage“遗传”；-ability 后缀表示“性质；能力”。该单词也可拆分成 her+it+ability。

⑪ phenotype *n.* 表型；表现型；显型。

[记忆窍门] type *n.* 类型

⑫ interaction *n.* 相互作用

[记忆窍门] inter-前缀表示“在一起；交互”；action *n.* 行动；活动。

⑬ nucleate *adj.* 有核的；*vt.* 使成核；*vi.* 成核

[记忆窍门] “nucl”表示“核”。

⑭ genome *n.* 基因组；染色体组

[记忆窍门] geno-“基因族群”。

⑮ transduction *n.* [遗] 转导；转换；换能；变频

[记忆窍门] trans- 前缀表示“转运；转移”；-duction 后缀表示“导”。

⑯ bacteriophage *n.* [病毒] 噬菌体

[记忆窍门] 可以联想到 bacteria *n.*细菌；phage *n.* 噬菌体。

⑰ pronuclear *adj.* 原核的

[记忆窍门] pro-前缀表示“某种事物的先驱、前身或原始状态”；nucleare *adj.* 细胞核的

⑱ microinjection *n.* 显微镜下注射

[记忆窍门] micro *adj.* 微小的；injection *n.* 注射

⑲ plasmid *n.* [遗] 质粒；质体

⑳ electroporation *n.* [遗] 电穿孔

[记忆窍门] electro-前缀表示“电；电子的；用电”。

㉑ permeability *n.* 渗透性；通透性

[记忆窍门] -ability 后缀表示“性质；能力”。

㉒ chromosome *n.* [遗] 染色体

[记忆窍门] chromo-前缀表示“色彩”

㉓ remedy *vt.* 补救；治疗；纠正 *n.* 补救；治疗；赔偿

[记忆窍门] re-前缀表示“重新；再；又”。

㉔ herbicide *n.* [农药] 除草剂

[记忆窍门] herb 草本植物；-cide 后缀表示“杀；消灭”。

㉕ insecticide *n.* 杀虫剂；农药

[记忆窍门] insect 昆虫；-cide 后缀表示“杀；消灭”。

㉖ isolate *vt.* 使隔离；使孤立；使绝缘 *n.* [生物] 隔离种群

[记忆窍门] iso-前缀表示“相同；相等”；late *adj.* 迟的；晚的。

㉗ bacterium *n.* [微] 细菌

[记忆窍门] -ium 后缀表示“场所，如 auditorium（礼堂）；表示金属元素，如 sodium

（钠）；也可以表示某种性质、状态或概念的集合体。bacteria，bacterium 的复数形式。

㉘ lethal *adj.* 致命的；致死的 *n.* 致死因子

㉙ larva *n.* [水产] 幼体，[昆] 幼虫，larvae，larva 的复数形式

㉚ virus *n.* [病毒] 病毒；毒害

㉛ fungi *n.* 真菌；菌类；蘑菇（fungus 的复数）

㉜ antifreeze *n.* 抗冻，防冻剂

[记忆窍门] anti-前缀表示"反对；抵抗"；freeze *n.* 冻结；冷冻。

㉝ seedling *n.* 秧苗；幼苗；树苗

[记忆窍门] seed *n.* 苗；种子

㉞ salinity *n.* 盐度；盐分；盐性

[记忆窍门] 可以联想到 salt *n.* 盐

㉟ malnutrition *n.* 营养失调；营养不良

[记忆窍门] mal-前缀表示"坏；不良"；nutrition *n.* 营养

㊱ impoverished *adj.* 穷困的；用尽了的

[记忆窍门] im-前缀表示"否定；poverty *n.* 贫困；-ed 附在规则动词和名词后构成同义形容词。

㊲ main staple *n.* 主要食物

㊳ deficiency *n.* 缺陷；缺点；缺乏；不足的数额

[记忆窍门] deficit 赤字；不足

㊴ alleviate *vt.* 减轻；缓和

㊵ a strain of 一种；一系

㊶ beta-carotene *n.* β-胡萝卜素

[记忆窍门] beta-, β；carrot *n.* 胡萝卜

㊷ vaccine *n.* 疫苗；菌苗 *adj.* 疫苗的；菌苗的

㊸ injectable *adj.* 可注射的

[记忆窍门] inject *v.* 注射；-able 后缀表示"可以……的"。

㊹ phytoremediation *n.* 植物修复

[记忆窍门] phyto-前缀表示"植物"；remediation *n.* 补救；矫正；补习。

㊺ caterpillar *n.* [无脊椎] 毛虫

[记忆窍门] cater *v.* 提供饮食及服务；pillar *n.* 柱子

㊻ perish *vt.* 使麻木；毁坏 *vi.* 死亡；毁灭；腐烂；枯萎

㊼ allergenicity *n.* 致敏性

[记忆窍门] allergen *n.* 过敏原；-icity 后缀表示"性质"。

㊽ incorporate *vt.* 包含；体现；把……合并 *vi.* 合并；混合

[记忆窍门] corporate *n.* 公司。

㊾ amino acid *n.* 氨基酸

[记忆窍门] amino *n.* [化学] 氨基；acid *n.* 酸

㊿ irrespective *adj.* 无关的；不考虑的

[记忆窍门] ir-前缀表示“不”，“非”；respect *n.* 尊敬；尊重

51 intestine *adj.* 内部的；国内的； *n.* 肠

[记忆窍门] in-前缀表示“在……内”。

52 testicle *n.* [解剖] 睾丸

53 embryo *n.* [胚] 胚胎；胚芽；初期 *adj.* 胚胎的；初期的

[记忆窍门] em-前缀表示“置于……之内”。

4.1.2 Texts and Translations

课文及翻译

A Review on Impacts of Genetically Modified Food on Human Health

转基因食品对人类健康影响的综述

Abstract

摘要

Genetically modified organisms (GMOs) are defined as organisms (except for human beings) in which the genetic material has been altered in a way that does not occur naturally by mating and/or natural recombination. GMOs have widespread applications as they are used in biological and medical research, production of pharmaceutical drugs, experimental medicine, and agriculture. The use of gene technology in food production has become interesting due to increased needs of food as well as its improved quality. With the application of gene technology to plants and animals, goals can be achieved more quickly than by traditional selection. Consequently, ethical dilemmas are opened concerning the eventual negative effects of production of genetically modified food. It seems that supplementation of nutraceuticals and wild foods as well as wild lifestyle may be protective, whereas western diet and lifestyle may enhance the expression of genes related to chronic diseases. Our genes or pathways are most likely regulated by microRNA. The prevalence and mortality due to multifactorial polygenic diseases; hypertension, coronary artery disease (CAD), diabetes and cancer vary depending upon genetic susceptibility and environmental precursors because they have identifiable Mendelian subsets. Rapid changes in diet and lifestyle may influence heritability of the variant phenotypes that are dependent on the nutraceutical or functional food supplementation for their expression. It is possible to recognize the interaction of specific nutraceuticals, with the genetic code possessed by all nucleated cells. There is evidence that South Asians have an increased susceptibility to CAD, diabetes mellitus, central obesity and insulin resistance at younger age, which may be due to interaction of gene and nutraceutical environment.

Keywords: *Bacillus thuringiensis*, genetically modified food, Gene Technology, Human Health, Pharmaceutical Drugs, transgenic plants

转基因生物（GMOs）被定义为遗传物质不经过杂交和/或自然重组就发生生物改变的生物（人类除外），转基因技术现已被广泛应用于生物与医学研究、药品生产、实验医学

和农业等领域中。由于人们对食品数量和质量的需求不断增长，基因技术在食品生产中的应用已引起重视。相较于传统选择，人类可通过对动植物采取基因技术而更快实现上述目标。因此，关于转基因食品可能产生的负面影响也陷入一个伦理困境。添加营养品、食用野生食物与天然的生活方式虽对身体有保护作用，但西方的饮食和生活方式可能也加速了与慢性疾病有关基因的显现。我们的基因一般由 microRNA 调控，多因素多基因遗传性疾病，如高血压、冠状动脉疾病（CAD）、糖尿病、癌症的患病率与死亡率根据遗传易感性和环境前体变化，这是由于如上疾病均有可识别的孟德尔亚单位。饮食和生活方式的快速变化可能影响到依赖于保健品或功能性食品供给量的不同表型遗传率。人类有可能认识到特定保健品和所有有核细胞具备遗传密码间的相互影响。有证据显示，南亚人民对冠状动脉疾病、糖尿病、向心性肥胖和胰岛素抗性的易感率呈低龄化，这可能是基因和保健品、环境间相互作用的结果。

关键词：苏云金芽孢杆菌，转基因食品，基因技术，人类健康，药品，转基因植株

4.1.2.1 Technology to Produce Genetically Modified Organisms 转基因生物的生产技术

Several methods of genetically modified organisms (GMO) production are known. The foreign gene that has been inserted into the cell of a microorganism, a plant or an animal is called a transgene. It is integrated into the genome of the recipients which are called transgenic. The transgenes are genes with known traits or mutated variants of known genes. In most cases, marker genes are used because of transgenic organism identification. The integration of transgene into the cell is carried out by different methods; (a) Transduction with the use of bacteriophages; (b) Transgene injection using pronuclear microinjection; (c) Transfer using modified viruses and plasmids; (d) Electroporation method by which higher permeability of cell membrane is achieved.

已知有几种生产转基因生物（GMO）的方法。插入微生物、植物或动物细胞中的外源基因称为转入基因。该基因被整合至受体基因组的过程称为转基因过程。转入基因是具有已知特征或具有突变体的基因。在大多数情况下，由于转基因生物的身份证明，标记基因也被用来作为转入基因。转入基因整合入细胞中的方法有以下几种：（a）利用噬菌体转导；（b）利用显微注射法注入转入基因；（c）利用重组病毒或质粒转入基因；（d）通过高渗透细胞膜电穿孔法。

For transfer of foreign，gene, also artificial chromosomes or fragments of chromosomes can be used. Transgenes can be transferred into the egg-cell by spermatozoa containing fragments of chromosomes. Developed world, having material and intellectual capacities, leads the studies on transgenic technology for production increase and improved food quality. In fact, there is not only enough but even too much food in the developed world. However, developing countries that need this technology to overcome the food shortage cannot afford it. Hence, gene technology is not a remedy to prevent the world from starvation. Transgenic seeds that developed countries can provide to developing countries to diminish the rate of malnutrition seems to be the best idea of genetic engineering. Transgenic plants that are resistant to pests will cause higher resistance in pests; consequently，stronger herbicides and insecticides should be used in the future. Finally, it has been proposed that transgenic food can cause certain allergies.

人工染色体或染色体片段也可用于外源基因的转入。转入基因可由包含其染色体片段的精子转移入卵细胞中。发达国家引领着以增加食物产量和质量为目标的转基因技术。事实上，发达国家不仅有足够食物，甚至食物充裕。然而，需要此项技术来克服食品短缺的发展中国家却无法负担起该技术。因此，基因技术不是一项阻止世界远离饥饿的补救措施。发达国家可提供给发展中国家转基因种子，以减少营养不良率，这似乎是基因工程的最佳意图。对害虫有抗性的转基因植物将导致害虫更高的抗性，因此将来会需要更强力的除草剂和杀虫剂。最后，已有人提出转基因食品能引起某些过敏症状。

(1) GM Foods are Promoted Why?

为什么要提倡转基因食品？

The term GM foods or GMOs (genetically-modified organisms) is most commonly used to refer to crop plants created for human or animal consumption using the latest molecular biology techniques. These plants have been modified in the laboratory to enhance desired traits such as increased resistance to herbicides or improved nutritional content. Genetic engineering can create plants with the exact desired trait very rapidly and with great accuracy. For example, plant geneticists can isolate a gene responsible for drought tolerance and insert that gene into a different plant. The new genetically-modified plant will gain drought tolerance as well. Not only can genes be transferred from one plant to another, but genes from non-plant organisms also can be used. The best-known example of this is the use of B.t. genes in corn and other crops. B.t., or *Bacillus thuringiensis*, is a naturally occurring bacterium that produces crystal proteins that are lethal to insect larvae. B.t. Crystal protein genes have been transferred into corn, enabling the corn to produce its own pesticides against insects.

术语"转基因食品"或"转基因生物"最常被用于利用最新的分子生物学技术生产出的用于人类或动物消费的农作物。这些植物在实验室中被改良，以增强人类需要的性状，如增加对除草剂的抗性或营养成分。基因工程可非常迅速并准确创造出具有所需特征的植物。例如，植物遗传学家可分离出耐旱基因并将该基因迁入到另一种植物中。新的转基因植物也将获得耐旱性征。基因不仅可从一种植物转移到另一种植物，非植物生物的基因也可被运用。最著名的例子是在玉米及其他农作物中使用 *B.t.* 基因，即苏云金芽孢杆菌，这是一种天然存在的，对昆虫幼虫有致命性的晶体蛋白的细菌。*B.t.* 晶体蛋白基因转入玉米并使玉米能够抵抗昆虫。

(2) Advantages of GM Foods

转基因食品的优点

Pest resistance: Farmers typically use many tons of chemical pesticides annually. Consumers do not wish to eat food that has been treated with pesticides because of potential health hazards, and run-off of agricultural wastes from excessive use of pesticides and fertilizers can poison the water supply and cause harm to the environment. Growing GM foods such as B.t. corn can help to eliminate the application of chemical pesticides and reduce the cost of bringing a crop to market.

抗虫性：每年农民都要使用大量化学农药。因为存在潜在的健康危害，消费者不希望食用使用过农药的食物。此外，过度使用农药和化肥而产生的农业废弃物会污染供水系统并引起环境危害。不断增加的转基因食物例如 *B.t.* 玉米能帮助减少化学农药的使用并降低农作物进入市场的成本。

Herbicide tolerance: Crop plants genetically-engineered to be resistant to one very powerful herbicide could help to prevent environmental damage by reducing the amount of herbicides needed.

除草剂耐受性：能抵抗强力除草剂的转基因农作物可通过降低除草剂用量而防止环境破坏。

Disease resistance: There are many viruses, fungi and bacteria that cause plant diseases. Plant biologists are working to create plants with genetically-engineered resistance to these diseases.

抗病性：有很多病毒、真菌和细菌会引起植物病害。植物生物学家正在努力创造可抵抗这些疾病的基因工程植物。

Cold tolerance: An antifreeze gene from cold water fish has been introduced into plants such as tobacco and potato. With this antifreeze gene, these plants are able to tolerate cold temperatures that normally would kill unmodified seedlings.

耐寒性：一种在冷水鱼类中存在的抗冻基因已经被引入到烟草和马铃薯等植物中。拥有这种抗冻基因的植物可耐受一般情况下会杀死未修饰植物幼苗的低温环境。

Drought tolerance/salinity tolerance: As the world population grows and more land is utilized for housing instead of food production, farmers will need to grow crops in locations previously unsuited for plant cultivation. Creating plants that can withstand long periods of drought or high salt content in soil and groundwater will help people to grow crops in formerly inhospitable places.

耐旱性/耐盐性：随着世界人口的增长，更多土地被用于居住而不是粮食生产，农民需要在之前并不适合栽培植物的土地上种植农作物。创造出可耐受长期干旱或高盐土壤和地下水的农作物将会帮助人类在从前荒凉的地方种植农作物。

Nutrition: Malnutrition is common in third world countries where impoverished peoples rely on a single crop, such as rice for the main staple of their diet. However, rice does not contain adequate amounts of all necessary nutrients to prevent malnutrition. If rice could be genetically engineered to contain additional vitamins and minerals, nutrient deficiencies could be alleviated. For example, blindness due to vitamin A deficiency is a common problem in third world countries. Researchers at the Swiss Federal Institute of Technology Institute for Plant Sciences have created a strain of "golden" rice containing an unusually high content of beta-carotene (Vitamin A). Plans are underway to develop golden rice that also has increased iron content.

营养性：第三世界国家的贫困人民饮食中的主食依赖于单一农作物如大米，因此营养不良很常见。然而，大米不含有足够的必需营养素来防止营养不良。如果大米可通过基因工程改造，含有额外的维生素和矿物质，那么营养缺乏就可以得到缓解。如，由于维生素A 缺乏症导致的失明在第三世界国家中广泛存在。瑞士联邦植物技术研究所的研究人员已研发出一种“黄金大米”，这种大米中含有大量的β-胡萝卜素（可转化成维生素 A）。开发高铁“黄金大米”的计划也在进行中。

Pharmaceutical medicines and vaccines are often costly to produce and sometimes require special storage conditions. Researchers are working to develop edible vaccines in tomatoes and potatoes. These vaccines will be much easier to ship, store and administer than traditional injectable vaccines.

药物和疫苗生产成本往往很高，有时还需要特殊的储存条件。研究人员正在研究开发含有番茄和土豆成分的口服疫苗。比起传统的注射疫苗，口服疫苗更易运输、贮藏和管理。

Phytoremediation: Plants such as poplar trees have been genetically engineered to clean up heavy metal pollution from contaminated soil.

植物修复：经过基因工程改造，杨树等植物可以清理被污染土壤中的重金属污染。

(3) Some Criticisms against GM Foods

对转基因食品的一些反对意见

GM foods fall into two categories: environmental hazards and human health risks.

转基因食品包括对环境危害和对人类健康产生的风险等两个方面。

① Environmental Hazards

环境危害

Unintended harm to other organisms: pollen from *B.t.* corn caused high mortality rates in monarch butterfly caterpillars. Monarch caterpillars consume milkweed plants, not corn, but the fear is that if pollen from B.t. corn is blown by the wind onto milkweed plants in neighboring fields, the caterpillars could eat the pollen and perish.

意外伤害其他生物：*B.t.*玉米的花粉可造成黑脉金斑蝶毛虫的高死亡率。黑脉金斑蝶毛虫以马利筋植物为食，而非玉米。令人担忧的是，如果 *B.t.*玉米的花粉被风吹到邻近领域的马利筋叶片上，毛毛虫就会因吃掉花粉而死亡。

Reduced effectiveness of pesticides just as some populations of mosquitoes have developed resistance to the now-banned pesticide DDT; many people are concerned that insects will become resistant to *B.t.* or other crops that have been genetically modified to produce their own pesticides.

农药的作用效果正在减弱，如一些蚊子种群可抵抗农药 DDT（滴滴涕，该农药现已禁用）；许多人担心昆虫会对 *B.t.*玉米或其他能够自身产生杀虫剂的转基因农作物产生抗药性。

Gene transfer to non-target species is another concern that crop plants engineered for herbicide tolerance and weeds will cross-breed, resulting in the transfer of the herbicide resistance genes from the crops into the weeds. These "super weeds" would then be herbicide tolerant as well.

基因被嵌入至目标物种是另一个令人担忧的问题，经基因工程改造的抗除草剂的农作物会与野草杂交，从而导致抗除草剂的基因从农作物转移进入杂草中。这些“超级杂草”也将有抗除草剂的特性。

② Human Health Risks

人类健康风险

Allergenicity: Many children in the US and Europe have developed life-threatening allergies to peanuts and other foods. There is a possibility that introducing a gene into a plant may create a new allergen or cause an allergic reaction in susceptible individuals. A proposal to incorporate a gene from Brazil nuts into soybeans was abandoned because of the fear of causing unexpected allergic reactions.

致敏性：美国与欧洲的很多儿童对花生等食物过敏而危及生命。其中一种可能性是引入某种基因进入植物，可能在易感个体中造成了一种新型过敏原或引起了一种过敏反应。一项从巴西坚果中合并基因进入黄豆的提案因怕造成意外的过敏反应而被舍弃。

4.1.2.2 Application of Transgenic Plants in Human Nutrition 转基因植物在人类营养中的应用

Genetically modified foods are classified into three categories according to their usage and legal regulations.

① Food is genetically modified (potato, tomato, soya, maize, sunflowers, rice, pumpkins, melons, rape, etc.).

② Food contains components of genetically modified plants (starch, oil, sugar, amino acids, vitamins, etc.).

③ Food contains genetically modified organisms (yoghurt contains transgenic microorganisms). Gene technology enables higher yields in plants, resistance to pests and frost, as well as mechanical properties of fruits, etc. We can also modify physical and chemical composition in order to improve the nutritional and physiological value of foods. Transgenic plants also enable production of more healthy food (more unsaturated fatty acids, transfer of proteins from legumes into wheat, increased content of essential amino acids, transfer of proteins from sunflowers into maize, etc.). Thus, dangers of heart diseases, allergies are diminished and malignancy prevented.

转基因食品根据其用量和法律法规规定，分为三类：

① 完全转基因食品，如马铃薯、番茄、大豆、玉米、向日葵、大米、南瓜、甜瓜、油菜等。

② 食物中含有转基因作物成分，如淀粉、油、糖、氨基酸、维生素等。

③ 食品含有转基因有机物，如酸奶中含有转基因微生物。

基因技术使植物产量提高、抵抗害虫和冰冻，以及提高水果的机械性能等。我们还可通过修改物理和化学成分以提高食品的营养和生理价值。转基因植物也能提高更多健康食品的产量（较多的不饱和脂肪酸，将豆类中的蛋白质转移到小麦中，增加必需氨基酸含量，将向日葵中的蛋白质转移到玉米中等）。因此，心脏病的危险性和过敏都会减少，恶性肿瘤也会被防止。

(1) Health Risk of Genetically Modified Organisms

转基因生物的健康风险

Several animal studies indicate serious health risks associated with GM food, including infertility, immune problems, accelerated aging, insulin regulation, and changes in major organs and the gastrointestinal system.

一些动物研究表明，很多严重的健康风险都与转基因食品有关，包括不育、免疫问题、老化加速、胰岛素调节、主要器官及胃肠系统的变化。

(2) GMOs are Inherently Unsafe

转基因生物本质上的不安全性

There are several reasons why GM plants present unique dangers. The first is that the process of genetic engineering itself creates unpredicted alterations, irrespective of which gene is transferred. This creates mutations in and around the insertion site and elsewhere. The biotech industry confidently asserted that gene transfer from GM foods was not possible; the only human feeding study on GM foods later proved that it does take place. The genetic material in soybeans that make them herbicide tolerant transferred into the DNA of human gut bacteria and continued to function. That means that long after we stop eating a GM crop, its foreign GM proteins may be produced inside our intestines.

转基因植物表现出独特的危险性有以下几个原因。第一，不管是哪个基因转移，基因工程本身在过程中会产生不可预知的变化，这将在基因嵌入点及其周围产生突变。生物技术产业信心满满地声称转基因食品中是不可能有基因转移。然而，人类后来的喂养研究证明这一现象确实存在。第二，大豆中耐除草剂的遗传物质转移到人体肠道细菌的 DNA 上并继续发挥作用。这意味着即使在我们停止食用转基因作物很长一段时间后，外源的转基因蛋白质可能仍会在我们的肠道内产生。

(3) Reproductive Failure and Infant Mortality

繁殖障碍和婴儿病死率

The testicles of both mice and rats fed roundup ready soybeans showed dramatic changes. In rats, the organs were dark blue instead of pink. In mice, young sperm cells were altered. Embryos of GM soy-fed mice also showed temporary changes in their DNA function, compared to those whose parents were fed non-GM soy.

喂食基因改造大豆的小鼠和大鼠的睾丸出现了巨大的变化。大鼠器官呈蓝色，而不是粉红色。小鼠的精子细胞发生变化，相比那些父母被饲喂非转基因大豆的老鼠胚胎，转基因大豆喂养中的老鼠胚胎的 DNA 功能也表现出暂时的变化。

4.1.2.3 Conclusions 结论

The latest development of biotechnology, particularly molecular biology, genetic engineering and transgenic technology has a very large number of potential applications in food production, including micro-organisms, plants and animals. Transgenesis is much more difficult to apply to farm animals than to plants or micro-organisms. Genetic modification has increased production in some crops. But the technology has too few challenges in few crops. Genetic modification is not a good thing in itself, but it is a tool where public & private science can balance each other. Genetically modified foods have various advantages like high yield, salinity tolerant, insect resistance etc. GM foods have a lot of health effects on living beings. GM foods have both positive and negative effects. These may be either direct effects, on organisms that feed on or interact with the crops, or wider effects on food chains produced by increases or decreases in the numbers of other organisms. As an example of benefits, insect-resistant *B.t.*-expressing crops will reduce the number of pest insects feeding on these plants, but as there are fewer pests, farmers do not have to apply as much insecticide, which in turn tends to increase the number of non-pest insects in these fields. Other possible effects might come from the spread of genes from modified plants to unmodified relatives, which might produce species of weeds resistant to herbicides. Conclusively, the present article is the compilation of various selective studies presenting both positive and negative impacts of GM foods on human health.

生物技术的最新发展，特别是分子生物学、基因工程和转基因技术在食品生产，包括微生物、植物和动物的生产中，潜在应用价值巨大。相比较于植物或微生物，转基因技术更难适用于农场动物。基因改造技术提高了农作物产量，但该技术在少数农作物上面临的挑战很小。基因改造本身并不是一件好事，而是一个让公共科学与私人科学相互平衡的工具。转基因食品有各种各样的优势，如高产、耐盐性、抗虫性等。转基因食品对生物也有保健作用。转基因食品是把双刃剑。它可能对以农作物为食或与农作物相互作用的生物产生直接影响，也可能是因其他生物数量的增加或减少而对食物链产生更广泛影响。举一个正面影响的例子：表达抗虫 *B.t* 基因的农作物可减少以这种农作物为食的害虫的数量，然而由于害虫的减少，农民就不必施用同样多的杀虫剂，这反过来就会有增加这一区域非害虫昆虫的数量。其他可能的影响也许来自转基因的植物向未转基因的亲缘植物的传播，这可能会产生抗除草剂的杂草物种。综上所述，本文是各种选择性研究的汇编，展示了转基因食品对人类健康的正面与负面影响。

4.1.3 Homework

课后作业

4.1.3.1 Sentence Translation

句子翻译

(1) Original Sentences

原句

① Rabbits fed GM soy showed altered enzyme production in their livers as well as higher metabolic activity.

② However, if the product has no natural equivalent, or shows significant differences from the unmodified food, then further safety testing is carried out.

③ Worldwide, reports of allergies to all kinds of foods, particularly nuts, fish and shellfish, seem to be increasing, but it is not known if this reflects a genuine change in the risk of, or an increased awareness of food allergies by the public.

④ Some sound requirements on adequate labeling of the genetically transformed food in EU have been passed so that consumers can choose according to believes (religious, ethic, medical).

⑤ It has been discussed whether the consumption of DNA in approved novel foods and novel foods ingredients can be regarded as safe as consumption of DNA in existing form.

⑥ Dr. Pusztai believes that the digestive tract, which is the first and largest point of contact with foods, can reveal various reactions to toxins and should be the first target of GM food risk assessment.

⑦ Genes which cause expression of desirable traits (e.g. modified starch production and disease resistance in potato es) were selected from organisms, such as bacteria, and transferred into plants, to alter their genetic material (DNA) in order to produce these desirable characteristics.

⑧ Today, the use genetic modification has already shown that an increased biological resistance to specific pests and diseases, including those caused by viruses, can reduce the need for chemical pesticides and decreasing the risk of crop failure.

⑨ In the future it will also be possible to enhance the nutritive value of crops by improving desirable functional characteristics, such as reduced allergenicity or toxicity as well as altered protein or fat content and increased phytochemical or nutrient content.

⑩ No adverse effects on human health have been scientifically recorded in commercialized GM foods, though there have been unconfirmed reports from various sources, some of which have been scientifically investigated and found not to be associated with GMOs.

(2) Translations

翻译

① 喂食转基因大豆的兔子肝脏酶产量发生变化，与此同时，其代谢活性也相应提高。

② 然而，如果产品没有自然对等物，或者与未转基因的食品有显著的不同之处，那么将进行进一步的安全测试。

③ 在全球范围内，关于各类食物，特别是坚果、鱼类和贝类过敏的报道似乎在增加。但这究竟反映了过敏风险的真实变化，还是公众对食物过敏的认识提高，目前还不得而知。

④ 欧盟已经通过了对转基因食品全面标示的合理要求，便于消费者根据其信仰（宗教，伦理，医疗）来进行选择。

⑤ 已获准的新型食品和新型食品成分中的食用 DNA 能否与自然存在的使用 DNA 一样安全，仍待商榷。

⑥ 普兹泰博士认为，消化道作为与食品的第一个也是最大的接触点，可显示出对于毒素的各种反应，应作为转基因食物风险评估的首要目标。

⑦ 为了得到某些理想特性，将影响其表达的基因（如改性淀粉生产和马铃薯的抗病性）从细菌等生物体中转移到植物中，以改变它们的遗传物质（DNA）。

⑧ 如今转基因的应用已表明，增强对特定害虫和包括病毒引起疾病的生物抵抗力，可减少对化学农药的需求和颗粒无收的风险。

⑨ 将来还可能通过改善作物理想的功能特性来提高其营养价值，例如降低过敏原性或毒性以及改变蛋白质或脂肪含量，增加植物化学或营养成分的含量。

⑩ 尽管有各种来源未经证实的报道，但没有科学研究记录商业化的转基因食品对人类健康造成不利影响，其中一些科学调查发现与转基因生物无关。

(3) 翻译文中划线句子

4.1.3.2 Common Sentence Patterns of Scientific Papers 科技论文常见句型

① 文章内容与作者观点

常用词：deal with, describe, explain, illustrate(vt.), introduce, present, report 等。

【例句】This article provided some descriptions of the API, along with some sample codes to illustrate how to make use of them.

这篇文章提供了应用程序编程接口的一些描述以及一些样本代码来阐明其如何使用。

② 综述某一个领域的研究课题

常用词：abstract, outline, review, summarize 等。

【例句】The influence which arose to the many kinds of disease does the outline on the trace element selenium.

就微量元素硒对多种疾病的影响做了概述。

③ 评估与比较

常用词：agree with, assess, compare, evaluate 等。

【例句】This paper will evaluate the development level of farmer vocational education and its influence factors by using the analytic hierarchy process and the ingredient analytic method.

文章将运用层次分析法和成分分析法对农民职业教育的发展水平及其影响因素进行

评价。

④ 论证与依据

常用词：be based on, take as reference 等。

【例句】 Methods you take natural calculus bovis as reference, the main content of cholic acid and bilirubin was determined by spectrophotometry.

方法是以天然牛黄为对照品，采用分光光度法测定其主要成分胆酸、胆红素的含量。

⑤ 观察与指示

常用词：demonstrate, exhibit, find, indicate, observe, point out, show 等。

【例句】Theoretical analysis and test research demonstrate that the two measures are effective ways to increase sticking strength between concrete interfaces as well as other performances.

理论分析与试验研究证明，这两种方法是提高混凝土界面黏结强度及其他性质的有效途径。

⑥ 运算与测量

常用词：calculate, determine, estimate, measure 等。

【例句】In this paper, parameter estimate algorithms are used to diagnose the burst fault in power system of carrier rocket.

本文将参数估计算法应用于运载火箭动力系统突发故障的诊断。

⑦ 成果的获取

常用词：achieve, construct, derive, design, develop, establish, give, improve, obtain, produce, provide, realize, record, reduce, solve 等。

【例句】The results show that both by chemical and physical methods of combining decentralized fumed silica, can obtain good decentralized results, the best dosage of A200 for 34 percent.

结果表明：用化学和物理两种相结合的方法分散气相二氧化硅，可获得很好的分散效果，A200 的最佳用量为 34%。

⑧ 应用与运用

常用词：apply, employ, use 等。

【例句】TLC is employed to identify radix paeoniae alba, radix scutellariae, radix angelicae dahuricae, radix notoginseng in precipitation.

采用薄层色谱法对沉淀中的白芍、黄芩、白芷、三七进行鉴别。

⑨ 实验与试验

常用词：experiment，test 等。

【例句】In this paper, we carry on experiment of comparing in 4℃, 25℃, 37℃ and 45℃ with natural thawing and vacuum thawing methods.

本文采用自然解冻和真空解冻的方式，在 4℃、25℃、37℃和 45℃条件下进行比较实验。

⑩ 结论

常用词：arrive at, conclude 等。

【例句】So, the authors conclude that the stratabound skarn of the Jiama deposit has nothing to do with magma hydrothermal solution, and however, has likely something to do with the hot brine in the basin.

因此，作者推断甲玛矿床的层控夕卡岩与岩浆热液无关，但可能与盆地热卤水有关。

4.2 Sanitation Standard Operating Procedures (SSOPs) and Good Manufacturing Practices (GMPs)

4.2 卫生标准操作程序和良好生产规范

4.2.1 Glossary

专业词汇分析

① sanitation *n.* 卫生，卫生设施

[记忆窍门] sanit，消毒，-ation 名词后缀；消费者健康的保障。

② procedure *n.* 程序，手续，步骤

[记忆窍门] pro-往前，ced-走，-ure 名词后缀；往前走的过程，进行下去的过程。

③ poultry *n.* 家禽

[记忆窍门] poul 发剖的音，try 尝试，尝试剖，家禽注定是要被宰割的。

④ manufacture *n.* 制造，加工；*vt.*（用机器大量）生产

[记忆窍门] manu-手，fact-作，制作，-ure 名词后缀；用手制作，古时生产全用手操作。

⑤ pesticide *n.* 杀虫剂

[记忆窍门] pest 害虫，cide“切开，杀”；杀灭害虫。

⑥ hygiene *n.* 卫生，卫生学

[记忆窍门] 源于希腊神话中的健康女神 Hygeia 黑吉尼亚。读 high gene，具有很 high 的 gene（基因），因为很注意个人卫生。

⑦ adulteration *n.* 掺杂，掺假

[记忆窍门] adult 成年人，er-音似儿，at（e）；eat 过去时，吃；-ation 名词后缀；成年人吃饭——“喜掺假”。成年人吃饭常有酒，但不是人人都能喝，所以总有人偷偷向酒里掺点儿茶、水。

⑧ contamination *n.* 污染

[记忆窍门] con-共同，tamin-拼音，他们；at(e)，eat 过去时，吃；-ation 名词后缀；他们共同用一份餐具吃饭——污染自己；吃完了还乱扔——污染环境。

⑨ disinfectant　*n.* 消毒剂，杀菌剂　*adj.* 消毒的，杀菌的

[记忆窍门] dis-不，in-向内部，fect-，make，-ant 通常与“人”、“物”或某种特性相关，即防止微生物等向内部扩散的试剂。

⑩ concentration　*n.* 浓缩，浓度

[记忆窍门] con-共同的，centr-，center，中心，-ation 名词后缀；向共同的中心聚集。

4.2.2 Texts and Translations

课文及翻译

Food safety guidelines for small size meat and poultry processing
Practices and programs relevant to SSOP and GMP
与 SSOP 和 GMP 相关的小型肉禽加工操作和程序的食品安全指南

Introduction

引言

A small size meat producer must understand the basic principles of Sanitation Standard Operating Procedures (SSOPs) and Good Manufacturing Practices (GMPs) and how to comply with them. For meat and poultry producers, SSOPs are the foundation of many food safety programs in the plants. Creating and complying with SSOPs can be challenging for the small size meat producers. Understanding the similarities and differences between SSOPs and GMPs is difficult. This fact sheet provides a basic understanding of these two food safety regulations and guidelines.

一个小型的肉品生产商需要理解卫生标准操作程序(SSOPs)、良好生产规范(GMPs)的基本原则，并知晓如何遵守这些规范。对于肉类及禽类生产商，SSOPs 是车间中许多食品安全项目的基础。建立和遵守 SSOPs 对于小型生产商而言，是具有挑战的。了解 SSOPs 与 GMPs 的相同点和不同点是有一定难度的。本文为理解这两种食品安全规范和指南提供了基础。

4.2.2.1 What are GMPs?

什么是 GMPs?

Good Manufacturing Practices (GMPs) contain both requirements and guidelines for manufacturing of food and drug products in a sanitary environment. The Food and Drug Administration has developed GMPs for all foods, and that agency enforces those GMPs for all foods except meat, poultry, and egg products. The U.S. Department of Agriculture's Food Safety Inspection Service has regulatory authority for those products. USDA-FSIS has developed a sanitation regulation (Code of Federal Regulations Title 9 Part 416 to address sanitary requirements for processing of meat and poultry products. The sanitation regulations are requirements to produce wholesome foods under sanitary conditions and specific Sanitation Standard Operating Procedures (SSOPs). When developing SSOPs to meet USDA-FSIS requirements, it is helpful to review GMPs for nonmeat products (21 CFR 110 www.access.gpo.gov/nara/cfr/waisidx_02/ 21cfr110_02.html), as FDA includes extensive details on defining sanitary conditions and feasible practices.

良好生产规范（GMPs）提供了在一个卫生的环境中生产食品和药品的要求和指南。（美国）食品药品监督管理局（FDA）对所有食品均制定了 GMPs，并对除肉类、禽类和蛋制品外的所有食品实施这些 GMPs。美国农业部食品安全检查局(USDA-FSIS, www.fsis.usda.gov)具有对这些产品的监管权。USDA-FSIS 制定了一项卫生细则（美国联邦法规，第 9 条， 第 416 部分以介绍规范肉类和禽类制品加工中的卫生要求。这个卫生细则要求在符合特定卫生标准操作程序（SSOPs）的条件下生产健康食品。在制定符合 USDA-FSIS 要求的 SSOPs 时，对非肉类食品 GMPs 进行审核（21 美国联邦法规是有帮助的，因为 FDA 包含了定义卫生条件及可行性操作的大量细节。

Good Manufacturing Practice (GMP) regulations were first introduced in 1969 by the FDA (Part 128 of the Code of Federal Regulations) to implement the Foods, Drug and Cosmetic Act. In 1977 this was recoded as Part 110. It was further revised and updated in 1986, and was named as cGMPs (current GMPs).

1969 年，FDA 首次引入良好生产规范（GMP）条例，以实施食品、药品、化妆品法案（美国联邦法规 第 128 部分）。1977 年，该条例被重新修订为第 110 部分。1986 年进一步修订和更新，并被命名为现行良好生产规范（cGMPs）。

4.2.2.2 GMPs categories GMPs 类别

① General maintenance of physical facilities

② Cleaning and sanitizing of equipment and utensils

③ Storing and handling of clean equipment and utensils

④ Pest control

⑤ Proper use and storage of cleaning compounds, sanitizers, and pesticides

⑥ Employee training

⑦ Plant design

⑧ Quality assurance assessment

① 物理设备的一般维护。

② 设备、器具的清洁和消毒。

③ 清洁设备和器具的存放和管理。

④ 虫害防治。

⑤ 清洁剂、杀菌剂和杀虫剂的合理使用和贮藏。

⑥ 员工培训。

⑦ 车间设计。

⑧ 品质的保证和评鉴。

These are the umbrella GMPs for all FDA-inspected food processing establishments regardless of size. In addition, specific GMPs are established for particular industries and products. For example, there are specific GMPs for processing seafood and dairy.

无论食品加工企业的大小，以上是 FDA 检查的总 GMPs。此外，还对特定的行业和产品建立了特定的 GMPs。如，海产品和乳品加工就有特定的 GMPs。

Meat and poultry producers are required to adhere to the Sanitation program requirements of 9 CFR 416. USDA enforces 9 CFR 416, while FDA enforces 21 CFR 110. Meat and poultry plants are responsible for preventing adulteration of their products through their written sanitation program. Practically speaking, the meat and poultry producers should comprehend GMPs, because they serve as a valuable guide and tool when formulating the plant's sanitation program.

肉类和禽类产品生产商必须遵守 9 CFR 416 中的卫生程序要求。USDA 实施 9 CFR 416，而 FDA 则实施 21 CFR 110。肉类和禽类生产车间有责任通过书面的卫生规范来防止产品掺杂。实事求是地讲，肉类和禽类生产商需要理解 GMPs，因为 GMPs 可以作为规范车间卫生准则的有价值的指导要求和工具。

4.2.2.3 Some cGMPs
一些 cGMPs

Let's look at the Code of Federal Regulations (CFR) under Title 21 and Part 110. Title 21 covers Food and Drugs; Part 110 is related to Current Good Manufacturing Practice in manufacturing, packing, and holding human foods.

让我们学习一下美国联邦法规（CFR）第 21 条，第 110 部分。第 21 条涵盖了关于食品和药品的相关细则，第 110 部是关于人类食品生产、包装、保存的现行良好生产规范。

(1) cGMPs and Personal Hygiene

cGMPs 和个人卫生

Cross-contamination of food by foodhandlers is the most frequent cause of contamination. Employee hygiene is essential, because the hygienic condition and habits of workers determine the amount of cross-contamination from worker to food products. It should be emphasized that clean, sanitary workers are necessary to produce clean, sanitary food products.

由食品从业人员造成的交叉污染是引起食品污染的最常见原因。员工的卫生至关重要，因为员工的个人卫生状况和习惯决定了由他们到食品的交叉污染的程度。应该强调的是，清洁卫生的员工是生产清洁卫生食品的必要条件。

Many cGMPs focus directly on reducing foodhandler contamination. For example, Code of Federal Regulations (CFR) Title 21, Part 110.10. Examples of personal hygiene include washing hands, removing jewelry, and maintaining personal cleanliness. Also, the food processor should provide training for new employees in personal hygiene based on cGMPs, which should be part of a formal, written training program that consists of instructions on hand washing, personal cleanliness, and sanitary hygiene.

许多 cGMPs 注重减少由食品从业人员造成的污染。例如美国联邦法规第 21 条，第 110 部分。以个人卫生为例，就包含洗手、摘除首饰、保持个人卫生等。此外，食品加工者必须根据 cGMPs 对新雇员进行关于个人卫生的培训，该培训应列入一个包含有洗手、个人清洁、卫生消毒等方面说明的正式书面培训项目中。

The small size producer should coach each employee to wash their hands in a correct way by describing, in detail, the correct amount of soap used, the correct water temperature, and the amount of lathering time, which is equal to the time needed to say the ABC's. The details of employee training should be written in the producer's employee training program, with instructions on how to coach employees. The GMPs about hand washing and facilities — such as sinks, toilets and towel racks — are presented in detail.

小型生产商应该指导每一位雇员以正确的方式洗手，如肥皂的正确用量、适宜的水温，以及与说出 ABC 时间相同的肥皂起泡时间等。要将员工培训的方方面面以及指导员工的说明都写在员工培训项目中。GMPs 对于洗手和相关设施如水槽、马桶、毛巾架等都进行了详细的介绍。

(2) Employer's Responsibilities

雇主的责任

① Provide training in food handling and personal hygiene.

② Conduct regular inspections of employees' hygiene and hygienic work habits. Violations should be handled as disciplinary violations, and incentives for superior hygiene should be provided.

③ Properly maintaining sanitary facilities and supplies. This includes ample quantities of soap, disinfectant, working sinks, hairnets, etc.

① 提供关于食品处理和个人卫生的培训。

② 定期检查员工的卫生及工作习惯。对违反者应进行违纪处理，对优秀卫生保持者应给予激励。

③ 合理维护卫生设施及用品。包括充足的肥皂、消毒剂、工作洗涤槽、发套等。

4.2.2.4 Complying with cGMP Regulations
遵守 cGMP 细则

As you may have noticed while browsing through the GMPs, some regulations are written so that compliance can be assessed. For instance, the regulation that "no pests shall be allowed in any area of the food plant" is clearly defined. If an inspector finds a pest, such as a mouse, or evidence of a pest in the food plant, then it is a violation of the regulation.

正如您在浏览 GMP 时已经注意到的一样，一些法规是为了评估合规性而编写的。例如，规定中"食品工厂的任何区域不得有害虫"是明确的。如果检查员在食品工厂发现有害生物，如老鼠或害虫的证据，那么这是违反规定的。

However, some GMPs contain phrases such as "clean as frequently as necessary to protect against the contamination of the food". This vague regulatory language obviously is subjective. How often is it "necessary" to clean the processing line: daily, every two shifts, or when we think it needs it? Other GMPs might use the terms "adequately" or "sufficient", which are both subjective terms. These issues highlight the potential problems of determining how often to clean and sanitize. USDA-FSIS has developed more prescriptive requirements for meat and poultry processing. The SSOPs require producers to document that the sanitation program and personal hygiene practices are adequate to ensure that foods are produced under sanitary conditions. As a producer changes technologies or practices, changes in the SSOPs are necessary and must be documented with appropriate validation.

然而，一些 GMPs 包含如“必要时需经常清洁以防止对食品的污染”的短语。这类模糊的监管语言明显是具有主观性的。对于清洗生产线而言，多长时间一次是必要的？每天？每两班？还是当我们认为该清洗的时候？其他 GMPs 还可能使用“足够的”或“充分的”等主观术语。这些内容突出了判断清洗和消毒频率的潜在问题。USDA-FSIS 对肉类和禽类加工制定了更多规范的要求。SSOPs 要求生产者提供文件证实其卫生计划和个人卫生规范足以确保在卫生条件下生产食品。当生产商更改其生产技术或操作时，SSOPs 也必须更改，且必须记录进行适当验证。

4.2.2.5 What are SSOPs?
什么是 SSOPs?

Sanitation Standard Operating Procedures — SSOPs — are the specific, written procedures necessary to ensure sanitary conditions in the food plant. They include written steps for cleaning and sanitizing to prevent product adulteration. SSOPs are required in all meat and poultry processing plants, CFR Title 9 Part 416. The cGMPs can help guide the plant when SSOPs are being developed in the plant. The SSOP procedures are specific to a particular plant, but may be similar to plants in the same or a similar industry. All SSOP procedures must be appropriately documented and validated.

卫生标准操作程序（SSOPs）是确保食品生产车间卫生条件的具体的书面准则。SSOPs 包含清洗、消毒等步骤以避免产品掺杂。美国联邦法规第 9 条第 416 部分指出，所有的肉品和禽类产品生产车间都要遵守 SSOPs。当车间制定 SSOPs 时，cGMPs 可以为其提供指南。SSOP 细则针对特定工厂，但可能与相同或类似行业的工厂相似。所有的 SSOP 细则必须合理制定并进行验证。

Both pre-operational (before daily processing begins) and operational (during processing) sanitation needs are included in SSOPs to prevent direct product contamination or adulteration. Therefore, the decision about how often to clean the processing line would be addressed in the SSOPs and supporting documentation of the plant.

SSOP 细则包含操作前（日常加工开始前）及操作时（加工期间）消毒需求以避免直接产品污染和掺杂。因此，关于多长时间清洗一次加工生产线的决定将在 SSOPs 和工厂的辅助文件中阐明。

(1) Pre-operational SSOPs

操作前 SSOPs

These are established procedures that describe the daily, routine sanitary procedures that occur before processing begins. The procedures must include the cleaning of product contact surfaces of facilities, equipment, and utensils to prevent direct product contamination or adulteration. These might include: 1. Descriptions of equipment disassembly, reassembly after cleaning, and use of acceptable chemicals according to label direction, and cleaning techniques. 2. Application instructions, including concentrations, sanitizers applied to product contact surfaces after cleaning.

以下是在加工之前描述其日常例行卫生程序的既定规程。该规程必须包括产品接触表面设施，设备和工具的清洁，以避免对产品的直接污染或掺杂。具体如下：

① 对仪器拆装、清洗后的重新组装、根据标签说明使用合适的化学品、清洗技术等

的描述；

② 使用指南：包含与清洗后的产品表面接触用的浓缩剂、消毒剂等。

(2) Operational SSOPs

操作时的 SSOPs

These are established procedures that describe the daily, routine sanitary procedures that will be conducted during operations to prevent direct product contamination or adulteration. Established procedures for operational sanitation must lead to a sanitary environment for preparing, storing, or handling any meat or poultry food products. Established procedures during operations might include, where applicable: 1. Equipment and utensil cleaning/sanitizing/disinfecting during production, as appropriate, at breaks, between shifts, and at mid-shift cleanup. 2. Procedures for employee hygiene, such as cleanliness of outer garments and gloves, hair restraints, hand washing, health, etc. 3. Product handling in raw and in cooked product areas.

以下是在操作过程中描述其日常例行卫生程序的既定规程，以避免对产品的直接污染或掺杂。建立的操作规程必须为肉类或禽类制品的准备、贮藏、处理提供一个卫生的环境。适用的操作包括：

① 在休息、换班以及每班次间的清扫工作期间，对仪器和用具进行适当的清洗、消毒、净化。

② 外工作服和手套的清洗，头发的束缚、洗手、健康情况等雇员卫生细则。

③ 生熟产品区的产品处理。

Meat and poultry plants are unique because they are required to develop, maintain, and adhere to written SSOPs. The plant must identify, by position, the officials who monitor daily sanitation activities, evaluate and document whether the SSOPs are effective, and take appropriate corrective action when needed. Finally, SSOPs must be routinely verified to ensure that they are working properly. <u>Microbiological testing should be done periodically on food and noncontact surfaces to verify the effectiveness of the established procedures.</u>

SSOP records must be maintained on-site for 48 hours and stored for a minimum of six months.

肉类和禽类制品生产车间是独特的，因为它们需要制定、保持、遵守书面的 SSOPs。车间必须由监管日常卫生活动的行政人员判别、评估、记录 SSOPs 是否有效，并在需要的时候采取适当的纠正措施。最后，必须定期查证 SSOPs 以确保其正常工作。对食品和非接触表面必须定期地进行微生物检测，以查证既定程序的有效性。

SSOP 记录必须现场放置 48h，并且存放至少 6 个月。

4.2.2.6 Meat and Poultry SSOPs 肉类和禽类制品 SSOPs

The SSOPs for meat and poultry plants must meet the following regulatory requirements:

① The plant has written SSOPs describing daily procedures that will be conducted before and during operations to prevent direct product contamination or adulteration. At a minimum, these procedures must address the cleaning of food contact surfaces, equipment, and utensils. The SSOPs state the frequency at which each procedure will be verified.

② The SSOPs should be signed and dated by plant management or plant owner. SSOPs should be reviewed periodically.

③ The plant must identify an individual(s) who will be responsible for implementing and monitoring SSOPs and the daily sanitation activities.

④ Written records of SSOP activities along with corrective actions must be maintained for a minimum of six months (48 hours on site).

肉类和禽类制品生产车间的 SSOPs 必须符合以下监管要求：

① 为避免直接产品污染或掺杂，生产车间要具有可指导操作前和操作中日常程序的书面 SSOPs。这些程序至少必须解决食品接触表面、设备、用具的清洁问题。SSOPs 规定了查验每个程序的频率。

② SSOPs 必须由车间管理者或工厂业主签字并且注明日期。SSOPs 需要定期审查。

③ 生产车间必须明确负责实施和监管 SSOPs 以及日常卫生活动的个人。

④ SSOP 活动及纠正措施的书面记录必须至少保存 6 个月(现场 48h)。

4.2.2.7 Guidelines for the Small Size Producer 小生产商的指导方针

Search, read, and keep a copy of the cGMPs for the specific type of food plant. These regulations are located in the Code of Federal Regulations (CFR), Title 21, and Part 110.

Search, read and keep a copy of the SSOP requirements for meat and poultry processing. CFR, Title 9, Part 416.

Develop written policies for personal hygiene that address SSOPs in the plant , including hand washing, gloves, jewelry, hairnets, policies for sick employees, etc.

Include written SSOPs in the employee training program, particularly those associated with personal hygiene and the policies of the plant on checking that employees are following the established procedures.

Include all sanitation procedures in the SSOPs. Ensure that all sanitation procedures document the verification frequencies, identify personnel who are responsible, and describe in detail all verification activities.

查找、阅读、保留一份适用于特定食品工厂的 cGMPs 的复印本，这些规章制度位于美国联邦法规第 21 条，第 110 部分。

查找、阅读、保留一份适用于肉类和禽类制品加工的 SSOP 要求的复印本。美国联邦法规第 9 条，第 416 部分。

通过提出洗手、手套、首饰、发套、对生病员工的相关政策等的工厂 SSOPs，制定个人卫生的书面政策。

在员工培训计划中包括特别是与个人卫生和工厂政策有关的书面 SSOPs，以检查员工是否遵守既定程序。

在 SSOPs 中包含所有卫生程序。确保所有卫生程序记录验证频率，确定负责人员，并详细描述所有验证活动。

4.2.3 Homework

课后作业

4.2.3.1 Sentence Translation

句子翻译

(1) Original Sentences

原句

① There should be specific person/persons (preferably manager) who are assigned responsibility for the food safety facility program.

② Highly visible and easy to understand signs supporting appropriate Good Manufacturing Practices (GMPs) should be put up to remind workers of proper practices. For example, not eating, chewing, drinking or smoking, hand washing, and specific clothing requirements etc.

③ Any trace of insects, rodents, birds; reptiles or mammals in products or ingredients are indicators of contamination, posting physical and microbiological hazards.

④ A pest control program is required to provide the basic environmental and operating conditions that are necessary for the production of safe, wholesome food.

⑤ To avoid any adulteration or possible cross contamination from other items, only essential products, packaging, chemicals and equipment should be stored in the facility.

⑥ Materials should be clearly marked or labeled with some kind of rotation coding that is understood by all staff to ensure FIFO and effective traceback/recall procedures.

⑦ There should be written SSOPs covering good manufacturing practice topics such as goods receiving/supplier approval, temperature controls, pest control, food safety training, shipping, foreign material control, etc.

⑧ Equipment Microbiological testing is used to determine the effectiveness of cleaning and sanitization programs.

⑨ Food safety issues mentioned either on the specific good safety meetings or other relevant meetings should be recorded as proof of the company's ongoing commitment to food safety (at least once every quarter).

⑩ Employees should be issued a list GMP of rules in the relevant languages. They may confirm by signing that they understand and agree to abide by the company's food safety policy rules regarding personal hygiene/GMPs and health requirements.

(2) Translations

翻译

① 应该指派专人（最好是经理）负责食品安全设施规划。

② 应张贴清晰易懂的标识，以支持良好的生产规范（GMP），提醒员工正确操作。如：禁止饮食、咀嚼吸烟，洗手要求以及特定着装规定等。

③ 产品或配料中出现任何昆虫，啮齿动物，鸟类，爬行动物或哺乳动物的痕迹，都是污染的标示，将造成物理和微生物危害。

④ 害虫防治方案为生产安全、卫生的食品提供必要的基本环境和操作条件。

⑤ 为避免掺假或其他物品的潜在交叉污染，设施场所内应存放必要的产品、包装、化学品和设备。

⑥ 材料应采用某种所有员工能理解的相关周转代码明确标识或标签，这些代码应确保先进先出和有效的追溯/召回程序。

⑦ 应当有书面的卫生标准操作程序涵盖良好生产规范的主题，例如：货物接收/供应商许可，温度控制，虫害防控，食品安全培训，运输，异物控制等。

⑧ 设备的微生物检测用来确定清洁和消毒程序的有效性。

⑨ 在专项良好安全会议或其他相关会议上提到的食品安全问题应记录下来，作为公司对食品安全持续承诺的证据(至少每季度一次)。

⑩ 发给员工一份他们可理解语言的 GMP 规则清单。他们可以通过签字确认，他们理解并同意遵守公司关于个人卫生/GMPs 和健康要求的食品安全政策规则。

（3）翻译文中划线句子

4.2.3.2 Common Sentence Patterns of Scientific Papers 科技论文常见句型

① 表示研究目的的常见基本句型

a. The purpose of the study was ...

b. The aim of this study was to ...

c. This study attempted to answer the following questions to test the hypothesis...

d. This study focused on the...

e. Our task in /of this article was to …

f. Our job in this paper was to …

g. The goal of this research was to…

② 介绍其他科学家研究成果的常见基本句型

a. In …(year),…(somebody) reported in his study that…

b. In …(year),…(somebody) found that…

c. In …(year),…(somebody) discovered that…

d. In …(year),…(somebody) concluded that…

③ 介绍研究意义的常见基本句型

a. …is important from the viewpoint that…

b. …is valuable from the viewpoint that…

④ 介绍需要解决的研究难题的常见基本句型

a. The problems to be solved are…

b. The largely unsolved problems are…

⑤ 介绍图（表）的常见基本句型

a. As shown in Table (Fig.)1, …

b. We can find in Table (Fig.) 1 that…

c. Table (Fig.) 1 summarized that …

4.3 HACCP

4.3 危害分析与关键控制点

4.3.1 Glossary

专业词汇分析

① legislation *n.* 立法

[记忆窍门] legal 意思是合法的。

② suitability *n.* 适宜性

[记忆窍门] suit 意思是套装，suitable 适当的，相配的。

③ food hygiene 食品卫生

④ implement *vt.* 实施，执行 *n.* 工具，器具

[记忆窍门] complete 完成；implementation 执行。

⑤ FAO (Food And Agriculture Organization) 联合国粮农组织

⑥ WHO (World Health Organization) 世界卫生组织

⑦ CAC（Codex Alimentarius Commission） 食品法典委员会

⑧ prerequisite programs 必备程序

[记忆窍门] pre-前缀表示预先的、在……前。require 表示要求、需要。

⑨ intrinsic *adj.* 内在的

[记忆窍门] in-前缀表示在……里面的。

⑩ obligatory *adj.* 必须的，必备的，有义务的

[记忆窍门] oblige 表示要求，迫使。

⑪ quality management system 质量管理体系

⑫ Certifying Bodies 认证机构

[记忆窍门] certify 表示证明，保证。

⑬ specification *n.* 规范

[记忆窍门] specify 表示明确指出，说明。

⑭ surveillance *n.* 监督

[记忆窍门] surveille 表示对……实行监督。

⑮ criteria *n.* 条款，标准

[记忆窍门] criticise 表示批评，评论。

⑯ accredited *adj.* 官方认可的，公认的

[记忆窍门] credit 表示名誉，信用。

⑰ Accreditation Body 计量认证机构

⑱ deduced from 推断，从……得出结论

[记忆窍门] de-前缀表示减去，除去，deduce 表示演绎，induce 表示归纳。

⑲ flow diagram 流程图

⑳ subcontract *n.* 分包合同，转包合同

[记忆窍门] sub-，在……下方，次于。

㉑ outsourced services 外包服务

[记忆窍门] out 表示在……之外。source 表示来源。

㉒ coordinate *n.* 协调　coordinator 协调人

[记忆窍门] co-，一起，共同，联合。

㉓ performance *n.* 执行情况，表演

㉔ schematic *adj.* 概要的

[记忆窍门] scheme *n.* 表示计划，策划。

㉕ interim *adj.* 临时的 *n.* 过渡期，中间期

[记忆窍门] intern 表示实习生。

㉖ loops *n.* 循环

[记忆窍门] loop 有表示圆圈的意思。

㉗ disinfection *n.* 消毒

[记忆窍门] dis-前缀表示否定，infect 是动词，意思是感染。

㉘ cleaning-in-place 就地清洗

㉙ infrastructure *n.* 基础设施

[记忆窍门] infra-前缀表示在……以下。structure 表示结构，建筑。

㉚ cross contamination 交叉污染

[记忆窍门] cross 有交叉的意思。*v.* contaminate 感染。

㉛ pallets *n.* 货盘、托盘

㉜ chlorine *n.* 氯

㉝ non-conforming products 不合格品

[记忆窍门] non-前缀表示否定，conform 意思是符合，遵守。

㉞ methodology *n.* 方法学，方法论

[记忆窍门] -ology，科学，学问。method，方法。

4.3.2 Texts and Translations

课文及翻译

Requirements for A HACCP Based Food Safety System
基于 HACCP 的食品安全体系要求

4.3.2.1 Introduction
绪论

Food safety is a global concern. Not only because of the continuing importance for public health, but also because of its impact on international trade. Effective Food Safety Systems shall therefore manage and ensure the safety and suitability of foodstuffs. In many countries world-wide, legislation on the safety and suitability of foodstuffs requires "HACCP" to be put in place by any food business or organisation, whether profit-making or not and whether public or private, carrying out any or all of the following activities: preparation, processing, manufacturing, packaging, storage, transportation, distribution, handling or offering for sale or supply of foodstuffs.

食品安全是一个全球关注的问题，这不仅仅是因为它一直对公共卫生非常重要，还因为它对国际贸易有很大的影响。因此，有效的食品安全体系可以管理和确保食品的安全性与适宜性。全世界已经有许多国家对食品的安全性与适宜性进行立法，要求规定，任何食品企业或组织，不论是否盈利，是公立的还是私人的，在以下食品的任何一个环节包括食品的准备、加工、生产、包装、贮藏、运输、销售、处理，销售或供给的全过程中，都必须执行危害分析与关键控制点（HACCP）法则。

The Joint FAO/WHO Codex Alimentarius Commission describes a series of steps, including the 7 HACCP principles giving guidance for the application of the HACCP system. Also, Codex advises that minimum hygiene measures should be in place before HACCP is implemented: "Prior to application of HACCP to any sector of the food chain, that sector should be operating according to the Codex General Principles of Food Hygiene, the appropriate Codex Codes of Practice, and appropriate food safety legislation."

联合国粮农组织/世界卫生组织下属的食品法典委员会介绍了包括 HACCP 七项原则在内的系列步骤，用来指导 HACCP 体系的运用。此外，法典建议，在实施 HACCP 之前，应执行有最低卫生措施："在将 HACCP 应用于食品链的任何部门之前，该部门应根据食品法典《食品卫生一般原则》、适当的食品法典操作规范和食品安全立法进行操作。"

For confidence , the Certifying Body must use the published "Requirements" and the "Certification Regulations" in an agreed manner. The "Requirements" are documented in such a way to allow an effective assessment of the status and performance of the HACCP-based Food Safety System, as implemented by the food business operator. In the "Certification Regulations", specific criteria are stated which have to be met by the Certifying Body when selecting a competent HACCP audit team, and rules which govern the way the certification process is designed and offered (e.g. the minimum auditor time) have to be followed. *Authority* is obtained when the Certifying Body is formally accredited by a recognised Body to operate the certification system for HACCP based Food Safety Systems and is audited regularly by this Accreditation Body. Accreditation concerns the reliability and competence of the Certifying Body. The document "Requirements for Certification Bodies" elaborates the accreditation requirements. It must be understood that certification of a HACCP-based Food Safety System is not a guarantee of a food business operator's continuous food safety performance. The value added to a food business operator with a certified HACCP-based Food Safety System lies in the efforts made by the operating company to maintain that HACCP system and its commitment to continuously improve its food safety performance.

为了保密，认证机构必须以协议的方式使用公开出版的"要求"或者是"认证规则"。"要求"以文件的方式允许对食品经营者执行基于 HACCP 食品安全体系的状态和绩效进行有效评估。在"认证规则"当中，规定了认证机构在选择合格的 HACCP 审核团队时必须满足的特定标准，以及必须遵守认证过程设计和提供方式的规则(如最低审核员时间)。得到授权就是认证机构获认可机构正式认可后，可运作以“HACCP”为基础的食物安全系统的认证系统，并由认可机构定期审核。官方认证涉及认证机构的可靠性与能力。文件“认证机构要求”详细阐述一些公认的准则。我们必须明白，通过了以 HACCP 为基础的食品安全体系的认证，并不代表食品经营者的食品安全就能永远得到了保证。对于食品经营者来说，通过食品安全体系 HACCP 认证的意义在于为了维持该体系所做的努力，并致力于持续改进食品安全的行动。

4.3.2.2 Scope of Application 应用范围

In this document, requirements have been specified to be used during the assessment of operational HACCP systems (HACCP-based Food Safety Systems) which ensure the safety of foodstuffs during preparation, processing, manufacturing, packaging, storage, transportation, distribution, handling or offering for sale or supply in any sector of the food chain. The “Requirements” are basically applicable to all food businesses or organizations, whether profit-making or not, and whether public or private.

在本文件中，详细规定了如何在评估中运用可操作的 HACCP 体系（基于 HACCP 的食品安全体系），该系统可确保食品在准备、加工、生产、包装、贮藏、运输、配送、销售或者售卖、供销等食品链任何环节的安全性。“要求”主要适用于所有从事食品的企业或组织，不论是否盈利，公立的还是私营的。

Obviously, the food business operators shall have identified any step in their activities which is critical to ensure food safety and shall have developed, implemented, maintained and reviewed adequate safety procedures, applying the principles of HACCP, including the general principles of food hygiene, and where appropriate the relevant codes of practice and the food safety legislation. These “Requirements” are not intended for application by suppliers and / or service companies to food businesses, like suppliers of packaging materials, food equipment, industrial cleaning services, etc.

很明显，食品经营者应确定其活动中对确保食品安全至关重要的任何步骤，应用 HACCP 原则，包括食品卫生一般原则、适当情况下的相关实践规范和食品安全法规，并应制定、实施、保持和审查适当的安全程序。该“规定”并不适用于像包装材料供应商、食品设备行业、工业清洗行业等等食品经营业的一些配套的服务行业。

4.3.2.3 HACCP System Requirements HACCP 体系要求

(1) Management Responsibility

管理职责

The food business operator is responsible for the safety (and suitability) of the produced food. Therefore, the food business operator shall include the policy with respect to food safety in the policy of the organization. The food business operator has ultimate responsibility for the policy of the organization and shall document, support and communicate this policy.

食品经营者应该对所生产食品的安全性（和适宜性）负责。因此，食品经营者应该将食品安全政策纳入企业政策。食品经营者对食品企业的政策负有最终责任，并且必须制定、支持、宣传该政策。

Periodically, the food business operator shall verify the implementation of the policy and review the outcome. The HACCP system enables the food business operator to demonstrate his commitment and his responsibility with respect to the supply of safe products. The HACCP system ensures that all required activities are effectively defined, implemented and maintained.

食品经营者应定期验证政策执行情况，并审查实施效果。HACCP 体系能够确保食品经营者证实其在提供关于安全产品方面的承诺和责任。HACCP 体系亦保证所有必要的措施都得到了有效的建立、执行和维持。

① Policy

方针

The food business operator shall define and document (in writing) the policy of the organization with regards to food safety. It will demonstrate the commitment of the organization to safe food. The policy shall demonstrate that the organization is fully aware of its position in the food chain. It will reflect the "farm-to-fork" approach, starting with the purchase and acceptance of raw materials. The policy shall be focused on the safety of foodstuffs and shall respond to the expectations and needs of its customers and consumers. The policy shall include concrete objectives (proposed actions) to ensure and improve food safety for the period under consideration. The food business operator shall ensure that the policy is understood, implemented and maintained at all levels in the organization.

食品经营者应该详细说明本企业关于食品安全的方针，并将它文件化。它将体现企业对安全食品的承诺。方针应该能够体现企业已经充分意识到本身在食品链中的位置。它反映了"农场到餐桌"的途径和原料从购进到接收的过程。方针应当以食品的安全、顾客和消费者的期望以及需求为关注焦点。为确保和提升食品安全，方针应该包括具体的周期性目标（提议的行动）。食品企业经营者应该确保组织内的各个层面都能理解、执行并维持该企业方针。

② Scope of the HACCP System

HACCP 体系的范围

The food business operator shall define the extent (the scope) of the HACCP system. The scope shall comprise that part of the food chain and those activities of the food business for which the food operator is responsible and can be held liable.

食品企业经营者应该界定 HACCP 体系的程度(范围)。HACCP 体系的范围应该包括食品链的环节和在食品交易中食品经营者应该负责任并能负责任的一些活动：

The part of the food chain for which the food business operator is responsible begins where the responsibility of the suppliers of raw materials and ingredients ends; the responsibility of the food business operator ends where another food business in the food chain takes over the responsibility. The scope shall therefore conform to purchase and sales contracts;

食品企业经营者所负责任的食品链的环节包括:从原料和配料供应商的责任结束时开始；食品经营者的责任结束于食品链中的另一家食品企业接管责任。因此，HACCP 体系的范围应该与购销合同相符。

All locations and process lines where food is manufactured and/or stored by the food business shall be properly indicated and be available for assessment;

食品企业经营者用来生产和/或贮存食品的场所和生产线都应该正确标示出来并可供评估。

All products which are supplied to the market by the food business, whether processed or handled, shall be properly specified;

食品企业供应市场的所有产品，无论是加工的还是处理的，都应该恰当说明。

All subcontracted activities（outsourced services, like packaging, storage, transport） shall be properly dealt with.

应该正确处理所有外包活动（像包装、贮存、运输一类的外包服务）。

A key principle is that no part of the operation of the food business can be excluded from the scope of the HACCP system; all activities must be available for assessment.

一个关键原则是食品经营操作的所有环节都不能排除在 HACCP 体系范围之外；所有的活动都必须得到可靠的评估。

③ Tasks, responsibilities and authorities

任务、职责和权利

The food business operator shall provide appropriate documentation with respect to the tasks, responsibilities and authorities of food business operator's employees who are in positions which involve handling food and/or controlling and ensuring the safety and suitability of the food. An organization chart and the organization's reporting structure shall be documented.

食品经营者应就涉及处理食品和/或控制和确保食品安全与适宜性的岗位上的食品经营者员工的任务、责任和权限提供适当的文件。组织架构图和报告结构应形成文件。

④ HACCP Team(s)

HACCP 小组

The food business operator shall assemble a HACCP team (or various HACCP teams if so required). The HACCP team shall develop, implement and maintain the HACCP system. The organization shall demonstrate that the members of the HACCP team have the knowledge, expertise and different disciplines available which are required to develop, implement and maintain a HACCP system covering the total scope of the HACCP system. Minimum qualification criteria, including required expertise, shall be defined and documented for all members of the HACCP team. In addition, the assignment (including tasks, responsibilities and authorities) shall be documented for the team members. Whenever more than one HACCP team has been assembled, a co-ordinator shall be appointed to co-ordinate the development, implementation and maintenance of the HACCP system.

食品企业经营者应该建立一个 HACCP 小组（如果有必要的话，可以组织多个 HACCP 小组）。HACCP 小组应该负责 HACCP 体系的建立、执行和维护。企业必须能够证明 HACCP 小组的成员具备建立、执行和维持 HACCP 体系所需的所有相关的知识、专业技术以及各种所需的多种学科能力。应进行定义和文件记录 HACCP 小组所有成员需具备的包括专业技术在内的最低的资格条件。此外，小组成员的分工（包括任务、职责和权力）都应该形成文件。不论什么时候，当至少两个 HACCP 小组集合时，就应该指定一个协调人负责协调 HACCP 体系的建立、执行和维护。

⑤ Resources

资源

The food business operator shall examine the requests and provide, in a timely manner, all the resources needed by the HACCP team(s) to develop, implement and maintain the HACCP system. When corrective actions, verification procedures or customers indicate that operational improvements are necessary, the food business operator shall examine the issues and provide appropriate resources to ensure food safety.

食品企业经营者必须及时掌握和提供建立、运行和维护 HACCP 体系所需的所有资源。当纠正措施、验证过程或者是顾客认为生产水平有待提高时，管理者应该审查相关的问题，并提供适当的资源来保证食品安全。

⑥ Management Review

管理评审

The food business operator shall review the HACCP system at planned intervals, of no more than 12 months, to ensure continuing suitability, adequacy and effectiveness. The review shall evaluate the need for changes to the HACCP system, including product safety, policy and objectives. The review shall provide evidence of the commitment to improve the HACCP system and its performance.

食品企业经营者应该以不超过 12 个月的计划间隔对 HACCP 体系进行评审，以保证体系的持续适宜、充分、有效。评审应该评估 HACCP 体系是否有变更的需要，包括产品的安全、方针和目标。评审应该提供改善 HACCP 体系和执行情况承诺的证明。

(2) Product Information

产品信息

① Product Characteristics

产品特性

Each product (or a group of similar products) shall be fully specified and documented, including its sensitivity to and potential for safety risks. This description of the safety of the product shall encompass the food chain, ranging from raw materials used to the distribution of the finished products. The traceability of the raw materials up to and including final supply shall be described.

每个产品（或者一组相似的产品）都应该有足够详细的产品描述和文件，包括它对安全风险的敏感性和潜在的安全风险。产品安全性的描述应该覆盖整个食品链，范围涉及从使用的原材料到最终产品的销售。应描述原材料直到最终供应的可追溯性。

An extensive specification of the end products is required to ensure a comprehensive assessment of the food safety procedures.

为了确保对食品安全程序的全面评估，需要对最终产品进行详尽的规范说明。

② Intended Use

预期用途

The intended use of the product shall be identified and documented since it has a direct influence on the required product characteristics.

产品的预期用途对所需的产品特性有直接影响，因此应加以识别并形成文件。

The intended use of the product shall be continually reviewed; relevant legislation and regulations shall be documented. When necessary, the product characteristics and manufacturing processes may need to be adapted to conform to special legislation. Information on the label, including directions for use, may also need to be adapted. These changes shall be recorded.

应该经常评估产品的预期用途，相关的立法和规章应该形成文件。必要时，为符合特定的法律可能需要调节产品特性和生产工艺。标签上的信息，包括使用说明，也需要与相关法律相适应。以上内容，当发生变化时都需要进行记录。

(3) Process Information

过程信息

① Flow Diagrams

流程图

The food business operator shall make available a complete and actual description of the operation in the form of flow diagrams (process steps) and layouts (production facilities). When applying HACCP to a given operation, consideration shall be given to steps preceding and follow the specified operation. These descriptions shall be drawn up and verified by the HACCP team.

食品企业经营者应该以流程图（过程步骤）和规划设计（生产设备）的形式制定一套完整真实的操作规范。当对一个给定的操作步骤应用 HACCP 体系时，应该考虑该操作步骤前后的相关步骤。这些描述应由 HACCP 小组拟订和验证。

② Layout

规划

All facilities which are part of the infrastructure of the food business, such as the production lines, storage areas and personnel facilities , shall be depicted in a layout plan.

所有设施作为食品企业基础设施中的一部分，例如生产线、贮藏区域和个人设施，都应该在平面图中描绘。

③ Control and Verification of Process Information

过程信息的控制和验证

Prior to the execution of changes in the production process and layout that could adversely affect food safety, these changes shall be reported to the HACCP team in order to evaluate potential hazards to food safety and take preventive actions accordingly.

在生产工艺和布局变化可能对食品安全产生不利影响之前，应将可能产生的变化报知 HACCP 小组，由 HACCP 小组来评估由此而产生的对食品安全的潜在危害并采取相应的预防措施。

In any case the accuracy and actuality of the flow diagrams and layout shall be verified by the HACCP team for compliance with the documented situation. This verification shall be repeated periodically (at least annually) in order to identify and document modifications to the process installation and layout. These periodic verifications shall be part of the verification procedure.

无论如何，流程图和规划的准确性、真实性都应该由 HACCP 小组来验证其与文件体系的一致性。验证应该周期性（至少一年一次）地重复进行，以确定并记录过程装置和布局的更改情况。周期性的验证是验证程序的一部分。

(4) Pre-requisite Program

必备程序

The food business operator shall make available a complete and actual description of the pre-requisite program (PRP) of the organization. The procedures belonging to the PRP shall be well established (appropriately specified and documented), fully operational and integrated in the HACCP system, and be verified.

食品企业经营者应该制订一套切实可行的、完整的企业必备程序（PRP）。属于 PRP 一部分的规程应建立完善(适当的规定和文件)，充分运行并融入 HACCP 体系，并得到验证。

The Codex General Principles of Food Hygiene lay a firm foundation for ensuring food safety and suitability. The food business operator shall decide which food hygiene principles, good manufacturing practices and food legislation must be included in the PRP of the organization.

食品法典委员会制定的《食品卫生一般原则》为确保食品的安全性和适宜性奠定了坚实的基础。食品经营者应该确定将食品卫生学原理、良好生产规范和食品法规中的哪些内容必须纳入企业的必备程序里。

(5) Hazard Analysis

危害分析

The food business operator (HACCP team) shall identify, analyse and evaluate all potential (biological, chemical and physical) hazards that can have an adverse effect on the safety of the products. Whenever the food business operation changes in a manner that could adversely affect food safety, all relevant steps of the Hazard Analysis shall be up-dated.

企业经营者（HACCP 小组）应该能够鉴别、分析、评估所有潜在的对产品安全产生不利影响的（生物的、化学的和物理的）危害。无论何时，当食品经营变化对食品安全产生不利影响时，应更新危害分析的所有相关步骤。

① Hazard Identification

危害的识别

The food business operator (HACCP team) shall identify and register all potential (biological, chemical and physical) hazards that can have an adverse effect on the safety of the products. The identification shall include all aspects of the operations within the scope of the HACCP system.

企业经营者（HACCP 小组）应该能够鉴别并登记所有潜在的对食品安全产生不良影响的（生物的、化学的、物理的）危害。鉴别应该涵盖 HACCP 体系范围内的所有操作。

The operations to be evaluated include all products, all processes and the pre-requisite program of the legal owner of the products. For service organizations (not legal owner, but holder of the products), the hazard identification and analysis is restricted to the services provided, for instance, cold/frozen storage, packaging and transport.

评估应包括所有产品、所有过程和产品合法所有者的必备程序。对服务机构（不是法定所有人的，而是产品持有者）、危害的鉴别和分析主要限定在提供服务的环节，例如，冷藏/冻藏、包装及运输。

② HACCP Analysis (risk)

HACCP 分析（风险评估）

The food business operator (HACCP team) shall conduct a HACCP analysis to identify which hazards are of such a nature that their elimination or reduction and control at acceptable levels is essential to the production of safe food. The results of the analysis shall be documented, including the concepts and principles utilized for determining/estimating the risks.

食品企业经营者(HACCP 小组)须进行 HACCP 分析，以确定哪些危害的性质足以使其消除或减少及控制在可接受的水平，这对安全食品的生产至关重要。分析的结果，包括对风险识别和评估时应用的概念和原理，应该形成文件。

The food business operator shall define permissible levels of risks. These levels (concentrations, product or process criteria) must comply, as a minimum, with legal requirements. When conducting the HACCP analysis, practical experiences, experimental data, professional literature, etc., shall be taken into account and be documented.

食品经营者应确定可接受的风险水平。风险水平（浓度、产品或工艺标准）必须与法规要求的最低限度相符。当进行 HACCP 的危害分析时，必须充分考虑并记录实践经验、实验数据、专业文献等，并形成文件。

(6) Control Measures

控制措施

The HACCP team shall identify and document the control measures that are to be applied or implemented when the hazard identification and HACCP analysis concludes that the risk of an identified hazard is significant and needs to be eliminated or reduced and controlled at an acceptable level.

当危害识别和 HACCP 分析得出识别的危害风险较大，需要消除或减少并控制在可接受的水平时，HACCP 小组应该鉴别并记录运用和执行的控制措施。

The HACCP team shall conduct an assessment of every step in the process, for example with the use of a decision tree. The assessment shall be based on, among other things, the differing expertise within the team and shall utilize external and internal information. For each step, including all products, all processes and all parts of the Pre-Requisite Program， the assessed aspects shall be identified. The reasons for deciding whether it is a CCP (critical control point) or not, shall be documented and traceable.

HACCP 小组应该对过程的所有步骤进行评估，例如决策树的使用。评估应基于团队内部不同的专业知识，除此之外，还应利用外部和内部信息。对每一步骤，包括所有产品、过程和必备程序的评估都必须进行确认。对关键控制点的确定理由应该进行记录并可追溯。

More than one control measure may be required to control a hazard and more than one hazard may be controlled by a control measure. Control measures shall be classified as specific or general control measures.

控制一个危害可能需要多个控制措施，一个控制措施有时也可以控制多个危害。控制措施应该分为一般控制措施和特殊控制措施。

① Specific Control Measures

特殊控制措施

Control measures related to CCP's shall be classified as specific control measures. Specific control measures are actions or activities, often measurable in terms of physical or chemical parameters such as temperature, time, moisture, pH, Aw, available chlorine, and sensory parameters such as visual appearance and texture.

与关键控制点相关的控制措施应该归类为特殊控制措施。特殊控制措施所采取的具体的行动或行为，常常是根据一些化学的或物理的参数，例如温度、时间、湿度、pH、水分活度、有效氯，以及外观和质地等一些感官参数来测量的。

Specific control measures based on subjective parameters, as in the case of visual inspection of a product, process, handling, etc., shall be supported by instructions or specifications, education and training.

基于主观参数的特殊控制措施，如对产品、工艺、操作等的目视检查，应辅以说明书或规范，对操作人员进行培训。

Specific control measures shall be monitored, be provided with corrective actions, validated and verified (see subsequent paragraphs).

应该对特殊控制措施进行监控，采取纠正措施，确认并验证（参见后面的章节）。

② General Control Measures

一般控制措施

Control measures not related to CCP's shall be classified as general control measures. General control measures are actions or activities which are part of the prerequisite program. In general, these measures will achieve control at acceptable levels.

与关键控制点不相关的控制措施应该归类为一般控制措施。一般控制措施中的行为活动是必备程序的一部分。一般来说，这些控制措施能够将危害控制在可接受水平之内。

General control measures shall be documented in specifications (raw materials, products, process, etc.), instructions (process, control, operations) and procedures or plans, e.g. purchase plan, hygiene plan (including personal), maintenance plan, cleaning and disinfection plan, and supported by education and training plans, operator-specific aspects, supervision, etc.

一般控制措施应该以规范（原材料、产品、过程等）、指令（过程、控制、操作）和程序或者是计划，例如，采购计划、卫生计划（包括个人卫生）、维护保养计划、清洁和消毒计划等形式记录下来，以及通过教育和培训计划、详细的操作、监督管理等内容进行支撑。

General control measures shall be validated in order to demonstrate the proper functioning of (the specific part of) the PRP and will subsequently be approved by the HACCP team.

为证明必备程序（细节部分）的正确运行，一般控制措施应该进行确认，然后由HACCP 小组批准后方可实施。

The effectiveness in controlling the identified hazards of the general control measures shall be verified at pre-defined, regular intervals.

对已识别的危害所采取的一般控制措施的效果，应该预确认并定期验证。

(7) Parameters and Critical Limits

参数和关键限值

① Critical process and product parameters

关键过程和产品参数

For each specific control measure related to a CCP the process and/or product parameters must be identified which are meant to demonstrate that control at the step is being maintained.

对于每个与关键控制点相关特殊控制措施的过程和/或产品参数都必须认真鉴定，从而证明该步骤得到了持续控制。

The food business operator shall document the parameters to be applied as well as the arguments for using these parameters.

食品经营者应该记录这些运用的参数以及运用这些参数的论据。

② Target values, action-limit values and critical limits

目标值、操作限值和关键限值

Further, the food business operator shall define for the various parameters the critical limit which must be met at all times during the operation. Also, normal operational target values are indicated for the various parameters as well as the action-limit values which indicate when intervention in the operation is required in order to continuously meet the critical limits.

此外，食品经营者应该详细定义不同参数的关键限值，保证在每次操作中都达到要求。另外，明确了各种参数的正常操作目标值以及操作限值，为了持续满足关键限值，何时需要对操作进行干预。

When determining the critical limits and the deduced action-limit and target values, the requirements of the relevant legislation and regulations and/or internal risk analysis for the safety of foodstuffs must be considered as (contractual) requirements.

在确定关键限值、推断的作用限值和目标值时，相关法律法规和/或内部食品安全风险分析的要求必须被视为(合同的)要求。

The food business operator must establish and maintain adequate provisions/procedures for the monitoring of the target values and the corrective actions to be executed whenever the critical limits are exceeded.

为监测目标值，食品企业经营者必须建立和维护适当的规定/程序，并执行超过关键限值时的纠正措施。

In addition, the effectiveness of the established parameters and operational values shall be validated to ensure food safety.

另外，为保证食品安全，企业应确定设立参数和操作限值的有效性。

(8) Monitoring and Measuring

监控和测量

The food business operator shall establish and maintain a monitoring (measuring) system for effective and efficient control of the Critical Control Points. The system includes all planned measurements, observations and analysis of the control parameters determining that the CCP's are under control.

食品经营者应建立并维护一套监控(测量)系统，对关键控制点进行有效、高效的控制。系统应当包括有计划地测量、观察以及控制参数的分析，从而确定关键控制点处于控制之中。

The justification for the development of the monitoring system shall be documented. The monitoring (measuring) devices shall be identified. The methodology of measurement and/or the instructions for measuring and recording of measurements shall be documented. In addition, the method for establishing the reliability of the measurements and/or the equipment (calibration) shall be documented.

建立监控系统的依据应该形成文件，监控（测量）装置应该加以标识。测量方法和/或测量说明、测量记录都形成文件。此外，建立测量值和设备(校准)可靠性的方法应该有文件记录。

(9) Corrective Actions

纠正措施

For each Critical Control Point, the food business operator shall document the corrective actions to be taken in case an action-limit value or critical limit is exceeded. The procedure will include the process to investigate the cause of the deviation.

对每个关键控制点，食品企业应该将超出操作限值或关键限值时所采取的纠正措施记录在案。纠正措施应当包括对偏差原因调查的过程。

A documented justification for the corrective action to be taken shall be available, including the responsibilities and authorities of the personnel which are involved. The actions to be taken must be established in advance. This could also involve the formation of a so-called 'emergency team'. This team shall evaluate the causes of the deviation and shall decide which additional preventive actions are to be taken.

所采取的纠正措施的记录文件中的合理解释应该是可用的，包含相关人员的职责和权限。必须预先建立需采取的纠正行动。这可能也涉及组建一个所谓的“应急小组”。小组成员应评估发生偏差的原因，并决定采用哪些额外的预防措施。

The food business operator shall also establish arrangements that provide procedures for recall of the products from the market place and/or from end consumers. Proper product identification and a “tracing & tracking” system shall be operational.

企业还应该建立从市场或者终端消费者手中召回产品的程序的安排，应有适当的产品标示和“追溯＆跟踪”体系。

All corrective actions taken, the causes and consequences, and the individuals involved in the corrective actions shall be recorded.

所采取的所有纠正措施，起因和结果以及涉及的人员都应该记录在册。

The effectiveness of the corrective actions, for both the process and the product, shall be evaluated.

应当对纠正措施中过程和产品的有效性进行评估。

(10) Validation

确认

Validation is not a part of verification, but a separate activity prior to authorizing the HACCP plan.

确认不是验证的一部分，而是在批准 HACCP 计划之前的一个独立的活动。

The objective of validation is to ensure that the hazards originally identified by the HACCP team are complete and correct and that they will be effectively controlled under the proposed plan. To meet the objectives of validation , it is necessary to review the effectiveness of the supporting evidence used in the HACCP study as well as the general and specific control measures, the monitoring system and corrective actions. Each time the food business operation changes in a manner that could adversely affect food safety , this review shall be up-dated.

确认的目的是保证由 HACCP 小组做出的最初的危害识别是完整而准确的，并处于提议计划的有效控制下。为了达到确认的目的，就必须对 HACCP 计划中的支撑证据、一般和特殊控制措施、监控系统和纠正措施的有效性进行审查。每次食品经营发生可能对食品安全产生不利影响的变化时，应更新审查。

To ensure the absence of bias, the food business operator shall form a validation team. The validation team may include members of the HACCP team, but must also include independent reviewers e.g. from within the food business operation, who have not been directly involved in the establishment of the HACCP plan.

为了保证没有偏见，食品企业应该有确认小组。确认小组可以包括 HACCP 小组成员，但也必须包括独立的审核员，例如，从事食品企业内部经营的、没有直接参与 HACCP 计划建立的人员。

Food business operators may have produced safe food for many years before the introduction of the HACCP system. Therefore, historical results from on-line Quality Control monitoring, end product testing, customer or consumer complaints may be used as evidence when validating HACCP plans. It is important to note that the data must be quantifiable and objective if it is to be useful.

企业在引入 HACCP 体系之前可能已经生产安全食品许多年了。因此，在线质量控制的监控、成品的检测、消费者的投诉等，都可以用作 HACCP 计划确认的依据。如果这些数据可以使用的话，要注意这些数据的量化和客观性是很重要的。

The composition of the validation team and the activities undertaken shall be clearly documented. The food business operator shall demonstrate satisfactory completion of validation.

确认小组的组成以及所采取的行动都应该以文件形式清楚地加以说明。食品企业经营者应该证明确认工作圆满完成。

(11) Verification

验证

The food business operator shall establish, document and implement procedures for verification of the HACCP system. The main purpose of verification is to determine compliance with the specifications of the HACCP system and to confirm that the HACCP system is working effectively through the application of (auditing) methods, procedures, tests (including random sampling and analysis) and other evaluations, in addition to monitoring.

食品企业经营者应该建立、记录并执行 HACCP 体系的验证程序。验证的主要目的是确定其是否符合 HACCP 体系的规范，并通过(审核)方法、程序、测试(包括随机抽样和分析)和其他评价，以及监测，确认 HACCP 体系有效地工作。

The food business operator shall plan an internal audit scheme, taking into consideration the status and importance of the processes and areas to be audited, as well as the results of previous audits. The audit criteria, scope, frequency and methods shall be defined.

食品经营者应策划内部审核方案，考虑待审核过程和领域的现状和重要性，以及以往审核的结果。应确定审核标准、范围、频率和方法。

Selection of auditors and the conduct of audits shall ensure objectivity and impartiality of the audit process. Auditors shall not audit their own work.

审核员的选择和审核的实施应确保审核过程的客观性和公正性。审核员不得审核本部门的工作。

The responsibilities and requirements for planning and conducting audits, for reporting results and maintaining records shall be defined in a documented procedure.

策划和实施审核、报告结果和保持记录的职责以及要求应在形成文件的程序中加以规定。

Management review: The food business operator shall review and evaluate the results of the entire verification process at planned intervals, of no more than 12 months. Therefore, the frequency of verification and internal audits shall be such that the food business operator can ensure continuing suitability, adequacy and effectiveness of the HACCP-based Food Safety System. Some requirements are to be verified at a higher frequency than other requirements. For instance, the effective control of CCP's may be evaluated with a frequency of at least twice a year, whereas a frequency of once a year may be sufficient to verify the actuality of process lines and layout.

管理评审:食品企业经营者应该以不超过 12 个月的计划间隔对整个验证过程的结果进行审核和评估。因此验证和内审的频率应确保食品经营者基于 HACCP 食品安全保证体系的持续适宜性、充分性和有效性。有些需求需要比其他需求更频繁地进行验证。例如，关键控制点控制的有效性应该在一年之内最少评估两次，然而，工艺路线和布局现状一年只要验证一次就足够了。

The food business operator shall collect and analyse the resulting data to evaluate where improvement is needed.

企业经营者应该收集、分析结果数据并评估需要改进之处。

The food business operator shall ensure that preventive actions are taken without undue delay to eliminate the causes of (potential) non-conformities in order to prevent recurrence (occurrence). The preventive actions shall be appropriate to the effects of the (potential) non-conformities encountered. The effectiveness of the preventive actions taken shall be validated.

食品企业应该确保及时采取预防措施以消除（潜在的）不合格的原因，从而防止其重复发生。预防措施应该与遇到的（潜在）不合格的因素相匹配。采取的预防措施的有效性还应该得到确认。

(12) Documentation and Records

文件和记录

① Documents and Document Control

文件和文件管制

The food business operator shall establish a documented HACCP system and shall maintain the HACCP system and corresponding documentation in order to ensure conformity with the requirements of this specification and the applicable legislation and regulations.

食品经营者应建立形成文件的 HACCP 体系，并保持 HACCP 体系和相应的文件，以确保符合本规范和适用法律法规的要求。

Documentation should be appropriate to the nature and size of operation.

文件应该与经营本身的特性和规模相适应。

② Records

记录

Efficient and accurate record-keeping is essential to the application of a HACCP System.

高效准确的记录保存对于 HACCP 系统的应用至关重要。

Records shall be established and maintained to provide evidence of conformity with the requirements and with the effective operation of the HACCP-based Food Safety System. Records shall remain legible, readily identifiable and retrievable. A documented procedure shall be established to define the controls needed for identification, storage, protection, retrieval, retention time and disposal of records.

应该建立并保持记录，以提供符合要求和基于 HACCP 食品安全体系高效运行的证据。记录应保持清晰，易于识别和检索。应该建立一套程序文件，就记录的鉴定、保存、保护、补救、保存时间及处理等需要控制的环节做出明确的规定。

4.3.3 Homework

课后作业

4.3.3.1 Sentence Translation

句子翻译

(1) Original Sentences

原句

① The food operation shall assure that the appropriate product, specific knowledge and expertise is available for the development of an effective HACCP plan. This may best be accomplished by assembling a multi-disciplinary team.

② The scope of the HACCP plan shall be identified. The scope shall describe which segment of the food chain is involved and the general classes of hazards to be addressed.

③ The HACCP team shall create the flow diagram. The flow diagram shall cover all steps in the operation. When applying HACCP to a given operation, consideration shall be given to steps preceding and follow the specified operation.

④ List all potential hazards associated with each step, conduct a hazard analysis, and consider any measures to control identified hazards. The HACCP team shall list all hazards which may reasonably be expected to occur at each step, from primary production, processing, manufacture and distribution until the point of consumption.

⑤ If a hazard has been identified at a step where control is necessary for safety, and no control measure exists at that step or any other, then the product or process shall be modified at that step, or at any earlier or later stage, to include a control measure.

⑥ Critical limits must be specified and validated, if possible, for each Critical Control Point. In some cases more than one critical limit will be elaborated at a particular step.

⑦ Managers and supervisors of food processes shall have the necessary knowledge of food hygiene principles and practices to be able to judge potential risks and take the necessary action to remedy deficiencies.

⑧ Food handlers shall have the necessary knowledge and skills to enable them to handle food hygienically. Those who handle strong cleaning chemicals or other potentially hazardous chemicals shall be instructed in safe handling techniques.

⑨ Cleaning chemicals shall be stored, where necessary, separately from food, in clearly identified containers to avoid the risk of (malicious or accidental) contamination of food.

⑩ Specific corrective actions must be developed for each CCP in the HACCP system in order to deal with deviations when they occur. The actions must ensure that the CCP has been brought under control.

(2) Translations

翻译

① 食品经营者应该确保有恰当的产品、特定的知识和专业技术，从而建立和实施一个有效的 HACCP 计划。最好通过组建一个多学科的团队来完成。

② 明确 HACCP 计划的范围。范围应该描述所涉及的食品链的哪个部分以及要处理的危害的一般类别。

③ HACCP 小组要绘制流程图。流程图应涵盖所有的操作步骤。在将 HACCP 应用于特定操作时，应考虑特定操作之前和之后的步骤。

④ 列出与每个步骤相关的所有潜在危害，进行危害分析，并考虑控制已识别危害的任何措施。HACCP 小组应列出从初级生产、加工、制造和分销到消费的每个步骤中可能合理发生的所有危害。

⑤ 如果在某一步骤上发现了对安全有必要进行控制的危害，而在该步骤或任何其他步骤上都不存在控制措施，则应在该步骤或任何早或晚的阶段修改产品或过程，使其包括控制措施。

⑥ 如有可能，每个关键控制点的关键限值必须明确并进行确认。在某些情况下，在某一特定步骤中将阐述一个以上的关键限值。

⑦ 食品加工的监督管理者应当具备必要的食品卫生原则和实践知识，能够判断潜在的风险，并采取必要的措施补救缺陷。

⑧ 食品操作人员应当具备卫生操作食品的必要知识与技能，那些使用强效清洁化学药品与有潜在危害化学品的操作人员应进行安全操作技术指导。

⑨ 清洁化学品根据需要应与食物分开存放，存放于有明确标识的容器内，以避免(恶意或意外)污染食物的风险。

⑩ 必须为 HACCP 体系中的每个关键控制点制定具体的纠偏措施，以便在偏差发生时进行处理。这些措施必须确保关键控制点处于控制之中。

(3) 翻译文中划线句子

4.3.3.2 Common Sentence Patterns of Scientific Papers 科技论文常见句型

① 前言中阐明目的

常用句型：Our task (job/mission/etc.) in/of this article (paper/work) is to …

The purpose (objective/goal/) of this study (research) is to …

【例句】The purpose of this study is to investigate the relationship between changes in leakage of the seeds and seed ageing and to search for an indicator of seed vigor based on it.

本研究旨在研究种子渗漏变化与种子老化的关系，并在此基础上寻找种子活力的标志。

② 前言说明讨论范围、焦点

常用句型：This study deals mainly with ...

The emphasis of this paper is put on ...

【例句】This study mainly deals with the influence of working memory capacity on the generation of predictive inference during text reading.

本研究主要探讨阅读过程中工作记忆容量对预测推理形成的影响。

③ 前言中表示有待解决的问题

常用句型：The problem to be solved is ...

The main problem seems to be ...

【例句】But the main problem seems to be demand for goods and energy, as lorries carrying coal crawl endlessly towards the city.

但主要问题似乎是对商品和能源的需求，因为运送煤炭的卡车没完没了地驶向城市。

④ 表示试验结果的句型：

常用句型：The experiments reported here showed (suggested /indicated) a correlation between ...

The highest (lowest/best) yield was obtained (came from/caused) the treatment of ...

The yield was highest with the treatment of ...

【例句】The experiments showed that the conversion ratio was concerned with reaction temperature, concentration of alkali and reaction time.

实验表明，转化率与反应温度、碱液浓度以及反应时间有关。

⑤ 表示结论的句型：

常用句型：From the experiment, it can be concluded that ...

The problem requires further research (study/investigation) in this area.

【例句】Compared to other methods, it can be concluded that the application of the fuzzy matter-element model method for evaluating region water environment is feasible and reliable.

并与其他方法加以比较，表明应用模糊物元模型法评价区域水环境是可行和可靠的。

⑥ 图表、公式的说明

常用句型：As shown in Table 1

We can find in Figure 1 that ...

【例句】As shown in Table E, this year the percentage of hoteliers is slowly but surely creeping back up.

如表 E 所示，今年酒店经营者的比例正在缓慢地回升。

⑦ 前言中在叙述前人成果之后，如何提出一种新方法或新方向。

常用句型：However, little information (little attention/little work/little data/little research......) (or few studies/few investigations/few researchers/few attempts......) (or no/none of these studies...) has (have) been done on (focused on/attempted to/conducted/investigated/studied (with respect to)) 。

【例句】However, there is little information on how different environmental conditions and materials affect H5N1's survival.

然而，关于不同的环境条件和材料如何影响 H5N1 的生存的信息很少。

⑧ 前言中研究方法和方向与前人一样时，如何强调自己工作。

常用句型：We need to (aim to, have to) provide more documents (data, records, studies).

Further studie is still necessary (essential)…

【例句】However, you still need to provide more configuration data to achieve the deployment goals listed earlier.

但是，您仍然需要提供更多的配置数据来实现前面列出的部署目标。

⑨ 连接词与逻辑

常用连接词：However, also, in addition, consequently, afterwards, moreover, furthermore, further, although, unlike, in contrast, similarly, unfortunately, alternatively, parallel results, in order to, despite, for example, compared with, other results, thus, therefore……

【例句】Compared with Europeans, Americans are more likely to receive medication if they have heart disease, high cholesterol, lung disease or osteoporosis.

与欧洲人相比，美国人如果患有心脏病、高胆固醇、肺病或骨质疏松症，更有可能接受药物治疗。

⑩ 讨论部分中的说明论证

常用词汇：Support, provide, indicate, identify, find, demonstrate, confirm

Chapter 5 Writing
第5章 写作

5.1 Translation Methods and Techniques of Food Science and Technology English
5.1 食品科技英语翻译方法和技巧

5.1.1 Glossary Analysis
专业词汇分析

伴随着不断涌现的新发现、发明与创造成果，新的科技词语随时在产生，仅化学专业词汇已增至数十万。科技工作者为了表达这些新物质与新概念，除了创造出全新的科技词汇，如基因、克隆、飞秒等之外，绝大多数均通过派生与合成新的词语来实现。

在食品科技英语中，合成词和派生词等也不容忽视。许多单词是由词缀和词根构成的。通过拆解单词，识别其词缀和词根，可把握其意义，并能够领略英语单词的构造奥妙。掌握构词技巧可极大地减轻记忆单词的负担，若真正领悟并进而拓展这种方法所蕴含的思路，将能触类旁通。

将两个独立的单词合并一起，这种构词法称为"合成词构词法"。通过不同词的合成可以构成名词、动词、形容词等新的合成词（compound word）。

名词	+	名词	cheese-cloth shelf-life dough-nut butter-fat lemon-drop blast-room	干酪包布，一种干粗布 货架期、货架寿命 面团坚果 乳脂肪 柠檬糖 鼓风室

续表

名词	+	形容词	water-soluble gas-tight heat-sensitive enzyme-resistant oxygen-impermeable	水溶性的 气密性的 热敏性的 酶抗性的 隔氧的
名词	+	动名词	photo-copying mouth-watering film-forming milk-handling water-holding	复印 润口的 成膜的 乳处理的 持水的
名词	+	动词过去分词	center-filled candy-coated spray-dried alkali-modified enzyme-catalyzed ion-exchanged	夹心的 糖衣的 喷雾干燥的 碱法改性的 酶促催化的 离子交换的
名词	+	动词	mouth-feel essence-recovery air-flow mold-release	口感 芳香物回收 空气流 脱模
形容词	+	名词	counter-current high-speed semi-solid low-viscosity double-helical macro-ingredient	逆流的 高速的 半固体的 低黏度的 双螺旋的 宏量组分
动词 ing 形式	+	名词	linking-device boiling-water	连接装置 沸水
形容词	+	动名词	fast-setting super-cooling dehydro-freezing deep-chilling	快凝 过冷 脱水冷冻 深冷
动词过去分词	+	名词	superheated steam fluidized-bed reduced-fat scraped-surface	过热蒸汽 流化床 降脂 刮板式

续表

副词	+	名词	up-date post-mortem under-season by-product	更新 宰后 欠味 副产物
介词	+	动词	through-put off-cut in-container off-flavor on-line	吞吐量 下脚料 灌装后 异味 在线
副词或形容词	+	动词过去分词	immediately-connected weak-bodied under-blanched	直接连接地 体弱的 漂烫不足的

派生词（derived word）指在已存在的某个词根基础上加上前缀或者后缀从而组成一个新词，通过派生法组成的词在科技英语词汇中占大多数。前缀或者后缀词数量很大，因而掌握一定的前缀和后缀的词素对掌握食品科技英语单词有很大的帮助。

一般情况下，词根加上前缀不会改变词性，只会改变该单词的词义。

有些前缀表示数量多寡、大小，比如 oligosaccharide 低聚糖、寡糖，polysaccharide 多糖，monosaccharide 单糖，polyalcohol 多元醇，diploe 偶极，multiple 多样的。

有些前缀表示否定的意思，比如 im-，in-，ir-，un-，mis，non，如：impossible 不可能的，insoluble 不溶解的，irregularity 不规则，unsaturated 不饱和的，misinterpretation 误释，non-homogenized 未经均质的。

有的前缀表示重复的意思，如 re-: refreshment 提神，精神恢复。有的前缀表示去除的意思，比如 depolymerization 解聚、debranching 去枝、dissolution 溶解、dehydrate 脱水。有的前缀表示过度、超过的意思，比如 supersaturated 过饱和、overconversion 过度转化。有的前缀表示一些专业领域的意思，比如 biopolymer 生物聚合物、electrostatic 静电的等。有的前缀表示上下级属性的意思，如 subion 次离子、subnetwork 子网络等。有些表示相互关系 inter-: intervening 介于中间的、interdependence 相互依赖等。有些会将词根构成动词，表示“使”的意思，如 en-: enlarge 使增大、encode 编码、enforce 使生效、encapsulation 胶囊化等。

通常情况下，词根加上后缀就会改变词性，但是原词义基本不会变化。当然也存在少数改变词根原词义的后缀，因而后缀多以词性来区分。有形容词性后缀，如-al: graphical 图解的；-able: applicable 适用的、objectionable 令人不快的、反感的；-less: odorless 无臭的、colorless 无色；-y: auxiliary 辅助的；-ic: electronic 电子的、dynamic 动力的等。有动词后缀，如-fy: satisfy 使满意、specify 指定、verify 核实、simplify 简化等。有副词词缀，如-ly: additionally 此外、permanently 永久地、arbitrarily 任意地等。也有名词词缀，如-ment: measurement 测量、nourishment 滋养、营养；-tion: nutrition 营养、communication 通信；-ant: antioxidant；-ability: traceability 溯源性，可追溯性等。

5.1.2 Sentence Translation

语句翻译

食品科技英语翻译不是科技专业词汇和英语语法的简单结合，对译者有很高的要求，需要比较系统地了解食品科技英语的特点、翻译方法和翻译技巧。

食品科技英语除具有普通英语的特征外，还具有用词严谨准确、陈述客观朴素、内容精练确切、时代感强以及文体国际化等特点。食品科技英语的翻译有别于其他英语文体的翻译，必须遵循其特定的翻译标准，采用特定的翻译方法和技巧。

5.1.2.1 Language Structural Features of Food Science and Technology English 食品科技英语中语言结构的特点

(1) Enriched by Impersonal Sentences

大量使用无人称句

由于食品科技英语文章所表述和探讨的都是客观事实或者发现等，主要是为了介绍或者说明这些事实或者发现本身，而不是为了突出强调这些事实或者发现是由哪些人或者组织发现和研究出来的，因而文章中多采用无人称句，物称的应用多于人称的应用。例如：Hold the casing back a little so that there are as few air bubbles as possible in the compact coil. “将肠衣往回拿一点，这样就可以使塞紧的香肠卷中的气泡尽量少。”

(2) Frequent Use of Passive Sentences

广泛使用被动句

因为科技文章侧重叙事推理，强调客观准确，尽量使用第三人称叙述，采用被动语态。避免因使用主动语态句的主观性而带来的弊端。The eggs are likely to be washed before they are broken. “打蛋前一般都先进行洗蛋。”

(3) Frequent Use of Nominalized Structures

经常使用名词化结构

食品科技英语文章中，在普通英语中用动词表达的内容在科技英语中常用名词表达，常用一个名词词组“表示动作意义的名词+of+名词+修饰语”代替一个句子，即名词化结构。例如：Archimedes first discovered the principle of displacement of water by solid bodies. “阿基米德最先发现了固体排水的原理。” 句中 of displacement of water by solid bodies 是一个介词短语结构，一方面代替了同位语从句（that water was displaced by solid bodies），另一方面强调了 displacement 这一事实。

(4) Frequent Use of Non-finite Verbs to Replace Clauses or Coordinate Clauses

常使用非限定性动词代替从句或并列分句

食品科技文章要求行文简练、结构紧凑，为此常常使用非限定性动词代替各种从句或并列分句，达到精简句子结构的目的。例如: To be a suitable substrate to support growth of micro-organisms, a food must have free water available for the micro-organisms. （如果要成

为支持微生物生长的适宜基质，食品就必须有可供微生物利用的游离水）。在上述的例句中，动词不定式短语 To be...of micro-organisms 作目的状语，代替了目的状语从句 If it is a suitable substrate ...of micro-organisms。

(5) Frequent Use of Postpositive Attributive

广泛使用后置定语

在食品科技文章中，由于对语言简练和内容准确要求较高，所以后置定语经常被使用。过去分词短语、不定式短语、介词短语、形容词及形容词短语均可作后置定语。例如: The estimated beef yield (in pounds), adequate to feed one individual for one year, from 10 acres of land devoted to raising cattle.（10 英亩❶专用于养牛的土地，预计它所产的牛肉（磅）足供一人一年食用。）在本句中，分词短语 devoted to raising cattle 作定语，修饰 10 acres of land。动词不定式短语 to feed one individual for one year 作定语，修饰 beef。又如: Even so, yields of both protein and of essential amino acids per acre of cultivated land are several times greater from corn when the seed is used directly as food rather than from animals fed the same amount of corn.（即使如此，当把玉米直接作为食物用时，每英亩耕地所获得的蛋白质和必需氨基酸得率均比来自同量玉米喂饲动物的得率要高出好几倍。）其中，介词短语 from corn ...as food 作后置定语，修饰主语 yields ...cultivated land。

(6) More Long Sentences and Complicated Structures

长句多，结构复杂

为了表述一个复杂概念，使之逻辑严密、结构紧凑，科技英语文章中经常使用结构复杂的长句。由于句子很长，常常带有短语、独立成分、后置修饰语、非限定性动词结构，以及各种从句，句子呈扩展型。因此，在翻译时，首先要对长句进行语法分析，弄清原文的语法结构，找出句子的中心内容，由几部分组成，连接它们的纽带及其修饰成分；再进行逻辑分析，分析各部分之间的逻辑关系，思维发展，分清其层次、重点及形式等，然后使用翻译方法和技巧以规范、流畅、简练的汉语表达原文的思想内容。例如: The person who seeks the answer to the question "What should eat for good nutrition?" might easily become lost in the maze of informational corridors, confused by the wealth of technical information provided by scientists or misled by simplistic answers provided by those with products to sell.（凡是渴望找到"应该吃什么才会有良好营养"这一问题答案的人也许很容易堕入复杂的知识迷宫，很容易被科学家所提供的丰富技术信息所迷惑，也很容易被售货员的三言两语弄得晕头转向。）该句是一个结构复杂的长句。主句的主语是 the person, who seeks the answer to the question "What should one eat for good nutrition ?" 为主语 the person 的定语从句，其中"What should one eat for good nutrition ?" 是 the question 的同位语从句，说明 the question, might easily become lost 及被略去 might easily become 以后的 confused 和 misled 则是主句的三个并列谓语，其动词形式都是被动语态。

❶ 1 英亩≈4046.86m^2。

5.1.2.2 Translation Methods of Food Science and Technology English 食品科技英语的翻译方法

普通英语翻译的方法包括直译与意译、增减词译法、词类转换法等，都适用于科技英语翻译中。同时，食品科技英语文献有其自身的特点，食品科技英语的翻译也应该有其独特的翻译方法和技巧。

例如: Until the factors operative in the thermal resistance of bacteria are understood, it will not be possible to control, other than by empirical means, the processes which are required for their success - the destruction of bacteria.(直到认识到这些对细菌耐热性起作用的因素之后，人们才能用经验方法以外的方法来成功地控制杀菌过程。)该句是一个结构复杂的长句。主句的形式主语是 It，其逻辑主语是不定式短语谓语 to control…of bacteria。主语的介词短语 other than by empirical means 为状语，修饰 control，the processes…of bacteria 是 control 的宾语。Until the factors…are understood 是时间状语从句，作状语修饰主句中的谓语部分 will not be possible. Which 引导的从句是定语从句，修饰 the processes. 该从句中，for their success 是状语，修饰从句谓语 require，而 the destruction of bacteria 是从句 require 的宾语。

在大多数情况下，对于科技文章中出现的，通过复合、派生等构词方式形成的技术术语，一般采用意译的方法进行翻译，而翻译的基础是对原文的思想内容有充分的理解。

例如：The term “fatis ” applicable to all triglycerides regardless of whether they are normally non-liquid or liquid at ambient temperatures. “油脂”一词适用于一切甘油三酸酯，而不论它们在室温下是固态或液态。

对于像计量单位、科技发明、材料、化学品名称等这样的技术术语，一般应使用音译法进行翻译。例如：The Maillard browning reaction occurs between a carbonyl found in a reducing sugar and an amine found in proteins and amino acids. 美拉德褐变反应发生在还原糖羰基与蛋白质和氨基酸的氨基之间。再如: cocoa 可可、ohm 欧姆、calorie 卡路里、joule 焦耳、nylon 尼龙、Vaseline 凡士林、sonar 声纳、quark 夸克、logic 逻辑等等。

对于有些技术术语来说，它们既有意译名，又有音译名，二者同时使用，翻译选择任何一个都可以。但应该注意到这样一种趋势，那就是意译逐渐取代音译。Fudge is a soft brown sweet that is made from butter, cream, and sugar. 乳脂软糖（福奇糖）是由黄油、奶油和糖制备得到的柔软的、棕色的糖果。再如：vitamin，维生素（意）/维他命（音）；jelly，凝胶糖果（意）/啫喱（音）；fondant，软糖（意）/方登糖（音）；penicillin，青霉素（意）/盘尼西林（音）；engine，发动机（意）/引擎（音）；marshmallow，棉花糖（意）/马希马洛糖（音）；laser，激光（意）/镭射（音）。

形译法也是科技词汇翻译常用的方法，此方法多用于用字母表示其外形的技术术语的翻译，可以选用近似该字母形状的汉语来翻译；也可保留原英文字母不做翻译，但保留的字母有时表示形状，有时表示概念，应注意区分。例如：T square，丁字尺；U steel，槽形钢；O ring，O 型环；A frame，A 型架；P/N region，P 区（电子不足区）/N 区（电子剩余区）；L electron，L 层电子（原子核第二层电子）。

有些技术术语在翻译中部分使用音译，部分使用意译，二者兼顾。例如：topology，拓扑学；motorcycle，摩托车；ampere meter，安培表；tannic acid，丹宁酸；neon sign，霓虹灯；Franklin antenna，富兰克林天线；chocolate，巧克力。

还有一些情况，在译文中直接用原英文，不做翻译，例如：Windows 98、Word 2000、Office star 等。

食品科技英语翻译具有其独特之处，主要表现在食品科技英语中出现的，通过复合、派生等构词方式形成的技术术语，一般采用意译，而准确的翻译要求对原文的技术内容、原理等科技因素有充分的理解，这一点比普通英语文体要求与难度更大了一些。很多科技英语术语或词汇都看似普通英语，但往往具有另外的科技领域方面的含义，翻译起来必须随行就市，不能望文生义。

总之，食品科技英语翻译既要熟悉普通英语的翻译方法和技巧，也要了解科技内涵，熟悉科技原理，掌握相关术语与准术语。

5.1.3 Homework

课后作业

Sentence Translation

句子翻译

(1) Original Sentences

原句

① Food Science has been defined as the application of physical, biological, and behavioral science to the processing and marketing of foods.

② All of these concerns fall within the realm of food science—a science that deals with the physical, chemical, and biological properties of foods as they relate to stability, cost, quality, processing, safety, nutritive value, wholesomeness, and convenience.

③ For example, conditions suitable for sustaining residual life processes are of concern to food chemists during the marketing of fresh fruits and vegetables, whereas conditions incompatible with life processes are of major interest when long-term preservation of food is attempted.

④ Having described the attributes of high-quality, safe foods, the significant chemical reactions involved in the deterioration of food, and the relationship between the two, we can now begin to consider how to apply this information to situations encountered during the storage and processing of food.

⑤ Of greater interest is the fact that the thermal conductivity of ice at 0°C is approximately four times that of water at the same temperature, indicating that ice will conduct heat energy at a much greater rate than will immobilized water (e.g., in tissue).

⑥ The highly electronegative oxygen of the water molecule can be visualized as partially drawing away the single electrons from the two covalently bonded hydrogen atoms, thereby leaving each hydrogen atom with a partial positive charge and a minimal electron shield; that is, each hydrogen atom assumes some characteristics of a bare proton.

⑦ Starch, lactose, and sucrose are digestible by humans, and they, along with D-glucose and D-fructose, and human energy sources, provide 70% ~ 80% of the calories in the human diet worldwide.

⑧ When aldoses or ketoses are heated in solution with amines, a variety of reactions ensue, producing numerous compounds, some of which are flavors, aromas, and dark-colored polymeric materials, but both reactants, disappear only slowly.

⑨ Maltose is produced during malting of grains, especially barley, and commercially by the specific enzyme-catalyzed hydrolysis of starch using β-amylase from Bacillus bacteria, although β-amylases from barley seed, soybeans, and sweet potatoes may be used.

⑩ Although gel-like or salve-like materials can be formed by high concentrations of particles (much like tomato paste), to form a true gel, the polymer molecules or aggregates of molecules must first be in solution, then partially come out of solution in junction zone regions to form the three-dimensional gel network structure.

⑪ Also, the amount of starch used in the preparation of food products, without counting that present in flours used to make bread and other bakery products, that naturally occurs in grains used to make breakfast cereals, or that is naturally consumed in fruits and vegetables, greatly exceeds the combined use of all other food hydrocolloids.

(2) Translations

翻译

① 食品科学可以定义为物理科学、生物科学和行为科学在食品加工及食品销售中的应用。

② 所有这些关注都落在食品科学领域——这是一门论述食品的物理、化学和生物学性质的科学。而这些性质涉及食品的稳定性、成本、品质、加工性、安全性、营养价值、卫生和便利性。

③ 例如，食品化学家关注在销售新鲜水果和蔬菜期间能维持残余生命的合适条件，而在尝试长期保藏食品时，他们主要关注的是与生命过程不相容的条件。

④ 已对高质量、安全食品的属性和与食品变质有关的重要化学反应以及两者之间的关系作了描述，目前我们正开始考虑如何将此信息应用于食品贮藏和加工期间出现的情况。

⑤ 最有意义的实验事实是在 0℃时冰的热导率为同温度下水的热导率的 4 倍，这意味着冰传导热能比非流动水（例如在组织中）快得多。

⑥ 可以将水分子中电负性高的氧设想为从两个共价结合的氢原子部分地引取单个电子，这样使得每个氢原子都带有部分正电荷，而且电子屏蔽达到最小，也就是说，每个氢原子具有一些赤裸质子的特性。

⑦ 淀粉、乳糖和蔗糖是可被人消化的，它们同 D-葡萄糖、D-果糖以及人类能源一起，为世界人类膳食提供 70%~80%热量。

⑧ 当醛糖或酮糖在胺溶液中加热时，各种各样反应接着发生，产生许多化合物，其中有些是风味物、香气以及暗色的高聚物材料，但是两种反应物消失非常慢。

⑨ 麦芽糖是在谷物（尤其是大麦）的麦芽化过程中产生的，在商业上是通过使用芽孢杆菌中的 β-淀粉酶对淀粉进行特定的酶催化水解而产生的，尽管大麦种子、大豆和红薯中的 β-淀粉酶也可以被使用。

⑩ 虽然凝胶状或者膏状材料可由高浓度颗粒（很像番茄酱）形成，但要形成真正的

凝胶，聚合物分子或者分子聚集体必须首先处于溶液中，然后部分的溶液从交界区分离出来形成三维凝胶网状结构。

⑪ 此外，在制备食品中使用的淀粉的数量，不包括用于制作面包和其他烘焙产品的面粉中的淀粉。用于制作早餐谷物的谷物中天然存在的淀粉，以及水果和蔬菜中自然消耗的淀粉，远远超过所有其他食品亲水胶体的总用量。

5.2 Introduction of Food Science and Technology Research Paper Writing

5.2 食品科技研究论文写作简介

5.2.1 Paragraph Writing

段落写作

食品科技论文是食品专业以及相关工作和研究人员相互交流的重要媒介，在互联网迅速普及，英语已经成为国际性语言的今天，食品专业大学生有必要熟悉英语食品科技论文的写作规范，以便为今后的学习深造和研究工作打下一定的基础。

文章一般都是由段落构成的，食品科技论文也不例外，写好段落是写好食品科技论文的基础。

5.2.1.1 Basic Elements of the Paragraph

段落基本成分

段落有长有短，但一般由主题句（Topic Sentences）、支撑句（Supporting Sentences）和结论句（Concluding Sentences）三个部分组成。

(1) Topic Sentences

主题句

主题句是一个段落中最重要的句子，用来阐述段落的中心思想，同时也描述了该段文字内容的发展方向与方式。在科技英语的写作中，往往把主题句放在段首，然后通过扩展细节和提供依据对主题句的内容进行论述。有时主题句也放在中间或结尾，甚至没有明确的主题句，而是隐含在段落内容中。

主题句的结构通常包括两个部分，即中心议题（Topic/Subject Part）和中心思想（Controlling Idea）。主题句的中心议题是该段文字所要涉及的人、事或问题，整个段落的文字内容都要围绕着这个人、这件事或这个问题展开；中心思想是决定该段文字的发展方向或扩展方法，它可能是一个词、短语或从句。

(2) Supporting Sentences

支撑句

支撑句也叫扩展句（Developing Sentences），用来对主题句作具体阐述。在扩展句中所要使用的是以事实、理由、原因、说明、图表、比较、对比、定义等方式来阐述主题句中控制部分的思想内容。一个段落一般都有两个以上的支撑句，从而可以从多个方面支撑和说明主题句。

(3) Concluding Sentences

结论句

结论句主要用来总结要点和提出供读者思考的一些见解等，同时表明段落的结束。要写结论句，就要抓住主题句中的关键词，或回答主题句中所暗示的提问。要总结一段的要点，有时会用到 to sum up、in short、in conclusion 等词组或词汇。需要指出的是，结论句并不是在所有的段落文本中都要表示出来。

5.2.1.2 Key Features of the Paragraph 段落特色

(1) Unity

一致性

一段好的文字最重要的特点是一致性，意思是一个段落只能有一个主题，段落中的所有句子都是用来解释和说明这个主题的。一切与该段落无直接关系的句子都不应该包括在其中，如果一个段落中包含了与主题无关的句子，就意味着该段落缺乏一致性。

(2) Coherence

连贯性

连贯性就是要在一段文字中将所有的句子清楚地、有逻辑地并按先后顺序联系在一起，共同说明这一段的主题。如果说一致性主要与段落内容相关，那么连贯性则主要关系到段落的形式或组织，写作手法上可按重要性顺序、时间顺序、空间顺序、实验过程、分类标准、因果关系、比较和对照、演绎和归纳法等展开段落。另外，通过使用相应的过渡词或短语可更好地把全段的意思连贯起来。

(3) Completeness

完整性

所谓段落的完整性体现在两个方面，一是在内容上完整，按照主题句所要求表示的内容来提供具体、翔实和具有说服力的事实，充分说明段落的主题，从而满足读者的需求；二是在形式上完整，要运用好各种写作技巧，使文章段落结构严谨，一般应包含主题句、支撑句和结论句三个基本成分。段落的完整性不是用字数多少来进行衡量的，如果主题句限制的内容较少，所写的段落就应较短；如果主题句限制的内容较多，那么该段的文字也就会较长。

5.2.2 Writing of Food Science and Technology Research Papers 食品科技论文写作

食品科技论文主要部分包括引言、材料与方法、结果与讨论、结论等几部分，在此之后的辅助部分一般还有致谢、参考文献和附录等。

5.2.2.1 Main Elements of the Food Science and Technology Papers 食品科技论文主要成分

(1) Introduction

引言

引言又称前言或绪论，是食品科技论文正文的第一部分，主要内容包括主题和目的，前人在本领域内的研究情况、必要的背景知识，以及本课题的研究价值和意义等，通过引言的初步介绍，读者便于阅读文章。例如：

It has been suggested that an intake of potassium below 70-120 mmol/day may encourage the development of several diseases, such as hypertension, cardiovascular diseases and osteoporosis. Raising dietary potassium has been shown to reduce blood pressure even at a low supplementary level and in young regular individuals.

From an analysis of the urinary excretion of potassium, it is reported that 84% of females and 66% of males do not reach the Reference Nutrient Intake of 90 mmol/ day. Furthermore,27% of females and 17% of males consume less than 50 mmol/day. Potassium inadequacy is particularly striking in the elderly and amongst the poorest members of the population, and has also been noted in young people.

The aim of the present study was to explore the extent to which NaCl in white bread could be reduced and the potassium content raised, and to assess the bioavailability of the potassium incorporated in bread. To this end, acceptability trials employing various salts of potassium partially substituting wheat flour with defatted soy flour (DSF) or a combination of both were carried out. This was followed by a feeding study to estimate the bioavailability of supplemental potassium added to a standard bread formula.

上面几段引言中，第一段介绍了论文研究的一些背景知识，即钾摄取量与某些疾病的发病率存在很大关系；第二段介绍前人在本领域内的研究情况，据报道的结果发现人群中缺钾比例很高，尤其是老年人和穷人；第三段是介绍针对以上提到的缺钾问题，本研究的目的是探索在白面包中减少氯化钠的量，提高钾盐的量，并简述了实现的手段。

(2) Materials and Methods

材料与方法

材料与方法部分主要包括实验条件、材料、设计或使用的方法等。一般先交代实验的时间、地点、材料、数量、条件、环境；然后描述实验的设计、基本过程和步骤；最后还要说明本实验的统计方法。如果偏理论模型的研究，要说明各参数、假设和理论模型，以便在后文中讨论。材料与方法写作时可以根据情况列出相应的小标题，例如：

① Plant materials

Individually quick-frozen (I.Q.F.) strawberries (Fragaria anannassa cv., Totem) were supplied by Conroy Packing Inc. (Salem, OR). Orange nasturtium flowers (Tropaeolum majus) were collected from local gardens during the summer season (Corvallis, OR). Stems and leaves were separated from the petals, which were then frozen with liquid nitrogen. Red radishes (*Raphanus sativus* L. cv., fuego) were obtained from the local market in Corvallis, OR. The radishes were peeled manually; the peel was washed and frozen under liquid nitrogen. All frozen materials were stored at −23℃ until further processing.

② Chemicals and reagents

Glycerol was supplied by Mallinckrodt Chemical, Inc. (Paris, KY), citric acid monohydrate was purchased from J.T. Baker (Phillipsburg, NJ), sodium citrate was obtained from Archer Daniels Midland (Faries Parkway, Decatur, IL), sodium benzoate was purchased from Chemical Works (St. Louis, MO), and potassium sorbate was acquired from Monsanto Company (St. Louis, MO).

③ Microbiological analysis

Sausage samples (10 g) were homogenized with 90 ml maximum recovery diluent (LAB M, Bury, UK) using a laboratory blender (Stomacher 400, Seward, London, UK) for 2 min and decimal dilutions were prepared. Lactic acid bacteria (lactobacilli) counts were determined by the overlay technique using MRS agar (LAB M, Bury, UK) and colonies were counted after incubation at 30℃ for 5 days. The numbers of staphylococci were determined on Baird-Parker agar (LAB M, Bury, UK) supplemented with Egg Yolk Tellurite Emulsion (Oxoid, Hampshire, UK) after incubation at 37℃ for 2 days; and black colonies were counted.

④ Statistical analysis

Data were analysed using the Statistical Analysis System (SAS, 1990). To compare drip loss and colour measurements for different pH and CO_2 "snow" treatment, the General Linear Models procedure was used to perform analysis of variance. Significance level was set at $P<0.05$.

上面摘录了几段食品科技论文中有关材料与方法的内容，第一段介绍了实验材料，第二段是化学药品和试剂，第三段是研究中采用的微生物分析方法，第四段是数据统计分析方法。

材料与方法是食品科技论文中较容易写作的部分，基本要求是既完整又简洁，其目的是专业同行能根据写的内容能够重复实验过程，同时还可以评价实验结果的科学性。在时态和语态方面，主要使用一般过去时和被动语态，因为所叙述的是已经发生过的客观事实。

(3) Results and Discussion

结果与讨论

结果与讨论是食品科技论文的主要部分，篇幅往往要占全文的一半以上。这一部分也可以将"Results"和"Discussion"两个部分分别写，特别是在结果和讨论可以明显区分开的情况下。结果部分主要是撰写研究发现，所以应当全面客观，适当使用图表可使结果的报道更为简洁、有效和直观。讨论部分主要是对实验结果的阐释，与前人研究的比较，以及本研究的局限性等，要注意分析实验结果的机理。例如：

The effects of the incorporation of three different commercial starch samples into the bread formulation were investigated in this research. Resistant starch (RS) contents of the Hylon Ⅶ, Novelose330 and CrystaLean samples were 59.8%, 46.4% and 44.9%, respectively.

Loaf volume values and quality characteristics of the breads supplemented with different levels of the commercial starch samples are presented in Table Ⅱ. Loaf volume values of Hylon Ⅶ-supplemented and CrystaLean-supplemented breads did not show significant differences as the addition level increased up to the 20% supplementation level. Significant decreases were observed in the loaf volume values of the Novelose330-supplemented breads above the 10% replacement level ($P<0.05$).

Firmness values and RS contents of breads supplemented with different levels of commercial starch samples are presented in Table Ⅲ. Within each storage day, the firmness values of HylonⅦ-supplemented and CrystaLean-supplemented bread samples did not significantly change up to the 20%

addition level, but Novelose 330 addition caused increases in firmness values above the 10% level. Although at 7 days of storage, the firmness values of the breads increased with increasing levels of starch supplementation, There were no statistically significant differences between the firmness values of the starch-supplemented breads (all levels) and control bread (0%) within each commercial starch supplementation group. Their firmness values were all high (including the control samples) and significantly higher than day 1 values, probably due to staling during extended storage.

在上面几个有关结果与讨论的段落中，第一段介绍了三种商业淀粉样品中抗性淀粉的含量。第二段介绍了表 2 中添加不同量的三种商业淀粉产品后面包体积的变化情况。第三段介绍了表 3 中添加了不同商业淀粉产品后面包的硬度与抗性淀粉含量随面包贮藏时间之间的变化关系。在用文字介绍研究结果时，切忌完全重复图表中的内容，要注意突出重点。

针对文中不同的实验或不同的研究模型，可以在结果和讨论中加入小标题分别加以论述。有时，在结果和讨论的最后就结束论文，因为在分析讨论本实验或研究的各项结果时，结论就已经得出了。

(4) Conclusions

结论

结论是文章逻辑发展的必然和自然结果，是作者通过正文的论述而形成的总的观念。结论应该全面、明确、合乎逻辑，但要突出论文的发现，它可以让读者在此基础上进一步思考或做进一步研究。例如：

The findings of this study show that indigenous enzymes are primarily responsible for the initial degradation of the sarcoplasmic proteins. However, bacterial enzymes also contributed to the initial breakdown of myofibrillar proteins, particularly myosin and actin. Furthermore, the RP-HPLC profiles showed that the release of hydrophilic 2% TCA-soluble peptides from both protein fractions was due to indigenous proteinases, while bacterial peptidases contributed significantly to the release of free amino acids. This study has also conclusively shown that many small hydrophilic peptides produced in fermented sausages originate from both the sarcoplasmic and myofibrillar proteins.

This study has demonstrated that common salt in white bread may be significantly reduced with the substitution of both chloride and non-chloride salts for potassium without compromising acceptability. This change in the dietary sodium-potassium ratio would have a beneficial effect on blood pressure. Similar modifications to the composition of popular processed foods that contribute a considerable amount of sodium to the diet might also be considered.

在上面这两个结论段中，第一段重点列举了本研究的主要发现，第二段在总结论文研究发现的基础上，最后一句自然地提出了合理的建议。

结论部分一般加标题 Conclusions，也有的不加结论标题，而在 Results and Discussion 中加以论述，得出结论。一般来说，这一部分只有一两小段的长度。

5.2.2.2 Supplementary Parts of the Food Science and Technology Papers 食品科技论文补充部分

(1) Acknowledgements

致谢

致谢一般写在正文之后。由于科学研究工作常常不是一个人或几个人的力量所能完成的，有时需要有关单位和个人的指导和协助，所以这一部分是作者向为本研究提供帮助、指导、资助的单位和个人表示感谢。除此之外，还需要写上资助的项目名称和编号。

例如：

The authors would like to thank Dr Fabien Puglia and Jaqueline Wynne for their help with blood sampling, Dr Hooshang Izadi for statistical advice, and all our volunteers for taking part.

The authors gratefully acknowledge the enthusiastic interest in the work and the skilled assistance of Annette A.M. Spanjer, Hanne L.M. Tjeerdsma-van Bokhoven, and Gert Keizer. Many thanks to Dr. Maria Schipper for her guidance and support with the statistical analysis. *(space)* This study was partly financed by Senter at The Hague.

The authors are grateful to Peter Milligan (Senior Application Advisor in Statistics, Computing and IT Services, King's College London) for advice on statistical procedures and to King's College Alumni association for a research grant to A.B.

This investigation was supported by a grant from the Northwest Center for Small Fruit Research and the Fruit Juice Advisory Committee. This is technical paper number 11,700 from the Oregon Agricultural Experiment Station.

常用来表示感谢的表达式有 Would like to thank…for…； Be grateful to…for…； Many thanks to…for…； Acknowledge…等。

(2) References

参考文献

根据英语科技论文写作的规定，凡是引用其他作者的文章、观点或研究成果，都应标明，并在参考文献栏中说明出处。参考文献可以引用杂志论文、专利、毕业论文、专著及未出版的著作。引用要完整、清楚，以便读者需要阅读该文献时可以找到。参考文献顺序的排列有两种形式。一种是按姓的首字母在字母表中的顺序进行排列，另一种是按在正文中引用的顺序排列。

① 按姓的首字母顺序排列

这是一种传统的排列方式，论文正文中不注明引文号码，在参考文献中依照作者的姓的首字母顺序排列，不编号码。例如：

Abers, J., & Wrolstad, R. E. (1979). Causative factors of color deterioration in strawberry preserves during processing and storage. *Journal of Food Science,* 44 (1), 75-81.

Baublis, A., Spomer, A., & Berber-Jimenez, M. D. (1994). Anthocyanin pigments: comparison of extract stability. *Journal of Food Science*, 59 (6), 1219-1221, 1233.

Cemeroglu, B., Velioglu, S., & Isik, S. (1994). Degradation kinetics of anthocyanins in sour cherry juice and concentrate. *Journal of Food Science*, 59, 1216-1218.

Erlandson, J. A., & Wrolstad, R. E. (1972). Degradation of anthocyanins at limited water concentration. *Journal of Food Science,* 37(4), 592-595.

② 按数字编号列出的参考文献

论文中的引文出处按出现先后顺序编上号码，所列出的参考文献应与论文中标注的顺序一致。例如：

[1] L. Lehane, J. Olley, Histamine (Scombroid) Fish Poisoning: a review and risk-assessment

framework, National Office of Animal and Plant Health, Canberra, Australia, 1999.

[2] W.F. Staruskiewicz, E.M. Waldron, J.F. Bond, J. AOAC. 60 (1977) 1125.

[3] V. Frattini, C. Lionetti, J. Chromatogr. A. 809 (1988) 241.

[4] M.T. Salazar, T.K. Smith, A. Harris, J. Agric. Food Chem. 48 (2000) 1708.

不论哪种排列法，都要规范一致，不能混用。投稿时，必须按照所投刊物要求的文献规范排序。

(3) Appendix

附录

附录一般放在论文的最后。与论文主题关系密切，但如包括在正文中会影响文章的连贯性的内容可放在附录内，这些内容包括复杂的计算、公式的推导、校核用的数表等项目。如果附录不止一个，可用 Appendix A 或Ⅰ，Appendix B 或Ⅱ等对其编号。

附录并不是每篇论文必备的，食品科技论文中大都没有附录，这一部分在有的论文中放在“致谢”之后。

5.3 Titles, Abstracts and Chart Titles Writing of Food Science and Technology English Papers

5.3 食品科技论文英文标题、摘要和图表标题的写作

5.3.1 Writing of English Titles

英文标题的写作

标题又称题名或题目，是文章的总纲，是能反映文章最重要的特定内容的词语逻辑组合，它是一篇论文给出的涉及论文范围与水平的第一个重要信息。为便于检索，标题一定要含有反映文章内容的关键词。论文标题十分重要，必须用心斟酌选定。对论文标题的要求是：准确得体，恰当反映所研究的范围和深度，避免过于笼统，题不扣文；简短精练，一般为 8~15 个英文实词；外延和内涵恰如其分；醒目，不使用非共知公认的缩写词、字符、代号等。

5.3.1.1 Structures of English Titles

英文标题的结构

英文标题以短语为主要形式，尤以名词短语最常见，即标题基本上由一个或几个名词加上其前置和（或）后置定语构成。例如：Advances in immunotherapy for food allergy（食物过敏免疫疗法研究进展）、Principles of food safety risk management（食品安全风险管理原则）。短语型题名要确定好中心词，再进行前后修饰，各个词的顺序很重要，词序不当，

会导致表达不准。对于较长的标题，可采取增加副标题的形式作补充解释以缩短主标题的长度。如：Consumer preferences and willingness to pay for food labeling: a discussion of empirical studies（关于消费者对食品标识的偏好与支付意愿的实证研究探讨）。对于一些研究型论文，名词短语的标题不能给读者一个确切的观点，需要读者去阅读文章，而陈述句构成的标题能更准确地表达作者的观点和文章的结论，让读者和编者一目了然。如：Standardised *Mangifera indica* extract is an ideal antioxidant （标准化的芒果提取物是一种理想的抗氧化剂）。少数情况（评述性、综述性和驳斥性）下可以用疑问句做题名，因为疑问句带有探讨性语气，易引起读者兴趣。例如：Can guava fruit intake decrease blood pressure and blood lipids?（番石榴摄入能够降血压血脂吗?）。

5.3.1.2 Word Length of English Titles 英文标题的字数

对于综述类论文，标题应确切、简练、醒目，在能准确反映论文特定内容的前提下，词数越少越好，一般不宜超过 10 个英文实词。而对于研究类论文，虽然对其标题的要求与综述类论文一致，但由于现代的高水平研究涵盖的内容越来越多，简单的几个词已经难以表达论文的主题，因此现代的研究性论文所用词数有大幅增加的趋势。最近几年发表的研究类论文，其英文实词数一般为 13~15 个，远大于十九世纪五六十年代论文的 8~12 个。

5.3.1.3 Upper Case or Lower Case Letters of English Titles 英文标题中的大小写

标题字母的大小写有以下三种格式。A.全部字母大写。例如：NMR STUDY OF HYDRATION OF NAVY BEAN DURING COOKING（菜豆烹调时水合作用的核磁共振研究）。 B. 每个词的首字母大写，但三个或四个字母以下的冠词、连词、介词全部小写。例如： Assessing Caffeine Intake in the United Kingdom Diet（英国日常饮食中咖啡因摄入的评估）。 C. 标题第一个词的首字母大写，其余字母均小写。例如：In vitro antioxidant properties of rutin（芦丁的体外抗氧化特性）。一般采用 B 格式。

5.3.1.4 Examples of English Titles 英文标题实例

(1) Review-based Titles

综述类标题

① A review of the health benefits of raisins

葡萄干健康益处的综述

② An overview of citric acid production

柠檬酸生产综述

③ Brazil nuts and associated health benefits: A review

巴西胡桃及其相关健康益处的综述

④ Advances in rapid detection techniques for fish meat

鱼肉鲜度快速检测技术研究进展

⑤ Recent advances in phosphorylation of food proteins: A review

食物蛋白磷酸化近期研究进展综述

⑥ Research development of beer staling flavor evaluation

啤酒风味老化评价的研究进展

⑦ Research progress of phenylalanine ammonialyase

苯丙氨酸解氨酶（PAL）的研究进展

⑧ Newest research on *Saccharomyces cerevisiae* in fermentation

酿酒酵母 *S.cerevisiae* 发酵研究新进展

⑨ Perspectives for chitosan based antimicrobial films in food applications

壳聚糖抑菌膜在食品中的应用前景

⑩ Current trends in traditional Turkish meat products and cuisine

传统土耳其肉制品及其烹饪的现状

⑪ Research status and the trend of development of sweetness agent

甜味剂的研究现状和发展趋势

⑫ Present situation and application prospect of immersion chilling and freezing in food processing

直接浸渍冷冻在食品加工中的应用现状与前景

⑬ Mechanisms of oxidative browning of wine

葡萄酒氧化褐变的作用机理

⑭ Applications for supercritical fluid technology in food processing

超临界流体技术在食品加工上的应用

⑮ Rheological properties of milkfat and butter

乳脂与黄油的流变学特性

⑯ Chemistry and reactions of reactive oxygen species in foods

食品中活性氧的化学过程与反应

⑰ Coffee and its consumption: benefits and risks

咖啡及其消费：益处与风险

⑱ Antioxidant activity of proteins and peptides

蛋白质与肽的抗氧化活性

⑲ Physiological function and application of milk basic protein

乳碱性蛋白的生理学功能及应用

(2) Research-based Titles

研究类标题

① Studies on cake quality made of wheat–chickpea flour blends

小麦-鹰嘴豆混合面蛋糕质量研究

② Preliminary study of the production of apple pomace and quince jelly

苹果渣与柑橘果冻生产的初步研究

③ Pharmacokinetic study of mangiferin in human plasma after oral administration

芒果苷口服后在人血浆中的药物代谢动力学研究

④ A comparative study of lipid and hypochlorous acid induced oxidation of soybean proteins

油脂与次氯酸诱导大豆蛋白氧化的比较研究

⑤ *In vitro* antioxidant study of vegetable oils containing conjugated linolenic acid isomers

含有共轭亚麻酸异构体的蔬菜油脂的体外抗氧化研究

⑥ Research on the preparation of antioxidant peptides derived from egg white with the assist of high-intensity pulsed electric field

高强脉冲电场辅助蛋白抗氧化肽的制备研究

⑦ Analysis of nutrient and antinutrient content of underutilized green leafy vegetables

未充分利用绿叶蔬菜的营养及抗营养成分分析

⑧ Investigation of α-glucosidase inhibitory activity of wheat bran and germ

麦麸与胚芽的 α-葡萄糖苷酶的抑制活性调查

⑨ Evaluation of quality during storage of apple leather

苹果泥干储藏期间的质量评价

⑩ Detection of H_2O_2 in food samples by FTIR

食物样品中过氧化氢的傅里叶变换红外光谱检测

⑪ Determination of melamine concentrations in dairy samples

乳样品中三聚氰胺浓度的测定

⑫ Assessment of the melatonin production in pomegranate wines

石榴酒中褪黑素生成的评估

⑬ Extraction of α-tocopherol and γ-oryzanol from rice bran

米糠 α-生育酚与 γ-谷维素的提取

⑭ Purification of soluble rice bran fiber using ultrafiltration technology

超滤法米糠可溶性纤维的纯化

⑮ Classification of Italian honey by mid-infrared diffuse reflectance spectroscopy

中红外漫反射光谱法分类意大利蜂蜜

⑯ Effects of extraction solvent on wheat bran antioxidant activity estimation

萃取剂对麦麸抗氧化活性评估的影响

⑰ Influence of flour particle size on quality of gluten-free rice bread

面粉颗粒大小对无谷蛋白大米面包质量的影响

⑱ The impact of Ca^{2+} combination with organic acids on green tea infusions

钙离子与有机酸结合对绿茶汤的影响

⑲ Properties of extruded expandable breadfruit products

面包果挤压膨化产品的特性

⑳ Characterization of juice in fruits of different *Chaenomeles* species

不同木瓜果实汁液的特征描述

㉑ Use of a free radical method to evaluate antioxidant activity

使用一种自由基方法来评估抗氧化活性

㉒ Relationship of acid phosphatase activity and Brix/acid ratio in cherries

樱桃中酸性磷酸酶活性与糖酸比的关系

㉓ Modifications of Kyoho grape berry quality under long-term NaCl treatment

长期氯化钠处理调控巨峰葡萄果实质量

㉔ Distribution of carotenoids in endosperm, germ, and aleurone fractions of cereal grain kernels

类胡萝卜素在谷粒的胚乳、胚芽及糊粉层中的分布

㉕ Removal of three kinds of phthalates from sweet orange oil by molecular distillation

分子蒸馏法除去甜橙油中三种邻苯二甲酸盐

㉖ Optimization of process parameters for continuous kheer-making machine

连续式印度炼乳生产机的工艺参数优化

㉗ Evolution of quality parameters during red wine dealcoholization by osmotic distillation

红酒渗透蒸馏脱醇过程中质量参数的演变

㉘ Flavour and texture changes in apple cultivars during storage

储藏中不同苹果品种的风味与质地变化

㉙ Protein enrichment and its effects on gluten-free bread characteristics

蛋白质强化及其对无麸质面包特性的影响

㉚ An innovative technique for extending the shelf life of strawberry: Ultrasound

延长草莓货架期的创新方法：超声

㉛ Dietary fiber from orange byproducts as a potential fat replacer

柑橘副产物来源的膳食纤维作为潜在的脂肪替代物

㉜ Quick cooking rice by high hydrostatic pressure processing

高静水压法速煮米饭

㉝ Assessing caffeine intake in the United Kingdom diet

英国饮食的咖啡因摄入评估

㉞ Optimizing the texture and color of sous-vide and cook-vide green bean pods

优化真空烹调与厨师烹调青豆荚的质地与颜色

㉟ Modelling of the aqueous debittering process of *Lupinus mutabilis* Sweet

南美五彩羽扇豆水相脱苦过程建模

㊱ Tuning color variation in grape anthocyanins at the molecular scale

在分子尺度调校葡萄花青素的色差

㊲ Structuring lipids by aggregation of acidic protein microspheres in W/O emulsions

在油包水乳状液中酸性蛋白微球聚集法构建脂肪

㊳ Melatonin is synthesized by yeast during alcoholic fermentation in wines

葡萄酒中酵母在酒精发酵过程中合成褪黑素

㊴ Curcumin inhibits invasion and metastasis of K1 papillary thyroid cancer cells

姜黄素抑制乳头状甲状腺癌 K1 细胞的侵袭和转移

㊵ Essential rosemary oil protects testicular cells against the DNA-damaging effects of H_2O_2 and DMNQ

迷迭香精油保护睾丸细胞对抗过氧化氢与二甲萘醌（DMNQ）引起的 DNA 损伤

5.3.2 Writing of English Abstracts

英文摘要的写作

摘要又称概要、内容提要，作为题目的补充对论文的内容进行准确、扼要的表达，不加解释和评论，使读者能够了解整篇论文的梗概并判定是否需要通读全文，并为科技情报文献检索数据库的建设和维护提供方便。几乎所有公开发表的科技论文都要有短小简洁的英文摘要，这是食品科技论文的一般要求。不仅英文论文如此，国内大多数中文科技论文也要求提供英文摘要。此外，论文的关键词是情报检索语言中的一个组成部分，其质量直接影响论文在情报检索系统中的检索效率，一般在科技论文的摘要之后列出 4~6 个关键词。

5.3.2.1 Features of Abstracts

摘要的特点

摘要的特点可以用三个字来概括：全、短、精。全是指摘要应是一篇相对独立的短文，应完整地揭示论文的主要内容；短是指摘要要尽可能言简意赅；精是指摘要应是原文的精华，也就是说它具有完整独立性、高度浓缩性和客观准确性。

5.3.2.2 Structures and Contents of Abstracts

摘要的结构和内容

(1) Research Objectives or Purposes

研究的目的

包括研究、研制、调查等工作的前提、背景和任务等，一般在摘要的开头用一到两句话简洁地概括研究范围及目的或研究背景。如：This study examined the effects of freezing temperature and duration of frozen storage on lipid and protein oxidation in chicken leg and breast meat.（本研究检测了冷冻温度与冻藏时间对鸡腿及鸡胸肉脂肪与蛋白质氧化的影响）。在一些专业性较强的科技刊物论文的英文摘要中，研究目的这一部分常常被略去，而把它放在论文的引言中，从而使论文摘要更加精炼。

(2) Process and Methods

过程与方法

介绍研究的内容和试验过程，包括所用的原理、对象、方法、材料、工艺、手段、装备和软件等。如：The meat was frozen at three different temperatures (−7℃, −12℃ and −18℃) and then stored at −18℃ for up to 6 months.（肉在−7℃、−12℃与−18℃ 3 个温度下冷冻，然后在−18℃条件下冷藏到 6 个月）。

(3) Results or Findings

结果或发现

实验或研究所取得的成果，包括观察、实验、研究的结果、数据或发现，得到的效果、性能等。如：A significant effect of frozen storage duration on lipid oxidation was detected in leg and breast meat, whereas freezing temperature had no significant effect.（冻藏时间对腿肉与胸肉的脂类氧化作用显著，而冷冻温度影响不大）。In leg meat, freezing at −7℃ had a significant impact on protein oxidation, measured as the increase in carbonyl groups and the decrease in total sulphydryl groups, after 3 months of frozen storage.（冻藏 3 个月时，−7℃冷冻对腿肉蛋白质氧化影响显著，腿肉中羰基含量增加，总巯基含量减少）。

(4) Conclusions or Inferences

结论或推论

结果的分析、比较、评价、应用，以及存在的问题，今后的课题、启发、建议和预测等。如：Lipid and protein oxidation appeared to occur simultaneously in chicken meat during frozen storage and was more intense in leg meat than in breast meat.（在鸡肉冻藏过程中，脂类与蛋白的氧化似乎同时发生，且在腿肉中比在胸肉中的氧化更剧烈）。

5.3.2.3 Classifications of Abstracts 摘要的分类

(1) Informative Abstracts

报道性摘要

报道性摘要（Informative abstract），也常称作信息性摘要或资料性摘要，其特点是全面、简要地概括论文的目的、方法、主要数据和结论。通常，这种摘要可以部分地取代阅读全文。

(2) Indicative Abstracts

指示性摘要

指示性摘要（Indicative abstract），也常称为说明性摘要、描述性摘要（Descriptive abstract）或论点摘要（Topic abstract），一般只用二三句话概括论文的主题，而不涉及论据和结论，多用于综述、会议报告等。该类摘要可用于帮助潜在的读者来决定是否需要阅读全文。

(3) Informative-indicative Abstracts

报道-指示性摘要

报道-指示性摘要（Informative-indicative abstract）是将原始文献中信息价值高的部分写成报道性摘要，其余部分则写成指示性摘要，起到检索、报道作用。它兼具报道性文摘和指示性文摘二者特点。

(4) Structured Abstracts

结构式摘要

结构式摘要（Structured abstract）是报道性摘要的改良版，是将报道性摘要结构化，使其重点突出、条理分明、内容完整，因而近年来被很多杂志所采用。如 *Journal of the Science of Food and Agriculture* 杂志的结构式摘要分为三部分：背景（Background）、结果（Results）与结论（Conclusion）。而 *European Journal of Nutrition* 杂志的结构式摘要则沿用报道性摘要的四要素：目的(Purpose)、方法(Method)、结果(Results)与结论(Conclusion)。每一部分在文中要用醒目的字体（黑体、全大写或斜体）直接标出，相当于小标题，利于检索和查看。

5.3.2.4 Persons in Writing Abstracts 摘要的人称

因为摘要是论文不加注释和评论的简短陈述，所以论文的英文摘要撰写多使用第三人称，如 the paper, the essay, this thesis, the author, this study；在需要使用第一人称时，用泛指 we，而不用 I。而目前的倾向是采用更简洁的被动语态或原形动词、介词短语、分词或分词短语作为摘要的开头，如：In order to, Based on, On the basis of, By using / analyzing, From the view of，As an example of，With regard to，To understand/overcome/enhance/investigate/analyze/seek，Taking advantage of，Compared with 等。

5.3.2.5 Tenses in Writing Abstract 摘要的时态

英文摘要的时态以一般现在时、一般过去式为主。一般现在时用于说明摘要开头的研究目的、研究内容与摘要结尾的结论和讨论部分，如：The aim of this study is to investigate the influence of certain factors on the yield, antioxidant activity (AA) and total phenolic content (TPC) of guava leaf extract.（本研究的目的是调查某些因素对番石榴叶提取物的产量、抗氧化活性与总酚含量的影响）。一般过去时用于叙述撰写论文前已完成的工作，如过去某时期的发现、实验、观察、调查、分析等过程，因此常用于摘要中的研究过程和研究结果两部分，如：The effects of pretreatment of leaf sample prior to extract, extraction method, and the leaf age were investigated.（调查了提取前预处理、提取方法与叶龄的影响）。

5.3.2.6 Voices in Writing Abstract 摘要的语态

英文摘要的语态应视具体情况而定。在不考虑动作的实施者、强调研究结果时采用被动语态，如：The production of low-temperature thermally-dried cells of *Saccharomyces cerevisiae* at 32℃ is examined in the present investigation.（研究了在 32℃条件下低温热干燥酿酒酵母细胞的生产）。而由于主动语态较被动语态表达更鲜明有力、严谨易懂，近年来主张摘要中尽量采用主动语态的言论越来越多，特别是在表达作者观点或引用有关专家的观点时，如：We have successfully developed a new process for manufacturing guava leaf tea with a unique polyphenolic profile.（我们已经成功地开发出了一种新的含有独特多酚组成的番石榴叶茶的加工工艺）。

5.3.2.7 Length of Abstracts 摘要的篇幅

对于英文摘要的篇幅，不同组织的要求不同。国际标准化组织（ISO）建议不少于 250

个词，最多不超过 500 个词。美国化学文献和医学文摘规定在 300 个词以内，而学术会议常要求 500 个词。根据中国科学技术期刊文献数据库英文版（CSTA）的要求，摘要长度以 50~150 字为宜。美国工程索引（EI）中国信息部要求：报道性摘要一般不超过 150 字，不少于 100 字。为使英文摘要的撰写与国际接轨，一般要求指示性摘要与报道-指示性摘要以 100~150 字为宜，而报道性摘要与结构式摘要长度最好为 250~300 字。

5.3.2.8 Common Abstracts Sentence Patterns 常用摘要句型

(1) Research Objective

表示研究目的

The (primary) purpose of this study (paper) is to...

本研究（本文）的（主要）目的是……

The object (aim) of this study (the present research) is to...

本研究旨在……

This (The present) study was designed (undertaken) to...

本研究旨在……

In this study, an attempt was made to (attempts were made to) ...

在本研究中，我们试图……

(2) Research Methods

表示研究方法

The method used in our study is...

我们的研究使用的方法是……

The technique we have applied is...

我们使用的技术是……

The procedure can be briefly described as...

这一步骤可以概括描述为……

The experiment, consisted of three steps, is described in...

这一试验有三个步骤，在……中给以描述。

The fundamental features of this theory are as follows...

这一理论的基本特征如下……

(3) Research Results

表示研究结果

The data obtained suggest that...

所取得的资料表明……

The analysis strongly suggests that...

这一分析有力地指出……

These findings indicate that...

这些发现表明……

In broad terms, the results favor...

宽泛地说，结果对……有利。

The study suggests that...

研究表明……

(4) Research Conclusions

表示研究结论

It is concluded that...

结论是……

These results demonstrate that...

这些研究结果证明……

We conclude that...

我们的结论是……

The authors are of the opinion that...

作者的意见是……

In conclusion, we state that...

总而言之，我们的结论是……

5.3.2.9 English Abstract Examples 英文摘要实例

(1) Informative Abstracts

报道性摘要

Effect of cooking on the antioxidant properties of coloured peppers（烹饪对彩椒抗氧化特性的影响）

Abstract: Pepper (*Capsicum annum* L.) has long been recognized as an excellent source of antioxidants, being rich in ascorbic acid and other phytochemicals. This study was conducted to investigate the effect of different cooking methods on the antioxidant properties of coloured peppers. Six varieties of peppers were subjected to different cooking methods, such as microwave heating, stir-frying and boiling in water, for 5 min individually. The cooked and raw peppers were analyzed for radical-scavenging activity (RSA) and total polyphenol content (TP) using 1,1-diphenyl-2-picrylhydrazyl–high-pressure liquid chromatography (DPPH)–HPLC and Folin-Ciocalteu methods, respectively. The samples were also evaluated for ascorbic acid content (AsA) by HPLC. Total carotenoid content was determined spectrophotometrically. Results suggest that there is no significant ($P > 0.05$) difference in RSA, TP, AsA and total carotenoid contents between the cooked and raw peppers when processed for 5 min. However, the cooked peppers show marked differences ($P < 0.05$) in the RSA, TP and AsA when cooked for 5 min in boiling water with further reduction observed after boiling for 30 min. This may be due to the leaching of antioxidant compounds from the pepper into the cooking water during the prolonged exposure to water and heat. Therefore, it is vital to use less water and cooking time and also to consume the water used for boiling so as to obtain the optimum benefits of bioactive compounds present in peppers. It is concluded that microwave heating and stir-frying without using water are more suitable cooking methods for pepper, to ensure the maximum retention of antioxidant molecules.

彩椒（*Capsicum annum* L）一直被认为是抗氧化剂的极好来源，其含有丰富的抗坏血酸与其他的植物营养素。本研究旨在调查不同烹饪方法对彩椒抗氧化特性的影响。使用不同的处理来烹饪六种彩椒，比如微波加热、炒与煮各 5min。处理后的彩椒与生彩椒使用 DPPH-HPLC 法检测其清除自由基活性（RSA），使用福林酚法检测其总酚含量（TP），使用 HPLC 法检测其抗坏血酸含量（AsA），使用分光光度法检测其总类胡萝卜素含量。结果显示，对比烹饪与未烹饪的彩椒，烹饪 5min 对 RSA、TP、AsA 与总类胡萝卜素含量的影响不显著（$P > 0.05$）。然而，经沸水烹饪 5min 的彩椒其 RSA、TP 和 AsA 与其他烹饪方法所得彩椒差异显著（$P < 0.05$），且煮制 30min 后各指标进一步降低。这可能是由于长时间暴露于水和热的过程促使彩椒中抗氧化成分浸出到烹饪用水中。因此，减少煮制用水量、缩短煮制时间、利用煮制用水，以获得彩椒中存在的生物活性成分的最佳效果。实验结果表明，不加水的微波加热与炒更适合彩椒的烹饪，可以确保最大限度地保留抗氧化分子。

(2) Indicative Abstracts

指示性摘要

Composition, industrial processing and applications of rice bran γ-oryzanol（米糠 γ-谷维素的组成、工业生产与应用）

Abstract: Rice bran oil (RBO) (20% ~ 25% in rice bran) is a unique rich source of commercially-important bioactive phytochemicals, most of them of interest in nutrition, pharmacy and cosmetics. The unsaponifiable constituents of RBO include mainly tocols (vitamin E, 0.10% ~ 0.14%) and γ-oryzanol (esters of *trans*-ferulic acid with sterols and triterpenic alcohols, 0.9% ~2.9%). The following topics concerning γ-oryzanol are reviewed: analytical methods for characterization and determination; influence of genetic and environmental factors on the composition of rice bran; extraction approaches, including supercritical CO_2 and subcritical water; and biomedical and industrial applications, including food and pharmaceuticals. Concentration ranges of γ-oryzanol, tocopherols and tocotrienols found in rice bran and RBO from different varieties and geographical areas are summarized.

米糠油（RBO）（占米糠质量 20%~25%）富含具有商业价值的生物活性植物营养素，其中大部分可应用于营养、制药和化妆品等行业。米糠油不皂化的组分主要包括生育酚（维生素 E 0.10% ~ 0.14%）与 γ-谷维素（反式阿魏酸酯以及甾醇和三萜醇，0.9% ~2.9%）。本文综述了关于 γ-谷维素的以下几个主题：表征与测定的分析方法；遗传及环境因素对米糠成分构成的影响；提取方法，包括超临界二氧化碳与亚临界水法；生物医学及工业应用，包括食品与制药。总结了不同品种与产地的米糠与米糠油中 γ-谷维素、生育酚与生育三烯酚的浓度范围。

(3) Informative-indicative Abstracts

报道-指示性摘要

Brazil Nuts and associated health benefits: A review（巴西胡桃及其相关健康益处的综述）

Abstract: Epidemiological studies have shown an inverse relationship between nut intakes and chronic diseases such as cardiovascular diseases and cancers. The composition of lipids, minerals, and phytochemicals, and their associated health functions in Brazil nuts are critically reviewed. The nuts have a high nutritive food value containing 60%~70% oil and 17% protein. Brazil nuts contain abundant dietary antioxidants, especially selenium (Se). One single Brazil nut provides 160% of the US Recommended Daily Allowance (RDA) of selenium - perhaps the best source of Se from plant-based foods. Brazil Nuts possess phenolics and flavonoids in both free and bound forms and are rich in tocopherol, phytosterols, and squalene. These compounds' possible beneficial effects are due to their antioxidant and antiproliferative activities, which are linked to a reduced risk of developing atherosclerosis and cancer.

流行病学研究已经显示出坚果摄入与慢性病比如冠心病与癌症的逆相关关系。本文综述了巴西胡桃的脂类、矿物质及植物营养素构成，以及与其相关的保健功能。巴西胡桃具有很高的营养价值，含有 60% ~ 70%油脂与 17%的蛋白质。巴西胡桃含有丰富的膳食抗氧化剂，特别是硒。一个巴西胡桃能够提供美国日推荐摄取量 160%的硒，也许是植物性食物中的硒的最佳来源。巴西胡桃含有游离与结合的酚醛树脂与黄酮，且富含生育酚、植物甾醇与鲨烯。这些化合物可能的有益作用是由于它们的抗氧化与抗恶性细胞增生活性，这些活性与降低动脉硬化和癌症的风险有关。

(4) Structured Abstracts

结构式摘要

Neuroprotective effects of digested polyphenols from wild blackberry species（野生种黑莓多酚分解物的神经保护作用）

Abstract:

Purpose: Blackberry ingestion has been demonstrated to attenuate brain degenerative processes with the benefits ascribed to the (poly) phenolic components. The aim of this work was to evaluate the neuroprotective potential of two wild blackberry species in a neurodegeneration cell model and compare them with a commercial variety.

Methods: This work encompasses chemical characterization before and after in vitro digestion and the assessment of neuroprotection by digested metabolites. Some studies targeting redox/cell death systems were also performed to assess possible neuroprotective molecular mechanisms.

Results: The three blackberry extracts presented some quantitative differences in polyphenol composition that could be responsible for the different responses in the neurodegeneration cell model. Commercial blackberry extracts were ineffective but both wild blackberries, *Rubus brigantinus* and *Rubus vagabundus,* presented neuroprotective effects. It was verified that a diminishment of intracellular ROS levels, modulation of glutathione levels and activation of caspases occurred during treatment.

Conclusions: This is the first time that metabolites obtained from an in vitro digested food matrix, and tested at levels approaching the concentrations found in human plasma, have been described as inducing an adaptative response.

目的：黑莓的摄入已被证明能减缓脑退化过程，此效果被归于其（多）酚类化合物。本研究的目的在于使用神经变性细胞模型来评估两种野生黑莓的神经保护潜力，并与一种商业黑莓做对比。

方法：本研究包含体外消化前后的化学表征与消化代谢产物的神经保护作用评估。也做了一些涉及氧化还原/细胞凋亡系统的实验来探讨可能的神经保护分子机理。

结果：三种黑莓提取物在神经变性细胞模型中产生了不同的应答，其原因可能是因为它们的多酚组成有一些含量上的差异。商业黑莓提取物被证明无效，而 *Rubus brigantinus* 与 *Rubus vagabundus* 两种野生黑莓则具有神经保护效果。且处理期间细胞内的活性氧水平下降，谷胱甘肽水平被调整，半胱天冬酶被激活。

结论：这是首次从体外消化的食物基质中获得的代谢物，并在接近人体血浆中发现的浓度的水平下进行测试，被描述为诱导适应反应。

5.3.3 English Chart Title's Writing

英文图表标题的写作

论文中精心设计的图和表能客观地展示作者的研究成果，起到文字叙述难以达到的效果，因此图表以其简明直观的表现形式深受读者喜爱，而一个好的图表标题更能吸引读者并提高读者阅读的兴趣，让读者在最短的时间内对图表内容有最全面的了解。通常撰写图表标题要求准确得体、简明精练，具有较好的说明性和专指性。不仅英文论文如此，国内一些高水平的中文科技论文也要求提供英文图表标题，以便国外专家学者能通过英文摘要和图表尽可能多地了解文章的内容，也有助于权威文献检索系统审查和收录。

5.3.3.1 Formats

书写格式

图题一般位于图的底部，题末使用英文句号，部分杂志要求加粗表示。如有相关的文字性描述，直接附在标题的后面即可。表题则一般位于表的上方，题末不用标点符号，相关注释则附在表的下方。论文中，如有多个图表，应按顺序标 Figure 1、Figure 2（Fig. 1, Fig. 2）或 Table 1、Table 2 等。如果全文只有一个图或表，也要标 Figure 1 或 Table 1。标题书写规则主要有以下两种：一是标题首词的第一个字母大写，其他词首均小写；二是标题中每个词的首字母大写，但冠词、连词和介词要小写。例如: Table 1. Total phenolic content and antioxidative activity of different parts of the yellow, red, and white onion cultivars / Table 1. Total Phenolic Content and Antioxidative Activity of Different Parts of the Yellow, Red, and White Onion Cultivars （表 1.黄、红、白洋葱品种不同部分的总酚含量与抗氧化活性）。论文作者向杂志投稿时，应事先了解其编写要求。

5.3.3.2 Grammatical Patterns

语法结构

标题一般以短语形式表达，多以名词加前位或后位修饰语构成，常见的前置定语有名词、形容词和分词，后置定语有介词短语、分词短语等。例如: Fig. 1. Total ion chromatogram of derivatized phytosterols in the GC-MS.（图 1. 气质联用中植物甾醇衍生物的总离子色谱图）/Table 4. Main characteristic ions with relative abundances and retention times of the derivatized phytosterols in the GC-MS full-scan mass spectra.（表 4.气质联用全扫描质谱中植物甾醇衍生物主要的特征离子的相对丰度与保留时间）。

5.3.3.3 Important Word's Position 中心词位置

中心词是指明图表的主题或要点，应放在首位。有的中心词可根据需要决定用单数还是用复数。例如：Table 2. Sterol levels (mg/100 g of oil) during storage at 60℃（表 2. 在 60℃储存时的甾醇水平，mg/100g）中，Sterol levels 指明了该表的要点。

5.3.3.4 Common Used Sentence Patterns 常用句式

如果图表用于说明通过一定的手段检测和观察某个变量的变化结果（效果、作用、影响），其规范的标题格式是：effect / influence of A on B in C；B in response to A in C；B during A in C；B before and after A in C；对于提供背景资料的图表，其格式为：B of C 或 B in C。其中 A 表示研究操作的因素（自变量），B 表示观察、测定的项目或背景资料的名称（因变量），C 表示被研究的对象，如动物、实验人群以及材料。如果研究对象是整个人群，不是某一特定的亚群，实验对象可以省略。例如：Table 1. Effects of cooking on the total carotenoids content of coloured pepper（表 1.烹饪对彩椒总类胡萝卜素含量的影响）/ Fig. 1. Sensory evaluation of argan oil during storage at 20℃.（图 1.在 20℃储存时摩洛哥坚果油的感官评价）。

除上述句式外，常见的句型还有：观察，an observation / observations of/on/in；调查，survey/investigation of/on；关系/相关/比较/对照，relationship/correlation/association/comparison/contrast 等作中心词，后接 of...and/with 或 between...and；特征/结果/证据，property/characteristics/feature/result/evidence/proof 等中心词，后接介词 for、of、to、in。

5.3.3.5 Examples of Chart Titles 图表标题实例

(1) Figures

图题实例

① Fig. 1. Formation of allicin and pyruvic acid from alliin.

图 1. 蒜碱由来的蒜素与丙酮酸的形成

② Fig. 2. Amount of acrylamide formed in the crust.

图 2. 面包皮中丙烯酰胺形成的量

③. Fig. 3. Change in total polyphenol content of coloured peppers after 5 and 30 min of boiling.

图 3. 煮制 5 分钟与 30 分钟后彩椒总酚含量的变化

④ Fig. 4. Texture profile analysis of the protein isolates studied.

图 4. 所研究的分离蛋白的质地剖面分析

⑤. Fig. 5. Schematic representation of the manufacturing procedure for synbiotic ice cream in this study.

图 5. 本研究中益生菌冰淇淋制造工序的图示

⑥. Fig. 6. Percentage contribution of ascorbic acid content to the radical-scavenging activity of raw coloured peppers.

图 6. 生彩椒抗坏血酸含量对其自由基清除能力的贡献率

⑦. Fig. 7. Comparison between the oil content of product fried in vacuum and traditional fryers.

图 7. 真空与传统油炸锅所得产品的含油量比较

⑧. Fig. 8. Relationship between crust colour, acrylamide formation, crust temperature and water content.

图 8. 面包皮颜色、丙烯酰胺形成、面包皮温度与含水量之间的关系

⑨. Fig. 9. Principal components analysis of ice creams (sensory attributes data) as they are affected by hydrocolloids, κ-carrageenan presence and storage time.

图 9. 水状胶、卡拉胶及储存时间对冰淇淋（感官性状数据）影响的主成分分析

⑩ Fig. 10. Pyruvic acid concentration as a function of water content in garlic slices dried at 40~60℃ cycling and at constant temperatures.

图 10. 40~60℃循环干燥与恒温干燥蒜片不同水分含量下的丙酮酸含量

(2) Tables

表题实例

① Table 1. Cyclic drying conditions

表 1. 循环干燥条件

② Table 2. Composition of spelt and common wheat bread formulas

表 2. 斯佩尔特小麦与普通小麦面包配方的构成

③ Table 3. Comparison of thermal properties of isolates prepared from soybeans stored under various conditions

表 3. 不同储藏条件下大豆所得分离蛋白的热力特性比较

④ Table 4. Effect of soaking, cooking and dehulling on protein, starch and ash content of peas

表 4. 浸泡、烹饪和脱壳对豌豆蛋白、淀粉及灰分含量的影响

⑤ Table 5. Interaction of fining treatment with storage time on quality attributes of clarified banana juice during storage

表 5. 澄清处理与储藏时间对储藏期内透明香蕉汁的品质特性的交互作用

⑥ Table 6. Analysis of variance of variety and treatment (soaking, cooking and dehulling) on composition of field peas

表 6. 品种与处理（浸泡、烹饪和脱壳）对紫花豌豆构成的方差分析

⑦ Table 7. Physicochemical properties of rice starches and flours

表 7. 米淀粉与面粉的理化特性

⑧ Table 8. Cholesterol biosynthesis inhibitory effects of lovastatin and tea polyphenols

表 8. 洛伐他汀（一种降脂药）与茶多酚的抑制胆固醇生物合成作用

⑨ Table 9. Parameters for kinetic model of oil content development in chicken nuggets during deep fat frying

表 9. 油炸时鸡块中油含量变化的动力学模型参数

⑩ Table 10. Regression analysis for loss factors of pre-cooked and liquid egg whites and whole eggs

表 10. 预烹饪与液态蛋白与全蛋损耗系数的回归分析

⑪ Table 11. Particle size distribution data for starch and starch–cassia gum pastes

表 11. 淀粉与淀粉-肉桂胶面团的粒度分布数据

⑫ Table 12. Correlation coefficients between starch fractions and digestion parameters

表 12. 淀粉分数与其消化参数的相关系数

⑬ Table 13. Standard references and ratings used in descriptive analysis of raw shrimp samples

表 13. 生虾样品描述性分析的参考标准与评级

参 考 文 献

[1] 秦荻辉. 实用科技英语写作技巧[M]. 上海：上海外语教育出版社，2001.

[2] 王建武，李民权，曾小珊. 科技英语写作（理论·技巧·范例）[M]. 西安：西北工业大学出版社，2008.

[3] 朱继武，王西玲. 英语写作基础[M]. 西安：西北工业大学出版社，2005.

[4] 陆则坚. 食品专业英语[M]. 北京：中国农业出版社，2003.

[5] 李传英. 医学论文英文图表写作中的文体特点[J]. 武汉大学学报（医学版），2006, 27（6）：820-822.

[6] 刘亚栋. 学术论文英文摘要的撰写[J]. 中国科技翻译，2007, 20（4）：48-50.

[7] 田凤英. 英语科技论文题目的新特点[J]. 大学英语（学术版），2010, 7（2）：42-44.

[8] 王应宽，蒲应䶮. 科技学术论文英文图表题名译写举隅[J]. 编辑学报，2001, 13（增刊）24-26.

[9] 余琳，黄拥军. 英文摘要的撰写及问题剖析[J]. 湖北经济学院学报（人文社会科学版），2010, 7（4）：119-120.

[10] BREWER S. Irradiation effects on meat color-a review [J]. Meat Science, 2004, 68: 1-17.

[11] DUUN A S, HEMMINGSEN A K T, HAUGLAND A, et al. Quality changes during superchilled storage of pork roast [J]. LWT-Food Science and Technology, 2008, 41(10): 2136-2143.

[12] GALLART-JOMET L, RUSTAD T, BARAT J M, et al. Effect of superchilled storage on the freshness and salting behaviour of Atlantic salmon (Salmo salar) fillets [J]. Food Chemistry, 2007, 103(4):1268-1281.

[13] MAGNUSSEN O M, HAUGLAND A, HEMMINGSEN A K T, et al. Advances in superchilling of food-process characteristics and product quality [J]. Trends in Food Science & Technology, 2008, 19: 418-424.

[14] NADEEM S, CHATTOPADHYAY U K, SHERIKAR A T, et al. Chemical sprays as a method for improvement in microbiological quality and shelf-life of fresh sheep and goat meats during refrigeration storage (5-7 degrees C) [J]. Meat Science, 2003, 63: 339-344.

[15] RIVAS-CANEDO E, FERNANDEZ-GARCIA M, NUNEZ M. Volatile compounds in fresh meats subjected to high pressure processing: Effect of the packaging material [J]. Meat Science, 2009, 81: 321-328.

[16] ROLLER S, SAGOO S, BOARD R, et al. Novel combinations of chitosan, carnocin and suplhite for the preservation of chilled pork sausages [J]. Meat Science, 2002, 62: 165-177.

[17] SAGOO S, BOARD R, ROLLER S. Chitosan inhibits growth of spoilage microorganisms in chilled pork products [J]. Food Microbiology, 2002, 19: 175-182.

[18] ATTENBOROUGH W M. Evaluation of processes for the production of low-and non-alcohol beer [J]. Ferment, 1988, 1 (2): 40-44.

[19] MONTANARI L, MARCONI O, MAYER H, et al. Production of alcohol-free beer. V. R. Preedy, (Ed.), Beer in Health and Disease Prevention [M]. Burlington, Elsevier Inc., 2009: 61-75.

[20] NARZISS L, MIEDANER H, KERN E, et al. Technology and composition of non-alcoholic beers. Processes using arrested fermentation [J]. Brauwelt International, 1992, 4: 396-410.

[21] Hans-Dietor Belitz Food Chemistry.

[22] Belitz H D, Grosch W, & Schieberle P. (2008). Carbohydrates. In (pp. 248-339).

[23] Demeyer, D., Toldrá, F., & Leroy, F. (2014). Fermentation. In M. Dikeman & C. Devine (Eds.), Encyclopedia of Meat Sciences (Second Edition) (pp. 1-7). Oxford: Academic Press.

[24] Food Processing. (2005). In T. E. Graedel & J. A. Howard-Grenville (Eds.), Greening the Industrial Facility: Perspectives,

Approaches, and Tools (pp. 239-255). Boston, MA: Springer US.

[25] Zhou, G. H., Xu, X. L., & Liu, Y. (2010). Preservation technologies for fresh meat-a review. Meat science, 86(1), 119-128. https://doi.org/10.1016/j.meatsci.2010.04.033

[26] Brányik, T., Silva, D. P., Baszczyňski, M., Lehnert, R., & Almeida e Silva, J. B. (2012). A review of methods of low alcohol and alcohol-free beer production. Journal of Food Engineering, 108(4), 493 506. https://doi.org/https://doi.org/10.1016/j.jfoodeng.2011.09.020.

[27] Verma, C., Nanda, S., Singh, R., Singh, R., & Mishra, S. (2011). A Review on Impacts of Genetically Modified Food on Human Health. The Open Nutraceuticals Journal, 4, 3-11. https://doi.org/10.2174/1876396001104010003.

[28] National Board of Experts-HACCP. (2002). Specification requirements for a HACCP based food safety system (3rd ed.). The Hague, Netherlands: National Board of Experts-HACCP.